THE TECHNICAL COLLEGE SERIES

Editor Emeritus: P. ABBOTT, B.A.

General Editor: W. E. FISHER, O.B.E., D.Sc.
(Formerly Principal, Wolverhampton and Staffordshire Technical College)

NATIONAL CERTIFICATE
MATHEMATICS

VOLUME III

THE TECHNICAL COLLEGE SERIES

Editor Emeritus : P. ABBOTT, B.A.

General Editor : W. E. FISHER, O.B.E., D.Sc.

(*Formerly Principal, Wolverhampton and Staffordshire Technical College*)

THE TECHNICAL COLLEGE SERIES

NATIONAL CERTIFICATE MATHEMATICS

VOLUME III

(THIRD YEAR COURSE)

By

G. E. MAHON, B.Sc.

Late Senior Lecturer in Mathematics, St. Mary's
College, Strawberry Hill, Middlesex, and late
Lecturer in Mathematics at the Polytechnic,
Regent Street, W.1

and

P. ABBOTT, B.A.

Formerly Head of the Mathematics Department,
and Head Master of the Secondary School, The
Polytechnic, Regent Street, W.1

ENGLISH UNIVERSITIES PRESS LTD.
ST. PAUL'S HOUSE, WARWICK SQUARE
LONDON, E.C.4

First published . *1938*
Twelfth impression . *1953*

*Printed in Great Britain for the English Universities Press, Limited,
by Richard Clay and Company, Ltd., Bungay, Suffolk*

PREFACE

THIS volume is essentially the work of Mr. G. E. Mahon and is based on the lectures given by him for many years to engineering students at the Polytechnic, Regent St., W.1.

The work is intended to provide a systematic and progressive text-book in mathematics for students taking mechanical or electrical engineering courses in a Technical Institution. It is in three volumes, which are planned to correspond to work which is usually done in the first three years of the senior course. The books include such mathematics as would normally be taken in a Technical Institution in which the students are preparing for a National Certificate. They also cover the syllabuses for the Examinations (S_1, S_2 and S_3) in practical mathematics conducted by the Union of Lancashire and Cheshire Institutes, the Union of Educational Institutions and the Northern Counties Technical Examination Council.

The practical requirements of technical students have been carefully borne in mind throughout the volumes, but an endeavour has also been made, within the limits necessarily imposed upon such a work, to provide a fundamental and theoretical basis such as is necessary for a more advanced study of the subject.

The authors acknowledge, with gratitude, the permission which has been kindly given by the Union of Lancashire and Cheshire Institutes, the Union of Educational Institutions, the Northern Counties Technical Examinations Council, and the Board of Education, to use questions which have appeared in their Examinations, and by Messrs. Longmans, Green and Company, Limited, to reproduce tables from " Mathematical Tables and Formulae." Thanks are given to Mr. A. F. Mahon for drawing the figures in this volume.

G. E. M.

P. A.

GENERAL EDITOR'S FOREWORD

THE Technical College Series today includes many books which are outstanding in their particular fields, and it is the aim of the publishers to maintain and develop the worthy tradition of the Series while meeting in full the increasing needs of technical and scientific education.

An outstanding contribution of the technical colleges to education has been the system of the National Certificates under which the Ministry of Education and the colleges work in association with leading professional institutions. The system has progressed from its early pre-occupation with engineering until the schemes now cover practically the whole field of higher technology and applied science. The major engineering institutions, the Royal Institute of Chemistry, the Institute of Physics, the Institution of Metallurgists are all associated with National Certificate schemes. There are National Certificates in Building and in Commerce, with each of which a group of professional institutions is associated. Though the pattern of National Certificate Courses was originally dictated by the needs and limitations of the evening student, the system of endorsements obtainable by further study has now brought about the result that these courses have been extended to meet the full requirements of practice in the subjects with which they deal. During recent years the system of part-time-day release of apprentices and learners has become common in all branches of industry as well as in the public services. This has effected something like a revolution in technical education; and in particular the treatment of National Certificate studies up to the standard already indicated has become much broader.

The books included in the Series will be planned to suit the requirements of three main groups : (i) the part-time and full-time students working in technical colleges for professional qualifications and university degrees; (ii) technologists, managers, and research workers in industry; (iii) teachers in technical colleges and elsewhere who require text-books of high standard, but broad enough in treatment of their subjects to be readily adaptable to local approved schemes of study.

W. E. FISHER.

CONTENTS

CHAPTER 1

THE SOLUTION OF EQUATIONS

1. The Quadratic Equation

Every quadratic equation can be reduced to the form $ax^2 + bx + c = 0$, where a, b, c are real numbers. It may happen that either b or c is zero.

We shall assume that the student is familiar with the solution of quadratic equations, either by factorisation or by the use of the formula

$$x = \frac{-b \pm \sqrt{b^2 - 4ac}}{2a}$$

In addition, he will know that if the roots of any quadratic equation are α and β

$$\left. \begin{array}{c} \alpha + \beta = -\dfrac{b}{a} \\[2mm] \alpha\beta = \dfrac{c}{a} \end{array} \right\}$$

Further, the roots are real, coincident, or imaginary when $b^2 - 4ac$ is positive, zero or negative. The graph of $y = ax^2 + bx + c$ cuts the x-axis in real points if $b^2 - 4ac$ is $+ ve$, touches the axis when $b^2 - 4ac = 0$, and, assuming a to be positive, lies above this axis when $b^2 - 4ac$ is negative.

Example 1

If one root of $x^2 - 6x + k = 0$ is 2, find k.
The sum of the roots is 6.
$\therefore$ The other root is 4.

$$k = \text{product of roots} = 8$$

Example 2

In drawing the graph of $y = x^2 - 3 \cdot 7x + 3 \cdot 12$, we find the curve cuts the x-axis where $x = 1 \cdot 3$. At what other point must it cut this axis?

The axis is cut where $x^2 - 3 \cdot 7x + 3 \cdot 12 = 0$. One root of this quadratic is $1 \cdot 3$.

The sum of the roots is $3 \cdot 7$.

∴ The graph again cuts the axis where $x = 2 \cdot 4$.

Also $2 \cdot 4 \times 1 \cdot 3 = 3 \cdot 12$, the constant term.

EXERCISE 1

1. Solve $\dfrac{x^2}{2} - \dfrac{x(3 - 2x)}{4} = \dfrac{x}{3} - \frac{1}{4}$.   (N.C.)

2. Factorise   (a) $x^2 - x - 20$,   (b) $\pi R^2 - 4\pi r^2$,   and
(c) $R^3 + 6R^2r + 8Rr^2$.

Use the results of (b) and (c) to find the values of these expressions when $R = 6 \cdot 5$, $r = 1 \cdot 75$ and $\pi = 3 \cdot 14$.

(N.C.)

3. Given that $f = \dfrac{p(D^2 + d^2)}{D^2 - d^2}$, express d in terms of the other quantities, and find d when $D = 8$, $p = 1100$, and $f = 3200$.   (U.L.C.I.)

4. Given $f = \dfrac{Wx}{S(a + b)} + \dfrac{Wd}{2Sk^2}\left[x - \dfrac{bx^2}{L(a + b)}\right]$, find the values of x given that $f = 4 \cdot 2$, $W = 1 \cdot 5$, $S = 10$, $k^2 = 11$, $L = 240$, $a = 12$, $b = 60$, $d = 8$.   (U.L.C.I.)

5. The lengths of the sides of a triangle are $5 \cdot 6$ ins., 5 ins., and $3 \cdot 4$ ins. Calculate the lengths of the two parts into which the longest side is divided by the perpendicular drawn to it from the opposite vertex.   (N.C.)

6. Fill in the blanks of

$$3a^2 + 5ab - 2b^2 = (3a^2 + 6ab) - (ab + \quad)$$
$$= 3a(\quad) - b(\quad)$$
$$= (\quad)(a + 2b)$$

and evaluate with as little labour as possible

$$3(8{\cdot}9)^2 + 5(8{\cdot}9)(25{\cdot}7) - 2(25{\cdot}7)^2.$$

(N.C.)

7. Without solving the equations, state whether the roots of the following equations are real, equal, or complex (imaginary) :

(a) $x^2 + 3x + 1 = 0.$ (b) $2x^2 - 3x + 4 = 0.$
(c) $x^2 + 4x + 4 = 0.$ (d) $0{\cdot}2x^2 - 0{\cdot}1x - 3 = 0.$

8. Given that the area of a rectangle, whose sides are x and y, is A, and that its perimeter is P, find a quadratic equation whose roots give the side of length x.

Find the sides given A = 12 sq. ins. and P = 18 ins.

9. Solve $\dfrac{3}{x + 2} - \dfrac{1}{x - 3} = \dfrac{4}{x}.$

10. When a body moves with a uniform acceleration f, we get $s = ut + \frac{1}{2}ft^2$, where s is the distance gone in time t, and u is the velocity of the body at zero time. Find t if $s = 3$ miles, $u = 8$ ft./sec., and $f = 4$ ft./sec.^{2}.

---

2. Equations Reducible to Quadratics

It will be found that there is but a single idea underlying the solution of the equations given in this section—viz., the use of a simpler symbol for a group of symbols, or for a more complicated one.

Example 1

Solve $x^4 - 5x^2 + 4 = 0$ . . . . . (1)

Writing z for x^2, the above becomes

$$z^2 - 5z + 4 = 0$$

i.e., $(z - 4)(z - 1) = 0$

Hence $z = 4$ or 1

i.e., $x^2 = 4$ or 1

giving $x = \pm 2$ or ± 1

The equation has four roots, $+ 2, - 2, + 1, - 1$, all of which satisfy it.

Example 2

Solve $x^{\frac{1}{2}} - 5x^{\frac{1}{4}} + 4 = 0$ . . . . . (2)

If $x^{\frac{1}{4}} = z$

then $x^{\frac{1}{2}} = z^2$, and (2) becomes

$$z^2 - 5z + 4 = 0$$

and just as before, we get

$$z = 4 \text{ or } z = 1.$$

Hence $x^{\frac{1}{4}} = 4 \text{ or } 1$

$\therefore$ $x = 256 \text{ or } 1.$

Example 3

Solve $x^2 = 4 + 5\sqrt{x^2 - 8}$ . . . (1)

Subtracting 8 from both sides, we get :

$$x^2 - 8 = - 4 + 5\sqrt{x^2 - 8} \quad . \;\; . \;\; . \;\; (2)$$

Put $z = \sqrt{x^2 - 8}.$

Then $z^2 = - 4 + 5z$, by substituting for z in (2),

i.e., $z^2 - 5z + 4 = 0$

or $(z - 1)(z - 4) = 0$

Giving $z = 1 \text{ or } 4$

i.e., $\sqrt{x^2 - 8} = 1 \text{ or } 4$

Giving $x^2 - 8 = 1 \text{ or } 16$

i.e., $x^2 = 9 \text{ or } 24$

or $x = \pm 3 \text{ or } \pm 2\sqrt{6}.$

Test if these roots satisfy equation (1).

They do so if $\sqrt{x^2 - 8}$ is regarded as positive.

Example 4

Solve $\dfrac{1}{y^4} - \dfrac{13}{y^2} + 36 = 0.$

Put $z = \dfrac{1}{y^2}.$

Then $z^2 - 13z + 36 = 0$

i.e., $(z - 4)(z - 9) = 0$

or $$\frac{1}{y^2} = 4 \text{ or } 9.$$

i.e., $y^2 = \frac{1}{4} \text{ or } \frac{1}{9}.$

Giving $y = \pm \frac{1}{2} \text{ or } \pm \frac{1}{3}.$

All four roots satisfy the original equation.

3. Trigonometrical equations are frequently simple examples of the quadratic.

Example 1

Solve for cos θ,

$$6 \cos^2 \theta - 5 \cos \theta + 1 = 0$$

We have $6x^2 - 5x + 1 = 0$ if $x = \cos \theta.$

Giving $(3x - 1)(2x - 1) = 0.$

$$\therefore \quad x = \tfrac{1}{3} \text{ or } \tfrac{1}{2}$$

i.e., $\cos \theta = \frac{1}{3} \text{ or } \cos \theta = \frac{1}{2}.$

Example 2

Solve $12 - 9 \cos \theta - 10 \sin^2 \theta = 0$ . . (1)

(1) can be written :

$$12 - 9 \cos \theta - 10(1 - \cos^2 \theta) = 0$$

i.e., $10 \cos^2 \theta - 9 \cos \theta + 2 = 0$

$$\therefore \quad (5x - 2)(2x - 1) = 0$$

where $x = \cos \theta$ as before.

Hence $\cos \theta = \frac{2}{5} \text{ or } \frac{1}{2}.$

Reference to a book of trigonometrical tables will give us the values of θ. Where $\cos \theta = \frac{1}{2}$, one value of θ is 60°

„ $\cos \theta = \frac{2}{5}$ „   „   66° 25′

EXERCISE 2

Solve the following equations :

1. $x^4 - 5x^2 + 6 = 0.$

2. $\dfrac{1}{y^4} + \dfrac{1}{y^2} - 6 = 0.$

3. $3x^{\frac{1}{2}} + 8x^{\frac{1}{4}} - 3 = 0.$

4. $x^2 - 2x - 5\sqrt{x^2 - 2x} + 4 = 0.$

5. $z = 4\sqrt{z - 3} + 8.$

6. $12 \sin^2 \theta - 13 \sin \theta + 3 = 0.$

7. $4 \tan^2 \theta + 19 \tan \theta - 5 = 0.$

8. Solve for $\sin \theta, 8 - 7 \sin \theta - 6 \cos^2 \theta = 0.$

9. Find $\tan \theta$, if $3 \sec^2 \theta - 10 \tan \theta - 11 = 0.$

Solve :

10. $3^x + \dfrac{27}{3^x} - 12 = 0.$

11. $2^{2x+2} - 17 \cdot 2^x + 4 = 0.$

12. Given that $\cos 2\theta = 2 \cos^2 \theta - 1$, solve
$$\cos \theta + \tfrac{2}{15} \cos 2\theta = 0 \text{ for } \cos \theta.$$

13. Solve   (i) $10^x(10^x - 2 \cdot 5) = -1 \cdot 5,$
      (ii) $5 \sin^2 x - 3 \cos^2 x = 1.$ (U.L.C.I.)

---

4. Equations Involving the Square Root of the Unknown

Example 1

Solve $\sqrt{2x + 3} = 4.$

Squaring, $2x + 3 = 16$

or $x = 6\tfrac{1}{2}.$

Strictly speaking, $\sqrt{2x + 3}$ should mean $+ \sqrt{2x + 3}$, or $- \sqrt{2x + 3}$, since any number has two square roots. To avoid ambiguity, the positive square root will always be understood.

Example 2

Solve $\sqrt{x+1} + \sqrt{x+8} = 7.$

We have $\sqrt{x+8} = 7 - \sqrt{x+1}$

Squaring, $x + 8 = 49 + x + 1 - 14\sqrt{x+1}$

$\qquad\qquad\quad = 50 + x - 14\sqrt{x+1}.$

i.e., $14\sqrt{x+1} = 42$

$\qquad\qquad \sqrt{x+1} = 3$

Giving $x = 8,$

which will be found to satisfy the given equation.

Example 3

Solve $\sqrt{2x+6} + \sqrt{3x+1} = 8$ . . . (1)

Transposing, $\sqrt{3x+1} = 8 - \sqrt{2x+6}$

Squaring, $3x + 1 = 64 + 2x + 6 - 16\sqrt{2x+6}$

$\qquad\qquad\qquad = 70 + 2x - 16\sqrt{2x+6}$

$\qquad \therefore\ 16\sqrt{2x+6} = 69 - x.$

Square again :

$\qquad\quad 256(2x+6) = 69^2 - 138x + x^2$

i.e., $512x + 1536 = 4761 - 138x + x^2.$

$\qquad x^2 - 650x + 3225 = 0$ . . . . (2)

$\qquad (x - 5)(x - 645) = 0.$

Giving $x = 5 \text{ or } 645.$

It is clear that $x = 645$ does not satisfy the original equation.

Hence $x = 5$ is the only solution. It will be found that $x = 645$ satisfies the equation

$$- \sqrt{2x+6} + \sqrt{3x+1} = 8.$$

Whenever we have to square twice, as in the above example, one of the roots found will not satisfy the original equation. In every case the values found for the unknown should be tried in the original equation.

Example 4

Solve for M *the equation* $T_e = M + \sqrt{M^2 + T^2}$, *given that* $T = 4 \cdot 22$ (*tons-ft.*) *and* $T_e = 18 \cdot 54$ (*tons-ft.*)   (U.L.C.I.)

Substituting, we get

$$18 \cdot 54 = M + \sqrt{M^2 + (4 \cdot 22)^2}$$

$$\therefore \quad (18 \cdot 54 - M)^2 = M^2 + (4 \cdot 22)^2$$

i.e., $(18 \cdot 54)^2 - 2M \times 18 \cdot 54 + M^2 = M^2 + (4 \cdot 22)^2.$

i.e., $\qquad (18 \cdot 54)^2 - (4 \cdot 22)^2 = 37 \cdot 08 M.$

$$\therefore \quad M = \frac{22 \cdot 76 \times 14 \cdot 32}{37 \cdot 08} \left(\begin{array}{l} \text{using difference} \\ \text{between two squares} \end{array}\right).$$

Notice that we could first solve the equation as given, thus

$$(T_e - M)^2 = M^2 + T^2$$

i.e., $\qquad T_e^2 - 2M \cdot T_e + M^2 = M^2 + T^2$

i.e., $\qquad T_e^2 - T^2 = 2M \cdot T_e.$

Giving $\qquad M = \dfrac{(T_e + T)(T_e - T)}{2T_e}$

With the given values $M = 8 \cdot 79$.

EXERCISE 3

Solve :

1. $\sqrt{3x - 4} = 5.$
2. $\sqrt[4]{x - 6} = 2.$
3. $\sqrt{x^2 - 8} = \sqrt{17}.$
4. $\sqrt{x - 2} = \sqrt{x} - 1.$
5. $\sqrt{3x + 1} + \sqrt{x + 3} = 2.$
6. $3\sqrt{y} + 2\sqrt{5 - y} = 8.$
7. $5\sqrt{z - 3} + 2\sqrt{z + 1} = \sqrt{z + 13}.$
8. $2\sqrt{x + 3} + \sqrt{x} = 5.$
9. $\dfrac{12}{\sqrt{x + 5}} + \sqrt{x + 5} = 7.$

10. A Board of Trade formula for determining the distances between the centres of rivets is

$$10c = \sqrt{(11p + 4d)(p + 4d)}.$$

Find p when $c = 1\frac{3}{8}$ and $d = \frac{3}{4}$.   (U.L.C.I.)

---

5. Simultaneous Quadratic Equations

Case I.

When one equation is of the first degree.

Solve

$$x^2 + 3y^2 = 13 \quad \} \quad . \quad . \quad . \quad . \quad (1)$$
$$2x + y = 4 \quad \} \quad . \quad . \quad . \quad . \quad (2)$$

From (2) $y = 4 - 2x.$

Substitute in (1) and get :

$$x^2 + 3(4 - 2x)^2 = 13$$

i.e., $x^2 + 3(16 - 16x + 4x^2) = 13.$

Simplifying, this gives :

$$13x^2 - 48x + 35 = 0$$

i.e., $(13x - 35)(x - 1) = 0$

From which, $x = 1$ or $\frac{35}{13}.$

Now substitute each of the above values for x in (2).

Putting $x = 1,$ we get $y = 2.$

Putting $x = \frac{35}{13},$ we get $y = -\frac{18}{13}.$

The values $(1, 2)$, and $(\frac{35}{13}, -\frac{18}{13})$, will be found to satisfy both equations.

The student will observe that the method of solution is to use the linear (first degree) equation to express y in terms of x (or vice versa). This value is then substituted in the other equation, and the resulting quadratic is then solved.

6. *Case II.*

Consider the equation

$$3x^2 + 2xy - y^2 = 0 \quad . \quad . \quad . \quad (1)$$

Every term is of two dimensions in x and y, and the equation is said to be homogeneous.

(1) becomes $(3x - y)(x + y) = 0$.   .   .   .   (2)

when we factorise.

Hence, either $3x - y = 0$.   .   .   .   (3)

or $x + y = 0$.   .   .   .   (4)

From (3) we get :

$$3x = y, \quad i.e., \quad \frac{x}{y} = \tfrac{1}{3}$$

From (4), $x = -y, \quad i.e., \quad \frac{x}{y} = -1.$

Such an equation as (1) cannot be solved for either x or y, but it can be solved for the ratio $\frac{x}{y}$, or $\frac{y}{x}$.

If the equation cannot be factorised, we could still find the ratio $\frac{x}{y}$.

For example, find the ratio $\frac{x}{y}$, if

$$x^2 - 2xy - 2y^2 = 0 \quad . \quad . \quad . \quad . \quad (5)$$

Dividing by y^2, we get :

$$\frac{x^2}{y^2} - \frac{2x}{y} - 2 = 0 \quad . \quad . \quad . \quad . \quad (6)$$

Put $\frac{x}{y} = z.$

(6) becomes :

$$z^2 - 2z - 2 = 0$$

Giving $z = \dfrac{2 \pm \sqrt{12}}{2}$

i.e., $\dfrac{x}{y} = 1 \pm \sqrt{3}.$

7. We can now apply the above method to the solution of a certain type of simultaneous quadratic equation.

Example 1

Solve
$$x^2 + y^2 = 5 \left.\vphantom{\begin{matrix}a\\b\end{matrix}}\right\} \quad \cdots \quad (1)$$
$$2xy - y^2 = 3 \left.\vphantom{\begin{matrix}a\\b\end{matrix}}\right. \quad \cdots \quad (2)$$

Observe that there are no terms of the first degree in either of the given equations.

We have, by cross-multiplication,
$$3(x^2 + y^2) = 5(2xy - y^2)$$

i.e.,
$$3x^2 - 10xy + 8y^2 = 0.$$

Factorising, we get :
$$(3x - 4y)(x - 2y) = 0$$

These give
$$x = 2y \quad \cdots \quad \cdots \quad (3)$$

or
$$x = \frac{4y}{3} \quad \cdots \quad \cdots \quad (4)$$

Substitute from (3) in (1) and get
$$5y^2 = 5$$
$$\therefore \quad y = \pm 1$$

and
$$\therefore \quad x = \pm 2.$$

The values $(2, 1)$, $(-2, -1)$ will be found to satisfy both equations.

Now take (4)—viz., $x = \frac{4y}{3}$—and again substitute in (1). We get :
$$\frac{16y^2}{9} + y^2 = 5$$

i.e.
$$\frac{25y^2}{9} = 5$$

or
$$y^2 = \tfrac{9}{5}$$

and
$$y = \pm \frac{3}{\sqrt{5}} = \pm \frac{3\sqrt{5}}{5}.$$

$$x = \tfrac{4}{3}y = \pm \frac{4\sqrt{5}}{5}$$

The values $\left(\dfrac{4\sqrt{5}}{5}, \dfrac{3\sqrt{5}}{5}\right)$ and $\left(-\dfrac{4\sqrt{5}}{5}, -\dfrac{3\sqrt{5}}{5}\right)$ satisfy both equations.

The methods used in Cases (1) and (2) are perfectly general, and will always solve simultaneous equations of the given types.

8. Notice the method used in solving the following :

Example 1

Solve
$$x + y = 7 \quad \text{. . . . . (1)}$$
$$xy = 12 \quad \text{. . . . . (2)}$$

Squaring (1) $x^2 + 2xy + y^2 = 49$
Multiply (2) by 4 $4xy = 48$
Subtract $x^2 - 2xy + y^2 = 1$
i.e., $(x - y)^2 = 1$
$$\therefore \quad x - y = \pm 1 \quad \text{. . . (3)}$$

Combine (3) and (1)

$$x + y = 7$$
$$x - y = 1 \quad \Big\} \text{giving } x = 4, y = 3$$

$$x + y = 7$$
$$x - y = -1 \quad \Big\} \text{giving } x = 3, y = 4.$$

The points **(4, 3)**, **(3, 4)** both lie on the curves (1) and (2).

Example 2

Solve
$$x^2 + y^2 = 170 \quad \text{. . . . . (1)}$$
$$xy = 13 \quad \text{. . . . . (2)}$$
$$x^2 + 2xy + y^2 = 170 + 26 = 196$$
$$\therefore \quad (x + y)^2 = 196 = 14^2$$
$$\therefore \quad x + y = \pm 14 \quad \text{. . . . . (3)}$$

Similarly $x^2 - 2xy + y^2 = 170 - 26 = 144$
i.e., $(x - y)^2 = 12^2$
$$\therefore \quad x - y = \pm 12 \quad \text{. . . . . (4)}$$

We now solve

$$x + y = 14 \quad \Big\} \qquad x + y = 14 \quad \Big\}$$
$$x - y = 12 \qquad \qquad x - y = -12$$

$$x + y = -14 \quad \Big\} \qquad x + y = -14 \quad \Big\}$$
$$x - y = 12 \qquad \qquad x - y = -12$$

These give the four solutions:

$$\begin{Bmatrix} x = 13 \\ y = 1 \end{Bmatrix} \quad \begin{Bmatrix} x = 1 \\ y = 13 \end{Bmatrix} \quad \begin{Bmatrix} x = -1 \\ y = -13 \end{Bmatrix} \quad \begin{Bmatrix} x = -13 \\ y = -1 \end{Bmatrix}$$

9. Simultaneous Equations of the First Degree with Three Unknowns

The method of solution is to eliminate one unknown—say, z—and get two equations involving x and y only.

The method of solving this pair is known.

Example 1

Solve

$$x + y + z = 6 \quad . \quad . \quad . \quad . \quad (1)$$
$$2x - y + 3z = 9 \quad . \quad . \quad . \quad . \quad (2)$$
$$x + 3y - z = 4 \quad . \quad . \quad . \quad . \quad (3)$$

Adding (1) and (3) we get:

$$2x + 4y = 10$$

or

$$x + 2y = 5 \quad . \quad . \quad . \quad . \quad (4)$$

Now multiply (3) by 3 and add to (2).

Then

$$5x + 8y = 21 \quad . \quad . \quad . \quad . \quad (5)$$

Solving (4) and (5), we get

$$x = 1, \quad y = 2.$$

Substitute these values in (1) and $z = 3$.

Example 2

It is known that the readings given below for x and y follow a law of the form $y = Ax^2 + Bx + C = 0$. Find A, B, and C.

x . . .	1	2	3
y . . .	1	3	12

Substituting the pairs of values for x and y in the given equation, we get:

$$A + B + C = 1 \quad . \quad . \quad . \quad . \quad (1)$$
$$4A + 2B + C = 3 \quad . \quad . \quad . \quad . \quad (2)$$
$$9A + 3B + C = 12 \quad . \quad . \quad . \quad . \quad (3)$$

Eliminate C from (1) and (2) by subtraction.   We get :

$$3A + B = 2 \quad . \quad . \quad . \quad . \quad . \quad (4)$$

Subtract (2) from (3) and get :

$$5A + B = 9 \quad . \quad . \quad . \quad . \quad . \quad (5)$$

Now eliminate B from (4) and (5), and

$$2A = 7$$
$$\therefore \quad A = \tfrac{7}{2}$$

Substitute in (4), giving $B = 2 - 3A = 2 - \tfrac{21}{2} = -\tfrac{17}{2}$.
From (1) $C = 1 - B - A = 1 + \tfrac{17}{2} - \tfrac{7}{2} = 6$.

Hence $$y = \frac{7x^2}{2} - \frac{17x}{2} + 6.$$

Other readings could be checked by the equation.

EXERCISE 4

1. Solve : $\left. \begin{array}{l} x^2 + y = 1 \\ y - 2x = 2 \end{array} \right\}.$

2. $\left. \begin{array}{l} x^2 - xy = 21 \\ x - y = 3 \end{array} \right\}.$

3. $\left. \begin{array}{l} x + y = 5 \\ xy = 6 \end{array} \right\}.$

4. $\left. \begin{array}{l} z^2 - 9w^2 = 28 \\ z - 3w = 2 \end{array} \right\}.$

5. $\left. \begin{array}{l} x^2 + xy = 3 \\ xy + y^2 = 6 \end{array} \right\}.$

6. $\left. \begin{array}{l} 3x^2 + 4xy + 5y^2 = 31 \\ x + 2y = 5 \end{array} \right\}.$

7. $\left. \begin{array}{l} x^2 + y^2 = 100 \\ xy = 14 \end{array} \right\}.$ (U.L.C.I.)

8. Find the values of $\dfrac{1}{x}$ and $\dfrac{1}{y}$ if $\dfrac{4}{x} - \dfrac{1}{y} = 13$ and $\dfrac{3}{x} - \dfrac{2}{y} = 6$.   (N.C.)

9. $3x^2 - 5xy = -2$
$\quad 4xy - 3y^2 = \ 1$

10. If $x = 4y$ and $\frac{1}{5}(2x + 7y - 1) = \frac{2}{3}(2x - 6y + 1)$, find x and y. (N.C.)

11. Find the values of x and y which satisfy

$$v = \tfrac{1}{2}\{x + \sqrt{y^2 + 4f^2}\}$$
$$\tan 2\theta = \frac{2f}{x}$$

Given that $\theta = 22\tfrac{1}{2}°$, $f = 50$, and $v = 150$. (U.L.C.I.)

12. S and T are connected by a relation

$$S = aT^3 + bT^2 + cT,$$

where a, b, c are constants, and $S = 11\cdot4$ when $T = 2$, $S = 42\cdot3$ when $T = 3$, and $S = 202\cdot5$ when $T = 5$. Find the values of a, b, c and deduce the value of S when $T = 4$. (U.L.C.I.)

13. The equation to a parabola is given by

$$y = A + Bx + Cx^2.$$

The parabola passes through the points $(1\cdot4, \ 3\cdot19)$, $(2, 4)$ and $(5, 10\cdot75)$. Find A, B, and C. (U.L.C.I.)

14. The parabola $y = a + bx + cx^2$ passes through three points whose co-ordinates are $(-h, y_1)$, $(0, y_2)$, (h, y_3). Insert these values and find a, b, c in terms of y_1, y_2, y_3, and h. (B.E.)

---

10. Some Other Types of Equation

Example 1

Solve the simultaneous equations $3^x = 27^{y-2}$ and $25^y = 5^{x-2}$.
  (U.L.C.I.)

Notice $25 = 5^2$ and $27 = 3^3$.
Hence

$$3^x = 3^{3(y-2)} \quad . \quad . \quad . \quad . \quad . \quad (1)$$
and
$$5^{2y} = 5^{x-2} \quad . \quad . \quad . \quad . \quad . \quad (2)$$

$\therefore$ Equating indices

$x = 3y - 6$ from (1)

and $2y = x - 2$ from (2).

Solving this pair of simultaneous equations we get :

$$x = 18 \text{ and } y = 8.$$

Example 2

If $5^x = 3^{x^2-4}$ find the values of x.   (U.L.C.I.)

Taking logs of both sides of the given equation we get :

$$x \log 5 = (x^2 - 4) \log 3.$$

$\therefore$ $\dfrac{x \log 5}{\log 3} = x^2 - 4$

whence $x^2 - 1 \cdot 465x - 4 = 0$

solving $x = \dfrac{1 \cdot 465 \pm \sqrt{(1 \cdot 465)^2 + 16}}{2}$

whence $x = 2 \cdot 862 \text{ or } - 1 \cdot 397.$

EXERCISE 5

1. The points $x = 2$, $y = 6 \cdot 49$, $x = 4$, $y = 15 \cdot 43$, and $x = 8$, $y = 40 \cdot 06$ lie on a curve whose equation has the form $y = a + bx^n$ where a, b, and n are constants. Find a, b, and n. (Note that the abscissæ form a G.P.)

(U.L.C.I.)

2. Three variables, p, v, T, are related by the formulæ $pv^{1 \cdot 3} = c$ and $pv = RT$ where c and R are constants. Given that $p = 150$ and $T = 500$ when $v = 31$, find the values of p and T when $v = 126$.   (N.C.)

3. Given that $\theta = 0 \cdot 8\pi$, $\mu = 0 \cdot 3$ and $N = Me^{\mu\theta}$, if $(N - M)V = 33000P$ when $P = 30$ and $V = 520$, find N.

(B.E.)

4. $y = a + bx^n$ is the equation to a curve which passes through the three points $x = 0, y = 1 \cdot 24$; $x = 2 \cdot 2, y = 5 \cdot 07$; $x = 3 \cdot 5, y = 12 \cdot 64$, find a, b, and n.   (B.E.)

5. If $v = be^{-\frac{t}{KR}}$, where b is a constant t is the time in seconds, $K = 0.8 \times 10^{-6}$. When $t = 0$, $v = 30$, and when $t = 15$, $v = 26.43$, find R. (B.E.)

6. There is a root of $x^3 + 5x - 11 = 0$ between 1 and 2. Find it, by calculation, by putting $(1 + h)$ for x, neglecting h^3 and solving the resulting quadratic for h.

7. Solve $3^{x^2 - 3} = 9^x$.

8. Solve $\left.\begin{array}{l} 2^{3x - y} = 4^{x - 2} \\ 4^{x + y} = 2^{x + 3} \end{array}\right\}.$

9. Solve $3^{x^2 - 5} = 81^x$.

10. Solve $\left.\begin{array}{l} 3^{2x - y} = 9^{x + 2} \\ 5^{x + y} = 25^{2x - 3y} \end{array}\right\}.$

11. Two variables, x and y, are connected by a law of the form $y = a + bx^c$, where a, b, c are constants. When x has the values 0, 6.33, 9.05, the values of y are 2.36, 13.46, and 20.66 respectively. Find (1) the values of a, b, and c and (2) the value of y when $x = 16$. (N.C.)

CHAPTER 2

GRAPHS. THE DETERMINATION OF LAWS. THE GRAPHIC SOLUTION OF EQUATIONS

1. In drawing the graph of $y = x^2$, it should be observed that the equation imposes a definite law on the point whose motion is represented by the graph.

We could translate the command " Draw the graph of $y = x^2$ " by the words, " Draw the path, on some suitable scale, of a point which moves so that its ordinate is always equal to the square of its abscissa."

We shall refer to the path of a point when it moves under a given law as the " locus " of the point; and if we can find an equation connecting the co-ordinates of the point with the law we impose on its motion, we call this equation the " equation of the path " or the " equation of the locus."

2. The Equation of a Straight Line

Find the equation of the path of a point which always moves in a given direction, and passes through a given point.

Case I.

The locus is a straight line, and we shall find an equation which is satisfied by the co-ordinates of every point on the line.

Suppose K is the given point. (Fig. 1.) Let the fixed direction make θ with the positive sense of OX. Clearly the locus is the straight line KP. For simplicity take the *y*-axis through K. Take any point O on this axis as origin and draw the other axis X_1OX.

Suppose K is the point $(0, c)$. Let P be *any* point on the straight line; let its co-ordinates be (x, y).

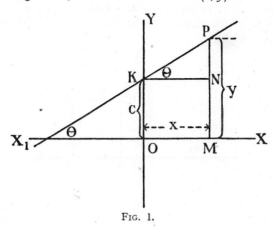

Fig. 1.

The law imposed on the moving point gives us the constants c and θ. We connect these with x and y, thus :

$$\frac{NP}{KN} = \tan \theta,$$

where KN is parallel to OX, and PM parallel to OY.
KN $= x$ and NP $=$ MP $-$ MN $= y - c$.

$$\therefore \frac{y - c}{x} = \tan \theta$$

i.e., $y = \tan \theta \,.\, x + c$ . . . . . . (1)

This is the required equation, usually written

$$y = mx + c \quad . \quad . \quad . \quad . \quad . \quad . \quad (2)$$

In this equation m ($= \tan \theta$) is called the *gradient* of the straight line; c is the intercept on the *y*-axis.

We make, then, the important inference that "*Every first degree equation in x and y (or any other two variables) represents a straight line.*"

This follows from the fact that any such equation can be put in the form (2).

3. Instead of taking the point K on the y-axis, take it anywhere in the plane—*i.e.*, let the co-ordinates of K be (x_1, y_1).   (Fig. 2.)

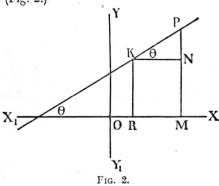

FIG. 2.

The equation of the straight line is got in exactly the same way as before—*i.e.*, we write down the value of $\tan \theta$ thus :

Let the co-ordinates of P be (x, y).

OR $= x_1$, OM $= x$ $\therefore$ RM $=$ KN $= x - x_1$
RK $= y_1 =$ MN $\therefore$ NP $= y - y_1$

$$\tan \theta = m = \frac{NP}{KN} = \frac{y - y_1}{x - x_1}$$

Hence

$$y - y_1 = m(x - x_1)$$

Example 1

The straight line through $(3, -4)$ inclined at $60°$ to the x-axis, is :

$$y + 4 = \sqrt{3}(x - 3).$$

Example 2

Find the equation to the straight line through $(-2, 3)$ *and* $(1, 4)$.

Let $y = mx + c$ be the straight line.

We must get values for m and c.

$(-2, 3)$ is on the line

$$\therefore \quad 3 = -2m + c \quad \cdots \cdots \quad (1)$$

Similarly $\qquad 4 = m + c \quad \cdots \cdots \cdots \quad (2)$

since $(1, 4)$ is on the line.

Solving (1) and (2) as simultaneous equations

$$m = \tfrac{1}{3}, \ c = \tfrac{11}{3}$$

$$\therefore \quad y = \frac{x}{3} + \tfrac{11}{3} \text{ is the required equation.}$$

It may be written $x - 3y + 11 = 0$, by clearing fractions.

4. The Determination of Laws of Linear Form

When we are given equations like

$$y = 3x + 4$$

or $\qquad\qquad y = 0 \cdot 2x^3$

it is a simple matter to get corresponding pairs of values of x and y, and so plot the graph.

The converse problem often confronts the student. He is given, or gets for himself in the laboratory, corresponding pairs of values of two variables—say, the extension of a spring under various weights, or corresponding values of the pressure and volume of a gas under certain constant conditions, or the voltage drop as known values of a current are passed through a resistance. From the data he is asked to find an equation connecting the two variables—*i.e.*, he must find the law connecting the variables.

In many cases we know the general fcrm cf the law. Thus Hooke's Law connecting the tension (y) of a spring with the extension x, is $y = kx$. In the case of a gas we get $pv^n = $ constant.

In these cases we find k for our particular spring, and n together with the constant for the gas.

In other cases, however, we have no indication of what the law may be, and we must use the method of " trial and error "—*i.e.*, we invent various forms of equations and test each one to see if the data given satisfy it.

5. The following examples illustrate some of the ways in which a non-linear law is reduced to a linear one.

Example 1

The following corresponding values of x and y are thought to be connected by the law $y = a + bx^2$. Test this and find the most probable values of a and b.

Note.—There may be slight experimental errors in the given values. (U.L.C.I.)

x . .	1	1·5	2	2·3	2·5	2·7	2·8
y . .	11	15	21·4	25·3	29	32	34·6
$x^2 = t$.	1	2·25	4	5·29	6·25	7·29	7·84

Since $$y = bx^2 + a$$
we write $$y = bt + a$$
where $$x^2 = t.$$

The values of x and y in the table are those given.

We find the values in the bottom line by squaring the x-values.

Now plot y against t.   (Fig. 3.)

The points lie almost on a straight line, AD.

Take any two points on the line.

We take the points C $(4, 21)$, and D $(8\frac{1}{3}, 36)$.

These must satisfy the equation :

$$y = bt + a$$
$$\therefore \quad 21 = 4b + a \quad . \quad . \quad . \quad . \quad . \quad (1)$$
and $$36 = 8\tfrac{1}{3}b + a \quad . \quad . \quad . \quad . \quad . \quad (2)$$

By subtraction $15 = 4\frac{1}{3}b$

$\therefore \qquad b = 3.5$ (nearly)

and $a = 7$

by substituting for (b) in (1).

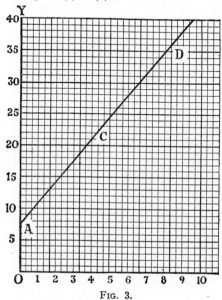

FIG. 3.

$\therefore$ The equation is

$$y = 7 + 3.5x^2.$$

Example 2

The following table gives the sectional areas of Whitworth bolts at the bottom of the thread for various diameters of bolts.

A = area in sq. ins.	0·13	0·3	0·9	1·3	1·8	2·28
d = diam. in ins.	0·56	0·75	1·25	1·5	1·8	2

*It is believed these figures are connected by a law in the form
of* $A = ad^2 + bd$. *Test this, and if correct find the most
probable values of a and b.*

We have $A = ad^2 + bd$

i.e., $\dfrac{A}{d} = ad + b$

viz., $y = ax + b,$

where $y = \dfrac{A}{d}$ and $x = d.$

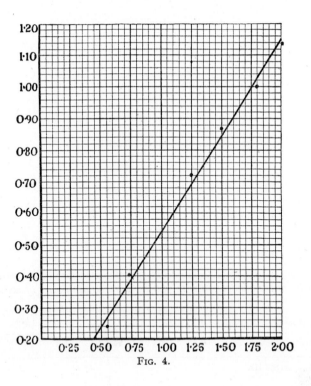

Fig. 4.

Now calculate $\frac{A}{d}$, and make the following table :

$x = d$ . .	0·56	0·75	1·25	1·5	1·8	2
$y = \frac{A}{d}$ . .	0·24	0·4	0·72	0·87	1	1·14

The graph is shown in Fig. 4.

We have taken the line through the points (1·75, 1) and (0·6, 0·3).

These points are on $y = ax + b$.

Substituting, we get :

$$1 = 1·75a + b \quad . \quad . \quad . \quad . \quad (1)$$
and
$$0·3 = 0·6a + b \quad . \quad . \quad . \quad . \quad (2)$$

Subtracting (2) from (1) :

$$0·7 = 1·15a$$
$$\therefore \quad a = 0·61$$
$$b = 0·3 - 0·366 \text{ (from (2))}$$
$$= -0·066$$
$$\therefore \text{ the law is A} = 0·61d^2 - 0·066d.$$

Example 3

Show that the following corresponding values of p and v can be represented by a law of the form

$$p = \frac{a}{v} + b$$

and find the most suitable values for a and b.   (U.L.C.I.)

p	100	120	140	160	180
v	4·29	3·57	3·16	2·75	2·49
$y = \frac{1}{v}$ . . .	0·233	0·28	0·316	0·364	0·402

Put $\dfrac{1}{v} = y$, and find the third row above.

Then : $p = ay + b$ . . . . . . (1)

Now plot y against p. See Fig. 5.

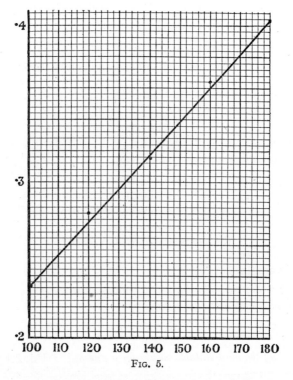

FIG. 5.

The line drawn passes through the points $p = 100$, $y = 0.236$ and $p = 150$, $y = 0.34$.

Hence, substituting in (1) we get :

$$100 = a \times 0.236 + b$$
$$150 = a \times 0.34 + b.$$

Solving, $a = 481$ and $b = -13.5$.
The approximate law is :

$$p = \frac{481}{v} - 13.5.$$

6. The Class of Curves

$$y = ax^n \quad . \quad . \quad . \quad . \quad . \quad (1)$$

whether n be positive or negative, can be reduced to the
linear form by taking logarithms of both sides to base 10.

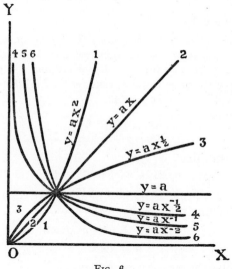

FIG. 6.

Clearly

$$\log y = n \log x + \log a$$

i.e., $$z = nt + c \quad . \quad . \quad . \quad . \quad . \quad (2)$$

where $z = \log_{10} y$, $t = \log_{10} x$, and $c = \log_{10} a$.

We thus plot $\log y$ against $\log x$.

The following points concerning the curves given by (1)
above, might be noticed.

(1) They all pass through the point $(1, a)$.

(2) Two of them are straight lines—viz.,

$y = a$, $(n = 0)$, and $y = ax$, $(n = 1)$.

(3) $y = ax^2$, a parabola, is a member of the family.

(4) $pv^n = $ constant, is also a member, and so is the rectangular hyperbola $xy = c$, $(n = -1)$.

A few are sketched in Fig. 6, for $+$ values of x.

Example 1

A curve showing the pressure p lb. per sq. in. and volume v cub. ft., of a gas in an engine cylinder passes through the points $p = 21$, $v = 0.175$, and $p = 112$ and $v = 0.045$. If the law of the curve is $pv^n = $ constant, find (1) the value of n, (2) the value of v when $p = 45$.   (N.C.)

Let $$pv^n = c$$

$$\therefore \quad \log_{10} p + n \log_{10} v = \log_{10} c$$

i.e., substituting

$$\log 21 + n \log 0.175 = \log c \quad . \quad . \quad . \quad (1)$$

and $$\log 112 + n \log 0.045 = \log c \quad . \quad . \quad . \quad (2)$$

Subtracting (1) from (2) gives :

$$\log \tfrac{112}{21} + n \log \tfrac{45}{175} = 0$$

giving $$n = 1.232.$$

To solve the second part, we have :

$$45v^{1.232} = c = 21 \times (0.175)^{1.232}$$

Hence

$$\log 45 + 1.232 \log v = \log 21 + 1.232 \log (0.175).$$

This is a simple equation for $\log v$.

Solving, we get $\log v = \bar{2}.982$

and $$v = 0.096.$$

Example 2

The following values of d and W *were obtained in a series of experiments on the strength of pillars.*

d	2·5	2·35	2	1·55
W	58,900	46,800	26,600	10,900

Find the law connecting d and W *of the form* W = kd^n, *where k and n are constants.*   (U.L.C.I.)

Here

$$\log W = n \log d + \log k \quad . \quad . \quad . \quad (1)$$

i.e.,
$$y = nx + c \quad . \quad . \quad . \quad . \quad . \quad (2)$$

Make the following table

$x = \log d$ . .	0·398	0·371	0·301	0·190
$y = \log W$ . .	4·77	4·67	4·425	4·037

Take the origin at (0, 4).   Unit on x-axis = 100 squares, on y-axis 10 squares.

Plotting y against x, it will be found that the points are almost co-linear.   See Fig. 7.

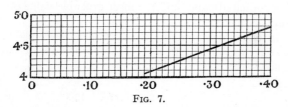

FIG. 7.

The line drawn passes through (0·25, 4·25) and (0·35, 4·60).

Substituting in (2) above :

$$4·25 = n \times 0·25 + c$$
$$4·60 = n \times 0·35 + c.$$

These give $n = 3\cdot5$ and $c = 3\cdot375 = \log k$ and the approximate law is

$$W = 2371d^{3\cdot5}.$$

EXERCISE 6

1. Find the equations to the straight lines :

(a) Through (2, 3) inclined at 30° to the x-axis.

(b) Through (− 1, 1) inclined at 120° to the x-axis.

(c) Through (− 3, − 2) inclined at 37° to the x-axis.

(d) Through (− 2, 3) and (5, 6).

(e) Through (4, − 1) and (− 2, 0).

2. In a certain experiment it is required to show that the product of two variables x and y is constant. In observing the value of y there is a constant error in the reading. The following table gives the experimental reading, y_1, for each value of x.

x . .	15	17	20	25	30	34	40
y_1 . .	5·00	4·34	3·60	2·76	2·20	1·87	1·5

Using squared paper find the most probable value of the constant error.

3. In experiments on the strength of a boiler-plate, to resist varying tensile stresses, the following results were obtained :

y	26·6	22·5	17·8	12·5	7·9	0·1
x	0	5	9·3	13	15·8	17·3

It is believed that the relation between y and x can be represented by a formula

$$y = + \sqrt{a - bx},$$

where a and b are constants. Test this graphically, and find the best values for a and b.   (U.L.C.I.)

4. The following results are found to obey, allowing for errors of observation, the law $x(y + n) = m$. Determine the values of the constants n and m.

y . . .	3	4	5	6	7	8	9	10
x . . .	2·35	2·1	1·9	1·75	1·58	1·45	1·35	1·25

(U.L.C.I.)

5. The following values of x and y were found in a certain experiment :

x . . .	5·5	6·0	6·5	7·0	7·5	8·0	8·5	9·0
y . . .	5·13	4·91	4·71	4·52	4·36	4·20	4·04	3·91

Show that the figures follow a law of the form $y = \dfrac{b}{1 + ax}$ and find the values of the constants a and b.

(U.L.C.I.)

6. The air resistance to the motion of a flat vane is given in the following table, where R = resistance in lb. and V = speed in ft./sec.

R . . .	30	105	163	230	313
V . . .	10	20	25	30	35

Determine whether these values are connected by a law of the form $R = a + bV^2$, and if so find this equation.

7. The following measurements were made from the expansion curve of an indicator diagram.

x . . .	4	5	6	7	8
y . . .	60·1	49·5	42·4	36·8	32·1

It is desired to represent the curve approximately by the equation $y = a + \dfrac{b}{x}$. Test this, and find good average values of a and b.   (B.E.)

8. A steamship at the following speeds, v knots, uses the indicated horse-power P.

v	10	12	14	16	18	20
P	1070	1910	3220	4950	7360	10,400

Is the law connecting v and P of the form $P = kv^n$? If so find the best values of k and n. There are experimental errors in the values of v and P.   (B.E.)

———

7. The student should train himself to recognise symmetry in a curve from its equation.

Take $y = x^2$.

We get the same value of y for $+$ or $-$ values of x. Hence the curve is symmetrical about the y-axis.

Similarly if we have only even powers of y, there is symmetry about the x-axis,

Where both powers are even, we have symmetry about both axes as in the circle $x^2 + y^2 = a^2$.

In $y = x^3$, if any point, say (2, 8), is on the curve, then $(-2, -8)$ is on the curve, and the curve lies only in the first and third quadrants. We need only find points in the first quadrant. The corresponding points in the third quadrant are obtained by a change of sign.

8. The Ellipse

The curve $\dfrac{x^2}{a^2} + \dfrac{y^2}{b^2} = 1$ is clearly symmetrical about both axes.

Since
$$y^2 = b^2\left(1 - \frac{x^2}{a^2}\right)$$
$$= \frac{b^2}{a^2}(a^2 - x^2)$$
$$\text{and } x^2 = \frac{a^2}{b^2}(b^2 - y^2)$$

x can never be greater than a; otherwise y^2 would be negative, and y imaginary. Similarly y can never be greater than b. The curve is an ellipse, whose semi-axes

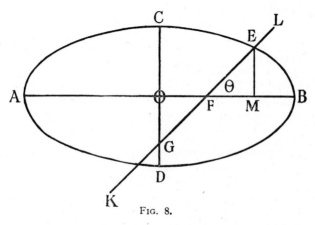

Fig. 8.

are a and b. If $a > b$, $2a$ is the major axis and $2b$ the minor axis.

The curve is readily drawn with the help of a trammel—say, the straight edge of a piece of paper.

Draw AB and CD (Fig. 8), the major and minor axes, each bisected at right angles at O.

KL is the edge of a sheet of paper.

Take any point E on the edge and make $EG = a = OB$ and $EF = b = OC$.

Keep G and F on the minor and major axes respectively, and mark the varying positions of E.

The locus of E is the ellipse :

$$\frac{x^2}{a^2} + \frac{y^2}{b^2} = 1$$

with O as origin.

Proof.—In any position of the trammel with G and F on the axes, let KL make θ with OB.

Then   OM $= x =$ the projection of GE on OB.
                $=$ GE cos θ

i.e., $x = a \cos \theta$.   .   .   .   .   .   (1)

Similarly

                $y =$ ME $=$ EF sin θ

i.e., $y = b \sin \theta$.   .   .   .   .   .   (2)

From (1)

$$\frac{x}{a} = \cos \theta$$

From (2)

$$\frac{y}{b} = \sin \theta$$

∴ Squaring and adding we get :

$$\frac{x^2}{a^2} + \frac{y^2}{b^2} = \cos^2 \theta + \sin^2 \theta = 1.$$

To draw $\dfrac{x^2}{16} + \dfrac{y^2}{9} = 1$

make AB $= 8$ units, CD $= 6$, EG $= 4$ and EF $= 3$.

We could, of course, graph the curve in the usual way.

EXERCISE 7

Plot the following curves :

1. $\dfrac{x^2}{9} + \dfrac{y^2}{4} = 1.$ 2. $\dfrac{x^2}{9} + \dfrac{y^2}{16} = 1.$

3. $3x^2 + 4y^2 = 48.$ 4. $x^2 + 2y^2 = 16.$

9. Graphic Solution of Equations

Notice the following method of solving a given equation graphically.

Example 1

Solve $x^3 - 8x - 5 = 0.$

This may be done by plotting $y = x^3 - 8x - 5$, and finding the points where the curve cuts the x-axis.

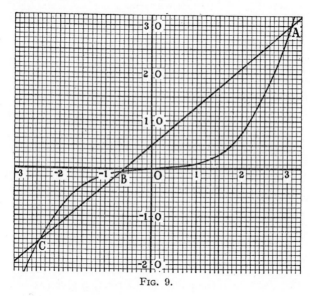

Fig. 9.

Or we may solve thus :

$$x^3 - 8x - 5 = 0$$
$$\therefore \quad x^3 = 8x + 5.$$

Now plot $y = x^3$
and $y = 8x + 5.$

The scale on the x-axis is ten times that on the y-axis.

The graph is shown in Fig. 9.   The points common to the

two curves are A, B, C and their abscissæ are 3·1, − 0·65, and − 2·5, respectively, true to two figures.   These are the roots required.

Example 2

Solve graphically

$$(x^2 - 6)(4 + x^2) = 32x$$

(N.C.   Slightly adapted.)

Clearly $\qquad x^2 - 6 = \dfrac{32x}{4 + x^2}.$

Now graph $\qquad y = x^2 - 6$

and $\qquad\qquad y = \dfrac{32x}{4 + x^2}$

These are shown in Fig. 10.

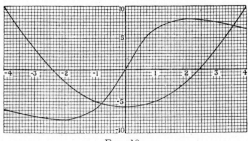

Fig. 10.

The abscissæ of the points of intersection give two of the roots.

These are $x = 3\cdot6$ and $x = -0\cdot75$.

10. The Cubic and Other Equations

The accurate graphing of a cubic function is more readily done when one knows how to get the turning-points on the curve.   See Chapter 7.

In solving any equation graphically say $f(x) = 0$, we are merely concerned with finding the points where the curve $y = f(x)$ cuts the x-axis—*i.e.*, the points where $y = 0$. For this purpose it is not necessary to draw the whole curve.

Suppose, in the curve $y = f(x)$, that when $x = 3$, y is positive, and when $x = 4$, y is negative.

Clearly the curve must cut the axis between $x = 3$ and $x = 4$. Hence we infer a root of $f(x) = 0$ between these two values. To find this root we need only plot values of x and y between these numbers. We may similarly limit our plotting for any further roots.

Example 1

Solve graphically the equation

$$x^3 - 1{\cdot}87x^2 - 4{\cdot}54x + 6{\cdot}41 = 0,$$

by plotting between $x = \pm 3$.

First, make the usual table

x. . .	0	1	2	3	-1	-2	-3
x^3 . .	0	1	8	27	-1	-8	-27
$-1{\cdot}87x^2$.	0	$-1{\cdot}87$	$-7{\cdot}48$	$-16{\cdot}83$	$-1{\cdot}87$	$-7{\cdot}48$	$-16{\cdot}83$
$-4{\cdot}54x + 6{\cdot}41$	$6{\cdot}41$	$1{\cdot}87$	$-2{\cdot}67$	$-7{\cdot}21$	$10{\cdot}95$	$15{\cdot}49$	$20{\cdot}03$
y. . .	$6{\cdot}41$	1	$-2{\cdot}15$	$2{\cdot}96$	$8{\cdot}08$	$0{\cdot}01$	$-23{\cdot}8$

Noting the changes in the sign of y, we see that the roots are between 1 and 2, 2 and 3, whilst the third root is -2 (nearly). Hence we need not plot for the negative values of x.

10 squares = 1 unit horizontally. 5 squares = 1 unit vertically. Fig. 11 (*a*).

To get the root between 2 and 3 :

The curve cuts the x-axis between $x = 2{\cdot}6$ and $x = 2{\cdot}7$.

When $x = 2 \cdot 64$, $y = -0 \cdot 2$

,, $x = 2 \cdot 66$, $y = -0 \cdot 08$ . . . . . (A)

,, $x = 2 \cdot 68$, $y = +0 \cdot 07$ . . . . . (B)

The root is between $2 \cdot 66$ and $2 \cdot 68$.

Plot the last two points, A and B, on the diagram. Fig. 11 (b).

50 squares $= 1$ unit on x-axis, 100 squares $= 1$ unit on y-axis.

The root is clearly $2 \cdot 67$ correct to three figures.

The other roots will be found to be $1 \cdot 2$ and -2.

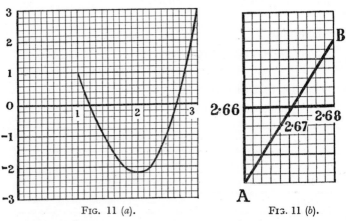

FIG. 11 (a).   FIG. 11 (b).

Example 2

Graph the functions $0 \cdot 08(4x - 3)(x^2 - 9)$ and $\frac{1}{3}(x + 1)$ for values of x from $-3\frac{1}{4}$ to $+3\frac{1}{2}$, using the same scales and reference axes for both graphs. By means of the graphs estimate to two significant figures the roots of

$$0 \cdot 24(4x - 3)(x^2 - 9) - x = 1. \quad \text{(N.C.)}$$

Plot $y = 0 \cdot 08(4x - 3)(x^2 - 9)$ . . . . (1)

i.e., $y = 0 \cdot 08(4x - 3)(x - 3)(x + 3)$ . . (2)

and the straight line

$$y = \tfrac{1}{3}(x + 1) \quad . \quad . \quad . \quad . \quad . \quad . \quad (3)$$

Plot the straight line first.

Where (1) cuts (3) we have, by equating ordinates,

$$0{\cdot}08(4x - 3)(x^2 - 9) = \tfrac{1}{3}(x + 1)$$

i.e., $0{\cdot}24(4x - 3)(x^2 - 9) - x = 1.$

Hence, the common abscissæ give the roots.

The graphs are shown in Fig. 12.

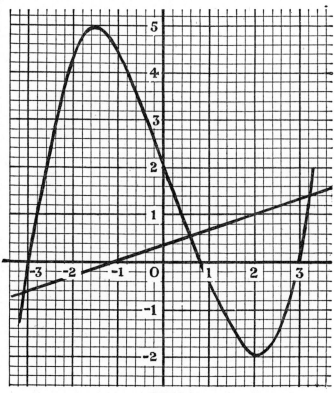

FIG. 12.

The roots are — 3·1, 0·56, *and* 3·3.

Example 3

Solve graphically the following equation

$$x^3 - 2x^2 - 2x + 1 = 0. \qquad \text{(U.E.I.)}$$

Put $y = x^3 - 2x^2 - 2x + 1$ and draw up the table below.

x	0	1	2	3	−1
y	1	−2	−3	4	0

From the table, one root is clearly $x = -1$.

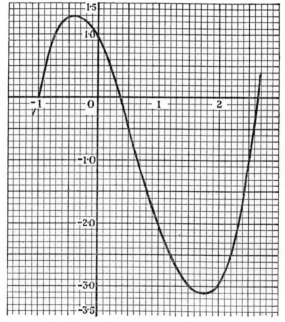

Fig. 13.

Since y changes sign between $x = 0$ and $x = 1$ there is a root between these values.

Similarly, y changes from negative to positive between $x = 2$ and $x = 3$; we thus infer a root between 2 and 3.

Actually we need only plot the curve between $x = 0$ and $x = 1$, and between $x = 2$ and $x = 3$, but the full curve is drawn in Fig. 13 between $x = -1$ and $x = 2.7$.

x	0	0·2	0·4	2	2·2	2·4	2·6	2·7
y	1	0·528	−0·056	−3	−2·432	−1·5	−0·15	0·703

The student should make the above table.   Joining the points (0·2, 0·528) and (0·4, − 0·056) to get one root and the points (2·6, −0·15) and (2·7, 0·703) to get the other.

The roots are seen to be − 1, 0·38, and 2·62.

Example 4

Show that $x^2 - 4 \log_e x = 2.86$ is satisfied by a value between $x = 2$ and $x = 3$, and by a graphic method or otherwise find this value correct to three significant figures.

(U.L.C.I.)

Put $y = x^2 - 4 \log_e x - 2.86$ . . . . . (1)

or $y = x^2 - 9.212 \log_{10} x - 2.86$. . . . (2)

since $\log_e x = 2.303 \log_{10} x$.

If a table of naperian logarithms is available use (1) above; otherwise use (2).

Putting $x = 2$ in (1) above we get

$$y = 4 - 2.77 - 2.86 = -1.63$$

Put $x = 3$,

$$y = 9 - 4.39 - 2.86 = +1.75.$$

Hence a root lies between $x = 2$ and $x = 3$.

Draw up the following table.

x	2·2	2·3	2·4	2·5	2·6
$x^2 - 2·86$.	1·98	2·43	2·90	3·39	3·90
$- 4 \log_e x$.	−3·15	−3·33	−3·50	−3·67	−3·82
y	−1·17	−0·90	−0·60	−0·28	+0·08

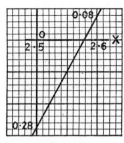

Fig. 14.

The root lies between $x = 2·5$ and $x = 2·6$.

Now join the points given by the last pair of coordinates in the above table and find $x = 2·58$ correct to three figures. (Fig. 14.)

EXERCISE 8

1. Plot
$$y = x^2$$
and
$$y = 5·2x - 6·4$$
Hence solve $x^2 - 5·2x + 6·4 = 0$.

2. Solve $x^2 - 6·4x + 9·43 = 0$ graphically.

3. On the same axes and to the same scale graph the functions $y = 2x^2$ and $y = 3x + 1$, and hence solve the quadratic $x^2 - \dfrac{3x}{2} - \dfrac{1}{2} = 0$.

4. Plot $y = x^3$ and $y = 9x - 3{\cdot}5$, and hence find one root of $x^3 - 9x + 3{\cdot}5 = 0$.

5. Graph each of the functions $[0{\cdot}2x^3(4 - x)]$ and $[0{\cdot}5(x - 2)^2 + 1]$ for values of x from $x = 0$ to $x = +4$, showing accurately the turning-point of each graph and using the same scales and reference axes for both graphs. By means of these graphs estimate within limits $\pm 0{\cdot}05$ the roots of the equation $x^3(x - 4) + 2{\cdot}5x^2 - 10x + 15 = 0$.

[Take the x-axis parallel to the longer side of your sheet of squared paper, and use a length of 8 ins. for the range $x = 0$ to $x = 4$, and a length of 6 ins. for the range $y = 0$ to $y = 6$.]   (N.C.)

6. Graph the function $\frac{1}{6}(x - 4)^2(x + 2)$ for values of x from -2 to $+6$. By means of the graph solve each of the equations

$$(x - 4)^2(x + 2) = 10$$
$$(x - 4)^2(x + 2) = 17. \qquad \text{(N.C.)}$$

7. Graph the function $(3x^2 - x^3)$ for values of x from -1 to $+3$. Find graphically within $\pm 0{\cdot}03$ the roots of each of the equations.

    (i) $x^3 - 3x^2 + 0{\cdot}25(x + 9) = 0$.

    (ii) $x^3 - 3x^2 - 0{\cdot}25(x - 11) = 0$.   (N.C.)

8. The equation $x^2 - 4{\cdot}485 + \dfrac{3{\cdot}25}{x} - 9{\cdot}4 \log_{10} x = 0$ has a root between $2{\cdot}5$ and 3. Find this root accurately to the third decimal place.   (U.L.C.I.)

9. Solve by plotting

$$3x^2 - 20 \log_{10} x - 7{\cdot}077 = 0.$$

                                                          (U.L.C.I.)

CHAPTER 3

PERMUTATIONS. COMBINATIONS. THE BINOMIAL THEOREM

1. No special mathematical knowledge is required to understand the method of finding the permutations or combinations of a given number of different things.

We must first understand the words " permutation " and " combination."

A " *Permutation* " is an arrangement.

A " *Combination* " is a group.

Thus *bac*, *abc*, *cab*, are different permutations of the same group *abc*.

Hence in arrangements order is the essential thing.

In groups or combinations the order of the things is of no importance.

If there are three members of a permutation or combination, we shall speak of it as a three-permutation or a three-combination.

Thus *pqr*, *rpq*, are three-permutations of the same three-combination.

2. The Fundamental Principle

Suppose there are four ways of going to school, and three different ways of returning home. We can clearly go to school and back in 4×3 ways, never using the same road twice in the return journey.

This is a simple illustration of a principle that is fundamental in dealing with the subject of permutations.

This principle is enunciated thus :

Suppose there are m ways of performing a certain action,

and when it has been done in any one of these ways, there are n ways of doing a second action, then the numbers of ways of performing the two actions in succession is $m \times n$.

The principle is almost self-evident, and can be extended to any number of consecutive actions.

Example 1

Take the popular pastime of filling in a football coupon. Suppose we have to predict the results of 7 matches.   Three results are possible in each match.   Each may be associated with the three results of any other match.   Hence the number of columns we require to make certain that one column is correct is 3^7 or 2187.

Example 2

How many possible sets of three letters are there available for the registration of motor cars, assuming that the twenty-six letters of our alphabet can be used.

The first letter may be chosen in 26 ways.   Since we may repeat any letter, the second and third letters may also be chosen in 26 ways each.

The required number is 26^3 or 17,576.

3. To find the number of ways of arranging n different things, using all of them in each arrangement

Suppose we have n different things, and we wish to find how many different ways they can be arranged, using all of them in each arrangement.

The problem is identical with that of seating n people on n chairs, in every possible way.

The first chair may be filled in n ways.

When this has been done the second chair may be filled in $(n - 1)$ ways

since we must leave one person on the first chair.

∴ Using our fundamental principle, the two chairs may be filled in $n(n-1)$ ways.

We go on in this way, until there is but one person to fill the last chair.

∴ The number of ways of arranging n things using all of them in each arrangement is

$$n(n-1)(n-2) \ldots 3.2.1 \quad . \quad . \quad . \quad (1)$$

This is the product of the first n integers, and is denoted by $\lfloor n$ or $n\,!$, and read " factorial n."

Thus $\lfloor 5 = 1 \,.\, 2 \,.\, 3 \,.\, 4 \,.\, 5 = 120 = $ " factorial five."

4. To Find ^nP_r

It often happens that we want to find how many r-permutations we can make from n different things.

Clearly r can never be greater than n.

This problem is stated shortly thus : " Find ^nP_r."

The " n " refers to the number of different things, whilst " r " tells us how many of them appear in each arrangement.

We now see that our problem is to find how many different arrangements of people we can get on r chairs if we have n people at our disposal.

The first chair can be filled by any one of the n people—i.e., it can be filled in n ways.

When it has been filled in any one of these ways the second can be filled in $(n-1)$ ways—i.e., in $(n-2+1)$ ways.

The third can be filled in $(n-2)$ ways—i.e., in $(n-3+1)$ ways, and reasoning in this way we see that the rth can be filled in $(n-r+1)$ ways.

Hence, using the fundamental principle we find :

$$^nP_r = n(n-1)(n-2) \ldots (n-r+1) \quad . \quad . \quad (2)$$

The number of factors is the same as the number of chairs —viz., r.

5. The problem solved in § 3 may now be stated as " Find ^nP_n "—*i.e.*, find the number of ways in which n different things may be arranged, using all of them in each arrangement.   Putting n for r in (2) above we get :

$$^nP_n = n(n - 1)(n - 2) \ldots 3 . 2 . 1 = \lfloor n.$$

Example 1

The number of arrangements of three coins which can be made from a penny, a shilling, a florin, and a half-crown is :

$$^4P_3 = 4 . 3 . 2 = 24.$$

Example 2

The number of three-permutations which can be made from a complete pack of cards is

$$^{52}P_3 = 52 \times 51 \times 50 = 132,600.$$

Example 3

Express $10 \times 9 \times 8 \times 7$ *in factorial notation.*

We have

$$10 \times 9 \times 8 \times 7 = \frac{10 . 9 . 8 . 7 . (6 . 5 . 4 . 3 . 2 . 1)}{(6 . 5 . 4 . 3 . 2 . 1)}$$
$$= \frac{\lfloor 10}{\lfloor 6}.$$

EXERCISE 9

1. Evaluate (*a*) $^7P_3$, (*b*) $^8P_4$, and (*c*) $^6P_6$.

2. Express (*a*) $^6P_2$, (*b*) $^5P_4$, and (*c*) $^8P_2$ in factorial notation.

3. Show that $^nP_r = \dfrac{\lfloor n}{\lfloor n - r}.$

4. If there are nine horses in a race, how many possible ways are there of nominating the first three horses ?

5. How many terms are there in the product

$$(a + b + c)(p + q + r)(x + y + z + w)?$$

6. If there are six stations between two towns, how many different kinds of single third-class tickets must be printed so that one may book from any station to any other?

7. How many numbers each containing three different digits can be made from 2, 3, 4, 5, 6? How many numbers of three digits can be made?

8. In how many ways may eight people sit on eight chairs arranged in a line, if two of them insist on sitting next to each other?

___

6. To Find ^nC_r

The notation ^nC_r means the number of groups (or combinations) each containing r things which we can get if we have n different things from which to choose them.

The problem is identical with that of finding how many different groups of r people we can get from n people.

Observe that any group of r people can be arranged in $\lfloor r$ ways. Thus a group of four people can arrange themselves in $\lfloor 4$, or 24 ways.

Putting $x = {}^nC_r$, we see that $x \lfloor r$ represents the number of ways in which the n people can form r-arrangements, since every group of r can arrange themselves in $\lfloor r$ ways.

Hence $\quad x \lfloor r = {}^nP_r$

$$= n(n-1)(n-2) \ldots (n-r+1)$$

$$\therefore \quad x = {}^nC_r = \frac{n(n-1)(n-2) \ldots (n-r+1)}{\lfloor r}$$

i.e., $\qquad {}^nC_r = \frac{n(n-1)(n-2) \ldots (n-r+1)}{1 \cdot 2 \cdot 3 \ldots r}$

The above formula is very important. Notice that the number of factors in both numerator and denominator is r.

e.g., $\qquad 5C_3 = \frac{5 \cdot 4 \cdot 3}{1 \cdot 2 \cdot 3} = 10.$

7. If we take a group of r from n things, we have a group of $(n - r)$ things left.   Hence the number of r-combinations equals the number of $(n - r)$-combinations.

i.e., $$^nC_r = {}^nC_{n-r}$$

Thus $$^{12}C_{10} = {}^{12}C_2 = \frac{12 \cdot 11}{1 \cdot 2} = 66.$$

Similarly

$$^nC_{n-3} = {}^nC_3 = \frac{n(n-1)(n-2)}{1 \cdot 2 \cdot 3}.$$

Example 1

The number of soccer teams that can be picked from 14 people is

$$^{14}C_{11} = {}^{14}C_3 = \frac{14 \cdot 13 \cdot 12}{1 \cdot 2 \cdot 3} = 364.$$

Example 2

Reverting to Example 1 above, find in how many of the teams a particular man, say Brown, appears, and in how many he does not appear :

(1) if he is in the team, pick 10 men from the remaining 13 men,

$\therefore$ he is in $^{13}C_{10}$—*i.e.,* 286 of the teams.

(2) He is not in $^{13}C_{11}$ of them—*i.e.,* he is not in $\frac{13 \cdot 12}{1 \cdot 2} = 78$ teams; since when he is excluded, we just pick 11 men from 13.

Observe that the number of teams Brown is in together with those he is not in = 364.

This example can be generalised; and it follows that

$$^nC_r = {}^{n-1}C_{r-1} + {}^{n-1}C_r$$

since the groups of r may be divided into (1) those in which a particular thing appears and (2) those in which it does not.

EXERCISE 10

1. Find (a) $^7C_4$, (b) $^8C_6$, (c) $^{10}C_1$, (d) $^5C_5$.

2. Express each of the above examples in factorial notation.

3. Show that $^8C_5 + ^8C_4 = ^9C_5$.

4. How many different triangles can be formed from 16 points in a plane, if no three of the points are in a straight line?

5. How many points of intersection have

(a) eight straight lines in a plane, no two of which are parallel,

(b) eight circles in a plane?

6. From eight white and six coloured balls in how many ways may three white and four coloured balls be selected?

7. In how many ways may seventeen articles be packed into two parcels one containing ten of them and the other seven?

8. If $^8C_r = ^8C_{2r-7}$, find r.

8. The Binomial Theorem

When n is a positive integer, we are now in a position to show that

$$(1 + x)^n = 1 + ^nC_1 x + ^nC_2 x^2 + \ldots$$
$$+ ^nC_r x^r + \ldots + ^nC_n x^n \quad (1)$$

i.e., that $(1 + x)^n = 1 + nx + \frac{n(n-1)}{1 \cdot 2} x^2 + \ldots + x^n \quad (2)$

The expansion in (2) above is known as the Binomial Theorem.

By actual multiplication we see that

$$(1 + x)^2 = (1 + x)(1 + x) = 1 + 2x + x^2 \quad . \quad . \quad . \quad \text{(A)}$$
$$(1 + x)^3 = (1 + x)(1 + x)(1 + x) = 1 + 3x + 3x^2 + x^3 \quad \text{(B)}$$
$$(1 + x)^4 = (1 + x)(1 + x)(1 + x)(1 + x)$$
$$= 1 + 4x + 6x^2 + 4x^3 + x^4 \quad \text{(C)}$$

Proceeding in this way, we observe that

(1) Each expansion is in ascending powers of x.

(2) Each expansion starts with x^0—*i.e.*, 1—and finishes with a power of x indicated by the particular index.

(3) The number of terms in the expansion is one more than the number expressed by the index.

We thus infer that, when n is a positive integer,

$$(1 + x)^n = 1 + a_1 x + a_2 x^2 + \ldots + a_n x^n \ldots \quad (3)$$

All we require to find is the value of each of the a's— viz., a_1, a_2, etc.

This is a simple problem in combinations.

When n is a positive integer

$$(1 + x)^n = (1 + x)(1 + x)(1 + x) \ldots \text{ to } n \text{ factors.}$$

The term in the product on the right-hand side which contains, say, x^3, is formed by taking x from three of its factors in every possible way. Since we have n factors, this may be done in $^nC_3$ ways. Similarly, for every other power of x; the coefficient of x^5 is, then, $^nC_5$, and that of x^r is ^nC_r.

Substituting for a_1, a_2, etc., in (3) we get :

$$(1 + x)^n = 1 + {^nC_1} x + {^nC_2} x^2 + \ldots + {^nC_r} x^r$$
$$+ \ldots + {^nC_n} x^n \quad \cdots \quad (4)$$
$$= 1 + nx + \frac{n(n - 1)}{1 \cdot 2} x^2 + \ldots + x^n \quad \cdots \quad (5)$$

The forms (4) and (5) above for the Binomial Theorem should be remembered.

Example 1

Expand fully $(1 + x)^6$.

We have

$$(1 + x)^6 = 1 + {^6C_1} x + {^6C_2} x^2 + {^6C_3} x^3 + {^6C_4} x^4$$
$$+ {^6C_5} x^5 + {^6C_6} x^6$$

Notice that $^6C_6 = 1$, and that $^6C_5 = {}^6C_1$, etc. So that the coefficients of terms equidistant from the beginning and end of the series are equal.

Writing out the coefficients fully, we get :

$$(1 + x)^6 = 1 + 6x + 15x^2 + 20x^3 + 15x^4 + 6x^5 + x^6.$$

From (4) above, the coefficient of any particular power of x may readily be written down.

Thus, in $(1 + x)^8$ the term involving x^5 is $^8C_5 x^5$—i.e., $56x^5$.

9. Now notice that :

$$(1 - x)^n = \{1 + (- x)\}^n$$

$$= 1 + n(- x) + \frac{n(n - 1)}{1 \cdot 2}(- x)^2 + \ldots$$

$$= 1 - nx + \frac{n(n - 1)}{1 \cdot 2}x^2 -, \text{etc.}$$

viz.—the terms are alternately positive and negative. Thus the first four terms of $(1 - x)^7$ are :

$$1 - 7x + 21x^2 - 35x^3$$

$(1 + 2x)^9$ is expanded thus :

$$(1 + 2x)^9 = 1 + {}^9C_1(2x) + {}^9C_2(2x)^2 + {}^9C_3(2x)^3 +, \text{etc.}$$
$$= 1 + 18x + 144x^2 + 672x^3 +, \text{etc.}$$

10. The form

$$(1 + x)^n = 1 + nx + \frac{n(n - 1)}{1 \cdot 2}x^2 + \frac{n(n - 1)(n - 2)}{1 \cdot 2 \cdot 3}x^3 + \ldots$$

we shall call the " Standard form of the Binomial Theorem." Any other form can be reduced to this one.

Example 1

Expand $(a + x)^n$.

$$(a + x) = a\left(1 + \frac{x}{a}\right)$$

$$\therefore (a + x)^n = a^n\left(1 + \frac{x}{a}\right)^n$$

$$= a^n\left[1 + {}^nC_1\frac{x}{a} + {}^nC_2\frac{x^2}{a^2} + \dots + {}^nC_r\frac{x^r}{a^r} + \dots\right]$$

i.e. $(a + x)^n = a^n + {}^nC_1 a^{n-1}x + {}^nC_2 a^{n-2}x^2 + \dots$
$$+ {}^nC_r a^{n-r}x^r + \dots \quad (6)$$

This expansion is more general than the one in standard form, but is not so useful.

Example 2

Expand $\left(3 + \dfrac{x}{2}\right)^6$ *as far as the term in* x^2.

$$\left(3 + \frac{x}{2}\right) = 3\left(1 + \frac{x}{6}\right)$$

$$\therefore \left(3 + \frac{x}{2}\right)^6 = 3^6\left(1 + \frac{x}{6}\right)^6$$

$$= 3^6\left(1 + 6 \cdot \frac{x}{6} + \frac{6 \cdot 5}{1 \cdot 2} \cdot \frac{x^2}{36} + \dots\right)$$

$$= 3^6\left(1 + x + \frac{5x^2}{12}\right).$$

11. The expansion of $(1 + x)^n$ preserves the same form when n is not $a +$ integer, provided that x is real and is numerically less than unity. The proof of this proposition is beyond the scope of this book.

Thus if $x < 1$ (numerically)

$$(1 + x)^{-4} = 1 + (-4)x + \frac{(-4)(-5)}{1 \cdot 2}x^2$$

$$+ \frac{(-4)(-5)(-6)}{1 \cdot 2 \cdot 3}x^3 + \dots$$

$$= 1 - 4x + 10x^2 - 20x^3 + \dots$$

N.B.—We cannot use the form involving ${}^nC_1$, etc.

In the above, observe that the series on the right-hand side is unending.

Similarly

$$(1 - x)^{-\frac{1}{2}} = 1 + (-\tfrac{1}{2})(-x) + \frac{(-\frac{1}{2})(-\frac{3}{2})}{1 \cdot 2}(-x)^2$$
$$+ \frac{(-\frac{1}{2})(-\frac{3}{2})(-\frac{5}{2})}{1 \cdot 2 \cdot 3}(-x)^3$$
$$= 1 + \frac{x}{2} + \frac{3x^2}{8} + \tfrac{5}{16}x^3 +, \text{ etc.}$$

12. We summarise our results thus :

$$(1 + x)^n = 1 + nx + \frac{n(n-1)}{1 \cdot 2}x^2 + \frac{n(n-1)(n-2)}{1 \cdot 2 \cdot 3}x^3 + \dots$$

   (a) *If n is a positive integer, the series terminates after (n + 1) terms have been written down, and the series gives the exact value of $(1 + x)^n$ for all values of x.*

   (b) *If n is a negative integer, or a positive or negative fraction, the " form " of the series is preserved, but gives the true value of $(1 + x)^n$ only when x is numerically less than unity.*

Example

$$\frac{1}{(1 + 2x)^3} = (1 + 2x)^{-3}$$
$$= 1 + (-3)(2x) + \frac{(-3)(-4)}{1 \cdot 2}(2x)^2 + \dots$$
$$= 1 - 6x + 24x^2 -, \text{ etc.}$$

In the above case $2x < 1$ (numerically),
i.e., $x < \frac{1}{2}$ (numerically).

N.B.—When we wish to refer merely to the numerical value of x, we write it thus : $|x|$ —*e.g.*,

if $x = -2.$
                      $|x| = \quad 2.$

$|x|$ is then read " the numerical value of x."

In the above example, we have, then :

$$|2x| < 1$$
$$|x| < \tfrac{1}{2}.$$

13. The following examples are typical of many which involve a knowledge of the Binomial Theorem.

Example 1

Find the term independent of x, i.e., the constant term, in the expansion of $\left(x - \dfrac{2}{x}\right)^8$.

$$\left(x - \frac{2}{x}\right) = x\left(1 - \frac{2}{x^2}\right)$$
$$\therefore \ \left(x - \frac{2}{x}\right)^8 = x^8\left(1 - \frac{2}{x^2}\right)^8$$

The required term will be the one containing $\dfrac{1}{x^8}$ when the binomial is expanded—*i.e.*, the fifth term.

Its value is $x^8 \, . \, {}^8C_4\left(-\dfrac{2}{x^2}\right)^4 = 1120.$

Example 2

Write down the expansion of $(x + a)^n$ where n is a positive integer. Give in full the $(r + 1)$th term. Find the constant term in the expansion of $\left(x^3 - \dfrac{2}{x^4}\right)^{14}$.   (U.L.C.I.)

$$(x + a)^n = x^n\left(1 + \frac{a}{x}\right)^n$$
$$= x^n\left(1 + {}^nC_1\frac{a}{x} + {}^nC_2\frac{a^2}{x^2} + \ldots + {}^nC_r\frac{a^r}{x^r} + \ldots + {}^nC_n\frac{a^n}{x^n}\right)$$
$$= x^n + {}^nC_1x^{n-1}a + {}^nC_2x^{n-2}a^2 + \ldots$$
$$+ {}^nC_rx^{n-r}a^r + \ldots + a^n.$$

The $(r + 1)$th term
$$= {}^nC_rx^{n-r}a^r$$
$$= \frac{n(n - 1)(n - 2) \ldots (n - r + 1)}{1 . 2 . 3 \ldots r}x^{n-r}a^r.$$

Also $\qquad \left(x^3 - \dfrac{2}{x^4}\right)^{14} = x^{42}\left(1 - \dfrac{2}{x^7}\right)^{14}.$

Hence (see example 1 above) the constant term is the seventh and is :

$$x^{42} \cdot {}^{14}C_6\left(-\frac{2}{x^7}\right)^6$$
$$= {}^{14}C_6 \cdot 2^6.$$

Example 3

$$\frac{1}{1+x} = (1+x)^{-1}$$
$$= 1 + (-1)x + \frac{(-1)(-2)x^2}{1 \cdot 2} +, \text{ etc.}$$
$$= 1 - x + x^2 - \ldots$$

If x is so small that x^2 and higher powers may be neglected, we get that :

$$\frac{1}{1+x} = 1 - x.$$

Similarly

$$\frac{1}{\sqrt{1+x}} = (1+x)^{-\frac{1}{2}} = 1 - \tfrac{1}{2}x$$

neglecting higher powers of x than the first.

Thus :

$$\frac{1}{\sqrt{0 \cdot 998}} = \frac{1}{\sqrt{1 - 0 \cdot 002}} = (1 - 0 \cdot 002)^{-\frac{1}{2}}$$
$$= 1 + \tfrac{1}{2} \times 0 \cdot 002 = 1 \cdot 001.$$

Example 4

Let $\qquad E = \dfrac{(1+x)^4}{\sqrt{1-x}}$

$$= (1+x)^4(1-x)^{-\frac{1}{2}}$$
$$= (1 + 4x + \ldots)(1 + \tfrac{1}{2}x + \ldots)$$
$$= 1 + 4x + \tfrac{1}{2}x + \ldots$$
$$= 1 + \frac{9x}{2}, \text{ neglecting } x^2, \text{ etc.}$$

Evaluate
$$\frac{(1 \cdot 02)^4}{\sqrt{0 \cdot 98}}$$

Here $x = 0 \cdot 02$

An approximate value is, therefore, by example 4 :
$$1 + \tfrac{9}{2} \times 0 \cdot 02 = 1 \cdot 09.$$

Example 5

Consider the formula $\dfrac{pv}{T} =$ constant, where p is the pressure of a gas in lb./sq. in., v the volume in cub. ins., and T the absolute temperature.

Suppose v increased by 3%, T diminished by 2%, what is the percentage change in p?

$$v \text{ becomes } v(1 + 0 \cdot 03)$$
$$T \text{ becomes } T(1 - 0 \cdot 02)$$
$$p \text{ becomes } p(1 + x), \text{ say}$$

$$\therefore \quad \frac{pv}{T} = \text{constant} = \frac{p \cdot v(1 + 0 \cdot 03)(1 + x)}{T \cdot (1 - 0 \cdot 02)}$$

$$\therefore \quad 1 + x = \frac{1 - 0 \cdot 02}{1 + 0 \cdot 03}$$
$$= (1 - 0 \cdot 02)(1 + 0 \cdot 03)^{-1}$$
$$= (1 - 0 \cdot 02)(1 - 0 \cdot 03)$$
$$= 1 - 0 \cdot 02 - 0 \cdot 03$$
$$= 1 - 0 \cdot 05.$$

Hence $x = -0 \cdot 05$ and p decreases by 5%.

EXERCISE 11

Expand to four terms, putting where necessary each binomial in " standard form."

1. (a) $(1 + z)^{\frac{1}{2}}$, (b) $(1 - h)^{-1}$, (c) $(1 + y)^{\frac{3}{2}}$, (d) $(1 - x)^{-\frac{4}{3}}$,
   (e) $\dfrac{1}{1 + x}$, (f) $\dfrac{1}{\sqrt{1 - x}}$, (g) $\dfrac{1}{\sqrt[4]{1 + x}}$, (h) $\dfrac{1}{(1 + x)^3}$,
   (k) $(a + x)^{-2}$, (l) $(a + 2h)^{\frac{1}{2}}$, (m) $(2 - 3x)^{-4}$.

2. Find approximately, using the Binomial Theorem,

    (a) $(1 \cdot 02)^5$,   (b) $(0 \cdot 997)^4$,   (c) $\sqrt{1 \cdot 006}$,   (d) $\dfrac{1}{0 \cdot 996}$,

    (e) $\dfrac{1}{3 \cdot 015}$, (f) $\sqrt[3]{1 \cdot 021}$.

3. Supposing h small compared with x find values for
$$\frac{(x + h)^8 - x^8}{h}, \quad \frac{(x + h)^{\frac{1}{2}} - x^{\frac{1}{2}}}{h}.$$

4. Using the Binomial Theorem, find the first five terms in the expansion of $\sqrt{1 + 2x}$.   (U.E.I.)

5. If x is so small that its third and higher powers may be neglected, show by the Binomial Theorem that the values of $\sqrt[n]{\dfrac{1 + x}{1 - x}}$ and $\dfrac{n + x}{n - x}$ may be considered equal.

    (N.C.)

6. Expand $\dfrac{(1 - x)^{\frac{5}{8}}}{(1 - x^2)^{\frac{1}{3}}}$ in ascending powers of x as far as the term containing x^2.

    Prove that $\dfrac{(1 - x)^{\frac{1}{2}}}{(1 + x)^{\frac{1}{3}}} = \dfrac{(1 - x)^{\frac{5}{8}}}{(1 - x^2)^{\frac{1}{3}}}$ and hence deduce that, when $x = 0 \cdot 12$, $\dfrac{(1 - x)^{\frac{1}{2}}}{(1 + x)^{\frac{1}{3}}}$ is approximately equal to $0 \cdot 9048$.

    (N.C.)

7. Find the coefficient of the seventh term in the expansion of $\left(\dfrac{2}{7} - \dfrac{x^3}{3} \right)^{10}$.   (U.L.C.I.)

8. Expand $(1 - 3x)^9$ for five terms and find the values of the fourth and fifth terms when $x = 0 \cdot 06$.   (U.L.C.I.)

9. Find the middle term in the expansion of $\left(x + \dfrac{a^2}{x} \right)^{12}$.

    (U.L.C.I.)

10. Expand $(x - y)^{\frac{1}{2}}$ to the first four terms, and when $x = 3$ and $y = - 0 \cdot 1$ find the numerical value of each of the first three terms of your result to four significant figures.

    (U.L.C.I.)

11. Using the Binomial Theorem find approximate values for (i) $\sqrt[3]{0\cdot985}$, (ii) $\dfrac{1}{\sqrt{0\cdot016}}$.   (U.L.C.I.)

12. Find the term containing x^{22} in the expansion of $\left(\dfrac{x^2}{2} - \dfrac{3}{4}\right)^{14}$.   (U.L.C.I.)

13. Given $F_1 = \dfrac{m}{(d - l)^2}$ and $F_2 = \dfrac{m}{(d + l)^2}$ find by using the Binomial Theorem the approximate value of $F_1 - F_2$, when l is so small compared with d that powers of $\dfrac{l}{d}$ above the first can be neglected.   (U.L.C.I.)

CHAPTER 4

FUNCTION. LIMIT. INFINITESIMAL. DEFINITION OF A DIFFERENTIAL COEFFICIENT

1. Functions of One Variable

In plotting $y = x^2$, we give a value to x, and then calculate a value of y. The two values, x and y, determine a point on the graph.

Both x and y are termed variables. In the above case x is the independent variable because any value whatsoever may be given to it. y is the dependent variable because its value depends on that given to x.

Definition

When a value given to x determines a value of y, y is called a function of x.

2. Notation

When y is a function of x, we express the fact by writing $y = f(x)$ or $y = F(x)$, and sometimes by $y = \phi(x)$. We shall use one or other of the first two forms.

Thus $\qquad y = f(x) = 3x^2 - 5x + 2$
and $\qquad y = F(\theta) = 3 \sin \theta + 2 \cos \theta$

are examples of functions of x and of θ. Both the above functions are called explicit functions, because one variable is expressed solely in terms of the other. In both cases we know the " form " of y.

On the other hand, if we merely know $y = f(x)$—*i.e.*, that y is some function of x—the only knowledge we get from the relationship is that values given to x determine values of y. We cannot calculate values of y, but can only say that when $x = 2, y = f(2)$, when $x = 0, y = f(0)$, etc.

Example 1

If
$$y = f(x) = 3x^2 - 4x + 2$$
$$f(2) = 3 . 2^2 - 4 . 2 + 2 = 6$$
$$f(-1) = 3(-1)^2 - 4 . (-1) + 2 = 9$$
$$f(\tfrac{1}{2}) = 3(\tfrac{1}{2})^2 - 4(\tfrac{1}{2}) + 2 = \tfrac{3}{4}.$$

Example 2

If $\qquad\qquad y = \sin 2\theta°$

we have $\qquad F(\theta°) = \sin 2\theta°$
$$F(15°) = \sin 30° = \tfrac{1}{2}$$
$$F(30°) = \sin 60° = \frac{\sqrt{3}}{2} = 0\cdot 866.$$

The student will now realise that all the formulæ he uses are examples of functions.

Thus : $\qquad\qquad V = \tfrac{4}{3}\pi r^3$

—the volume of a sphere is a function of the radius.

Again, if $\qquad\qquad f = \dfrac{Ex}{l}$

—the intensity of stress, f, is a function of the strain, x. Any other formulæ may be regarded in a similar way.

It should be observed that some functions of x are true only between certain values of x. For instance, $f = \dfrac{Ex}{l}$ holds only for values of x between the elastic limits.

Similarly $y = \dfrac{1}{x}$ is not a function of x for the value $x = 0$, since $\tfrac{1}{0}$ has no value.

Perhaps the student has been accustomed to state that $\tfrac{1}{0}$ is equal to " infinity," whatever he may mean by that word. He should, however, remember that we cannot divide by zero; and will convince himself of this fact if he tries to divide both sides of the equation $2 \times 0 = 3 \times 0$ by zero.

EXERCISE 12

1. Given that $f(x) = 3x^2 - 5x + 2$, find (a) $f(2)$, (b) $f(0)$, (c) $f(-3)$, (d) $f(\frac{1}{2})$.

2. If $f(\theta°) = 3 \sin 2\theta° + 4 \cos \theta°$, find (a) $f(0°)$, (b) $f(15°)$, (c) $f(30°)$.

3. If $F(x) = 3x^3 - 4x + 2$, find (a) $F(3) - F(2)$, (b) $F(-1) - F(-3)$.

4. If $f(x) = 2x^2 - x - 4$, find (a) $f(x + 2) - f(x)$, (b) $f(x + h) - f(x)$.

5. If $\phi(t) = 3t^2 + 2t - 1$, find $\phi(t + 2) - \phi(t + 1)$.

3. The Notion of a " Limit "

The use of the word limit in a mathematical sense is closely allied to many of the ways in which we use the word in everyday speech.

When we speak of " working to the limit," or say that a person has reached the " limit of endurance " we imply : (a) a boundary to the amount produced by, or to the possible endurance of, say, an individual, and (b) that the boundary has not quite been reached, otherwise the person could neither work nor endure.

This notion of " not quite reaching the boundary " is inherent in the mathematical notion of a limit.

Consider $$y = \frac{1}{x}$$

Case I.

Let x increase progressively.

If $\qquad x = 10^4, \quad y = \dfrac{1}{10^4} = 0.0001.$

If $\qquad x = 10^5, \quad y = \dfrac{1}{10^5} = 0.00001.$

as x gets larger and larger, we see that y gets smaller and smaller.

To express this progression of x through greater and greater values we shall use the symbol ∞, and call it infinity.

We then write :

$$\underset{x \longrightarrow \infty}{Lt} \left(\frac{1}{x}\right) = 0$$

Lt is an abbreviation of the word "limit." "$x \longrightarrow \infty$" should be read as "x tends to infinity" and the statement

$$\underset{x \longrightarrow \infty}{Lt} \left(\frac{1}{x}\right) = 0,$$

means that as x progresses through greater and greater values $\frac{1}{x}$ approaches nearer and nearer to zero.

Case II.

Let x decrease indefinitely.

When $\qquad x = 0{\cdot}001, \quad y = \dfrac{1}{0{\cdot}001} = 10^3$

When $\qquad x = 0{\cdot}0001, \; y = \dfrac{1}{0{\cdot}0001} = 10^4$

and again we see that as x gets smaller $\frac{1}{x}$ becomes greater— *i.e.*, that

$$\underset{x \longrightarrow 0}{Lt} \frac{1}{x} = \infty \quad . \quad . \quad . \quad . \quad . \quad (2)$$

We do not mean that ∞ (infinity) is a number, but the statement (2) is a short way of saying that no matter how great a number N may be named by some hypothetical person Z, we can always choose x so small that $\frac{1}{x} > N$.

All we need do is to choose x smaller than $\frac{1}{N}$. Further, notice that we never contemplate x as having the value zero.

If we graph $y = \dfrac{1}{x}$ for positive values of x we get a curve that approaches the x-axis as $x \longrightarrow \infty$, and approaches the y-axis as $x \longrightarrow 0$.

Example 1

$$y = f(x) = \frac{(3 - x)(x - 1)}{x - 1} \quad . \quad . \quad . \quad (1)$$

When $x = 1$, $y = \dfrac{2 \times 0}{0} = \dfrac{0}{0}.$

If we are asked " what is the value of y when $x = 1$?," we must reply that nobody knows, or that its value is indeterminate, which means the same thing.

Now, in (1) put $x = 1 + h$

Then $y = \dfrac{(2 - h) \cdot h}{h}$

$$= 2 - h,$$

provided h is not zero.

If, after dividing by h, we now make $h = 0$, we get $y = 2$.

We write this result :

$$\underset{x \longrightarrow 1}{Lt} \frac{(3 - x)(x - 1)}{(x - 1)} = 2$$

Thus, although we cannot find a value of y when $x = 1$, the result shows that if our hypothetical person Z names any small number ε, we can find a value of x that differs very little from unity, which will make y differ from 2 by less than ε.

In the above example, should Z give the number 0·00001, we merely choose h smaller than this—say, 0·000001.

Example 2

Evaluate $\underset{x \longrightarrow 2}{Lt} \dfrac{x^2 - x - 2}{x - 2}$

If the student will adopt the following method, he will have difficulty neither in evaluating examples similar to the above nor in understanding them.

Let $$f(x) = \frac{x^2 - x - 2}{x - 2}$$

If $x = 2$, $f(x)$ takes the form $\frac{0}{0}$.

Put $$x = (2 + h)$$

Then :

$$f(2 + h) = \frac{(2 + h)^2 - (2 + h) - 2}{h}$$

$$= \frac{4 + 4h + h^2 - 2 - h - 2}{h}$$

$$= \frac{h^2 + 3h}{h}$$

$$= h + 3.$$

Now put $h = 0$, and we see that the required limit is **3**.

EXERCISE 13

1. Evaluate $\underset{x \longrightarrow 1}{Lt} \dfrac{(x + 4)(x - 1)}{x - 1}$.

2. Find $\underset{x \longrightarrow 2}{Lt} \dfrac{x^2 + x - 6}{x - 2}$.

3. Find $\underset{x \longrightarrow 3}{Lt} \dfrac{2x^2 - 5x - 3}{x - 3}$.

4. Find $\underset{x \longrightarrow 0}{Lt} \dfrac{x^2 + 3x}{x}$.

5. Find $\underset{x \longrightarrow 3}{Lt} \dfrac{2x^2 - x - 15}{x^2 + 2x - 15}$.

6. Evaluate $\underset{x \longrightarrow 2}{Lt} \dfrac{x^2 - x - 2}{2x^2 - 3x - 2}$.

7. Find $\underset{t \longrightarrow 5}{Lt} \dfrac{3t^2 - 13t - 10}{2t^2 - 9t - 5}$.

8. Show that $\underset{h \longrightarrow 0}{Lt} \dfrac{(x + h)^3 - x^3}{h} = 3x^2$

5. The Differential Notation and Infinitesimals

Suppose ABK is any curve whose equation is $y = f(x)$.

Let   OM $= x$ $\therefore$ MA $= f(x)$.

MN is a positive increment of x. It will be written Δx. [Not $\Delta \times x$.] This is simply a notation, and may be read as " an increment of x " or " a bit of x," or " Delta x."

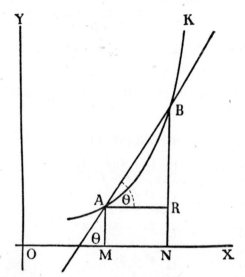

Fig. 15.

Δ is the Greek capital D, and is named Delta.

ON is then $= x + \Delta x$

          $\therefore$ NB $= f(x + \Delta x)$.

If AR is parallel to OX, we see that

          MA $=$ NR $= f(x)$

          $\therefore$ RB $= f(x + \Delta x) - f(x)$ . . .

and   AR $= \Delta x$.

It is clear that the gradient of the chord AB is tan θ, where

$$\tan \theta = \frac{f(x + \Delta x) - f(x)}{\Delta x}, \; i.e., \frac{RB}{AR}$$

Now let $\Delta x \longrightarrow 0$—*i.e.*, let N approach M so that no matter how small a number, ε, is named by our hypothetical Mr. Z, we can make Δx smaller than ε. We thus observe

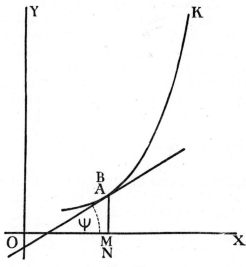

Fig. 16.

that although we never contemplate the actual arrival of N at M, it is impossible for Z to stop the approach of N to M, since no matter how small a number he names, we can make Δx smaller than this number.

As N approaches M, B approaches A, and the chord AB approaches coincidence with the tangent at A, as in the above figure.

The gradient of the tangent at A is $\tan \psi$. In the above work, Δx is an example of an infinitesimal, which we define as "a variable whose limit is zero."

Δx may now also be read as "the differential of x."

We shall often use the letter "h" instead of the symbol Δx.

Referring to Fig. 15 of this chapter, we see that

$$MA = NR = f(x) = y,$$

and $\qquad \therefore \quad NB = NR + RB = y + \Delta y,$

for by our definition RB is an infinitesimal, and may be regarded as the differential of y, or the increment of y.

6. We summarise the ideas of the last paragraph thus :

(1) For any curve, $y = f(x)$, θ is the angle made by any chord AB with the positive sense of OX.

(2) The gradient of this chord is $\tan \theta$, where

$$\tan \theta = \frac{RB}{RA} = \frac{f(x + \Delta x) - f(x)}{\Delta x} = \frac{f(x + h) - f(x)}{h}$$
$$= \frac{\Delta y}{\Delta x}$$

(3) Fig. 16 is what Fig. 15 becomes as $h \longrightarrow 0$, and we infer that the gradient of the tangent at any point A of the curve $y = f(x)$ is $\tan \psi$, where

$$\tan \psi = \underset{\Delta x \longrightarrow 0}{\mathbf{Lt}} \frac{\Delta y}{\Delta x} = \underset{h \longrightarrow 0}{\mathbf{Lt}} \frac{f(x + h) - f(x)}{h} \quad (1)$$

Example 1

Consider $y = f(x) = x^2$. Find the gradient of the chord joining $(1, 1)$ and $(2, 4)$.

If $\tan \theta$ is the gradient, we get :

$$\tan \theta = \frac{\text{Difference between the two ordinates}}{\text{Difference between the two abscissæ}}$$
$$= \frac{4 - 1}{2 - 1}$$
$$= 3.$$

The gradient of the chord joining two points on a curve is sometimes called the average gradient of the curve between the points.

Example 2

If $f(x) = 2x^2 + x + 1$, find the average gradient of the graph between the points where $x = \frac{1}{2}$ and $x = 2$.

$$\text{Average gradient} = \frac{f(2) - f(\frac{1}{2})}{2 - \frac{1}{2}}$$

$$= \frac{11 - 2}{\frac{3}{2}}$$

$$= 6.$$

In this example we have taken the average gradient of the graph between the two points as that of the chord which joins them.

Example 3

Find the gradient of the tangent at the point $(2, 4)$ on the curve $y = f(x) = x^2$.

This example shows how we apply to a particular curve formula (1), which is fundamental in much of the work of this book.

From formula (1), if $\tan \psi$ is the gradient we have :

$$\tan \psi = \mathop{Lt}_{h \longrightarrow 0} \frac{f(x + h) - f(x)}{h}$$

In our example

$$f(x) = x^2, \text{ and } x = 2$$

$$\therefore \quad \tan \psi = \mathop{Lt}_{h \longrightarrow 0} \frac{(2 + h)^2 - 2^2}{h}$$

$$= \mathop{Lt}_{h \longrightarrow 0} \frac{4h + h^2}{h}$$

$$= Lt (4 + h)$$

$$= 4.$$

Example 4

Find the gradient of the tangent to the curve, $y = 2x^2 + x - 1$, *at the point where* $x = 3$.

Here, $\qquad\qquad f(x) = 2x^2 + x - 1$

$$\tan \psi = \underset{h \to 0}{\mathrm{Lt}} \frac{\{2(3 + h)^2 + (3 + h) - 1\} - \{2 \cdot 3^2 + 3 - 1\}}{h}$$

$$= \mathrm{Lt} \frac{\{2(9 + 6h + h^2) + 3 + h - 1 - 20\}}{h}$$

$$= \mathrm{Lt} \frac{13h + 2h^2}{h}$$

$$= \mathrm{Lt} (13 + 2h)$$

$$= 13, \text{ if we put } h = 0.$$

Example 5

Find the equation to the tangent at the point (3, 20) *on the curve in the above example.*

We have just found the gradient of the tangent—viz., $\tan \psi$ to be **13**. Also, the tangent passes through the point (3, 20).

Hence its equation is

$$y - 20 = 13(x - 3)$$

i.e., $\qquad\qquad\qquad 13x - y - 19 = 0.$

EXERCISE 14

1. If $y = 3x^2$, find the average gradient between the points where $x = 1$ and $x = 2$.

2. If $y = x^2$, find the gradient of the chord joining the points where—

      (a) $x = 3$, and $x = 4$.

      (b) $x = -1$, and $x = 2$.

      (c) $x = 1$, and $x = 1 + h$.

3. Using the result of (c) above, find the gradient of the tangent at the point (1, 1) on the curve $y = x^2$. Write down the equation to the tangent at this point.

4. Find the equation of the tangent at the point where $x = 2$ on the curve $y = 4x^2$.

5. Find the equation to the tangent at the point where $x = 2$ on the curve $y = 2x^2 + x + 1$.

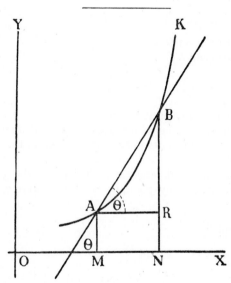

FIG. 17.

7. Differential Coefficient, or Derivative

The above figure is Fig. 15 of this chapter reproduced.

The equation of the curve is $y = f(x)$; $OM = x$ and $MN = h = \Delta x$.

Notice that A represents any point on the curve, and in order to get the gradient of the tangent at A, we let N approach M and use the equation from paragraph (6)

$$\tan \psi = \underset{h \to 0}{Lt} \frac{f(x + h) - f(x)}{h}$$

This limit is called " the differential coefficient of y or $f(x)$ with respect to x."

We write it $\dfrac{dy}{dx}$. It is also called the first derivative of the function of x, $f(x)$, with respect to x.

Similarly if $z = f(\theta)$, $\dfrac{dz}{d\theta}$ is the differential coefficient of z, or $f(\theta)$, with respect to θ.

The relationship

$$\frac{dy}{dx} = \operatorname*{Lt}_{h \to 0} \frac{f(x + h) - f(x)}{h}$$

is fundamental, and must be remembered.

It has already been used by the student, when finding the gradients of the tangents to the curves given in the last set of examples.

Geometrically, a differential coefficient is the gradient of the tangent at any point (x, y) of the curve $y = f(x)$.

Example 8

$If \qquad y = x^2 + x$, find $\dfrac{dy}{dx}$

$$\begin{aligned}
\frac{dy}{dx} &= \operatorname*{Lt}_{h \to 0} \frac{\{(x + h)^2 + (x + h)\} - \{x^2 + x\}}{h} \\
&= Lt \frac{(2hx + h^2 + h)}{h} \\
&= Lt(2x + h + 1) \\
&= 2x + 1, \text{ when } h \longrightarrow 0.
\end{aligned}$$

$2x + 1$ is then the gradient of the tangent at any point whose abscissa is x. Thus if $x = 2$, then $y = 6$, and $\tan \psi = 5$.

Hence the equation to the tangent at $(2, 6)$ is

$$y - 6 = 5(x - 2)$$

EXERCISE 15

1. Find the differential coefficients with respect to x of (a) x^2, (b) $3x^2 + x$, (c) x^3.

2. Get $\dfrac{d}{dt}(4t^2)$ and $\dfrac{d}{dz}(2z^2 + 3)$.

3. If $y = 3x^2 + 2x + 4$ find $\dfrac{dy}{dx}$. Then write down the equation to the tangent at the point where $x = 1$.

4. Find the gradient of the tangent where $t = 2$ on the curve $y = 4 - t + t^2$.

CHAPTER 5

DIFFERENTIATION OF FUNCTIONS OF A SINGLE VARIABLE

1. The Differentiation of x^n

It must be recalled that if $y = f(x)$, the gradient at any

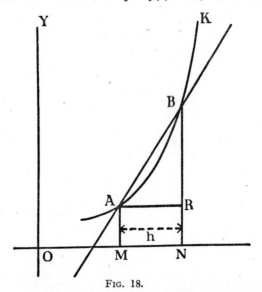

FIG. 18.

point A, where $OM = x$ and $MA = y = f(x)$, is calculated from the equation :

$$\frac{dy}{dx} = \underset{h \to 0}{Lt} \frac{f(x + h) - f(x)}{h} \qquad \cdot \quad \cdot \quad \cdot \quad \cdot \quad (1)$$

If $y = f(x) = x^n$

$$f(x + h) = (x + h)^n = x^n\left(1 + \frac{h}{x}\right)^n$$

Hence

$$\frac{dy}{dx} = \operatorname*{Lt}_{h \to 0} \frac{x^n\left(1 + \frac{h}{x}\right)^n - x^n}{h} \quad . \quad . \quad . \quad . \quad . \quad (2)$$

Before proceeding to evaluate (2), it is advisable to note the following points :—

(1) The letter "f" standing for "function" must be omitted from (2), since we have been given its form explicitly.

(2) $(x + h)^n$ has been put in "standard form."

(3) Since $h \longrightarrow 0, \frac{h}{x}$ may be taken as a proper fraction and therefore the expansion of $\left(1 + \frac{h}{x}\right)^n$ is true for all values of n, positive or negative, integral or fractional.

(4) In finding the gradient at A, x or OM remains *constant*; the independent variable is MN— *i.e.*, h or Δx.

Hence

$$\frac{dy}{dx} = \operatorname*{Lt}_{h \to 0} \frac{x^n\left(1 + \frac{h}{x}\right)^n - x^n}{h}$$

$$= x^n \operatorname{Lt} \frac{\left(1 + \frac{h}{x}\right)^n - 1}{h} \quad \text{[Taking out the common factor, } x^n \text{]}$$

$$= x^n \operatorname{Lt} \frac{\left(1 + \frac{nh}{x} + \text{terms in higher powers of } h\right) - 1}{h}$$

$$= x^n \cdot \frac{n}{x} \quad \left[\begin{array}{l}\text{The two units disappear; and the only term} \\ \text{without } h \text{ after division is } \frac{n}{x}\end{array}\right]$$

i.e.,
$$\frac{d}{dx}(x^n) = nx^{n-1} \quad . \quad . \quad . \quad . \quad (3)$$

This result holds for all values of n.

Further, if $y = ax^n$

$$\frac{dy}{dx} = nax^{n-1} \quad . \quad . \quad . \quad . \quad . \quad . \quad (4)$$

This will be clear by reference to (2). Instead of x^n in the numerator, we have ax^n and this expression will be carried through the whole of the subsequent work.

N.B.—If $\quad y = $ a constant, $\frac{dy}{dx} = 0$

Example 1

If $\qquad y = x^{-3}, \quad \frac{dy}{dx} = -3x^{-4}$

Example 2

If $\qquad y = x^{-\frac{1}{2}}, \quad \frac{dy}{dx} = -\frac{1}{2} \cdot x^{-\frac{3}{2}}$

Example 3

$$\frac{d}{dx}(4x^3) = 12x^2$$

Example 4

$$\frac{d}{dt}(3t^{-\frac{2}{3}}) = -2t^{-\frac{5}{3}}$$

Example 5

If $\qquad y = \frac{2}{\sqrt[3]{z^4}} = \frac{2}{z^{\frac{4}{3}}} = 2z^{-\frac{4}{3}}$

then $\qquad \frac{dy}{dz} = -\frac{8}{3}z^{-\frac{7}{3}}.$

EXERCISE 16

1. Differentiate

(i) x^7, (ii) $2x^{-4}$, (iii) $3x^{-2}$, (iv) $\dfrac{5}{x^3}$.

2. Evaluate $\dfrac{d}{dt}\left(\dfrac{2}{t^5}\right)$, $\dfrac{d}{dy}\left(\dfrac{5}{\sqrt{y}}\right)$, $\dfrac{d}{dz}\dfrac{3}{\sqrt[3]{z^2}}$.

3. In the following examples find y_1, where $y_1 = \dfrac{dy}{dx}$:

(a) $y = \dfrac{4}{x}$, (b) $y = \dfrac{5}{x^3\sqrt[3]{x}}$, (c) $y = 6x^2\sqrt[5]{x}$.

4. Differentiate the following functions with respect to the appropriate variable :

(i) $2x^{-\frac{2}{3}}$, (ii) $50^{\frac{2}{3}}$, (iii) $2z^{-4}$, (iv) $\dfrac{5t^3}{\sqrt[4]{t}}$.

5. Differentiate

(i) $2x^{3\cdot2}$, (ii) $x^{0\cdot13}$, (iii) $\dfrac{5}{x^{2\cdot14}}$, (iv) $\dfrac{3}{\sqrt[3]{2x^{1\cdot5}}}$, (v) $\dfrac{5x^{1\cdot3}}{\sqrt{x^{3\cdot6}}}$.

---

2. The Differential Coefficient of a Sum

The differential coefficient of a sum of a number of terms is *the sum of their separate differential coefficients.*

Thus :

$$\frac{d}{dx}(x^3 + 3x^2 + 2x + 4) = 3x^2 + 6x + 2$$

This follows from the fact that a differential coefficient is a limit; and that the sum of a finite number of limits equals the limit of their sum.   (See end of chapter for proof.)

The proposition remains true if some of the terms are negative.

Example 1

If $\qquad y = 2t^{1\cdot3} - 3\sqrt{t} + 6$, find $\dfrac{dy}{dt}$.

We put $\qquad y = 2t^{1\cdot3} - 3t^{\frac{1}{2}} + 6$

$$\frac{dy}{dt} = 2\cdot6t^{0\cdot3} - 1\cdot5t^{-\frac{1}{2}}$$

Example 2

$$y = \frac{z^4 - 3z^2 + 2z - 1}{z^3}$$

Write $\qquad y = z - 3z^{-1} + 2z^{-2} - z^{-3}$ (by division)

$$\frac{dy}{dz} = 1 + 3z^{-2} - 4z^{-3} + 3z^{-4}.$$

EXERCISE 17

1. Find $\dfrac{d}{dx}(2x^3 - 3x^2 + 4x - 2)$ and

$$\frac{d}{dt}\left(2t^{1\cdot3} - 4t^{-2} + \frac{3}{t}\right).$$

2. Differentiate with respect to the independent variable used :

   (i) $\dfrac{x^3 - 2x^2 + 3}{x^4}$,   (ii) $\dfrac{3t^{2\cdot6} - 4t^{0\cdot3} + 2}{t}$

   (iii) $(x + 4)(x - 5)$,   (iv) $(3x + 1)^2$

3. Give the derivatives with respect to x of :

   (a) $(2x^3)^3$,   (b) $1 - \dfrac{1}{3x^2}$,   (c) $x^{-1\cdot5}(x^2 - 4^2)$,

   (d) $\dfrac{x^6 - x^2}{2x^3}$,   (e) $(2x^2 - x^3)^2$.   (N.C.)

4. Give the derivatives of

   (i) $\left(\dfrac{4^3}{x}\right)^2$,   (ii) $x^2(2x^2 - 8^4)$,   (iii) $\sqrt[5]{x^3}$,

   (iv) $-2^7x^{0\cdot4}$,   (v) $\dfrac{x^{12} - x^3}{x^6}$.

Find, without using tables or slide rule, the values of the first four of these derivatives when $x = 2^5$.   (N.C.)

5. Find $\dfrac{dy}{dx}$ when $y = 3\sqrt[3]{x^2} + \dfrac{2}{x^{1\cdot5}} - \dfrac{5}{x^3}$.   (U.E.I.)

6. Find $\dfrac{dy}{dx}$ if

   (a) $y = x^3 + 2x^2 + 4$,   (b) $y = 6x^{3\cdot2} - \dfrac{2}{x}$,

   (c) $y = x(x^2 + 3)(x - 4)$.   (U.L.C.I.)

7. (a) Find from first principles the value of $\dfrac{dy}{dx}$ if $y = 3x^2 + 2x + 6$.

(b) Write down the value of $\dfrac{dp}{dv}$ at the point where $v = 6$, if $pv^2 = 100$.   (U.L.C.I.)

8. (a) Find $\dfrac{dy}{dx}$ in the following cases :

   (i) $y = 4x^2 + x$,   (ii) $y = \dfrac{3(x + 2)^2}{x}$.

(b) At what points on the curve $y = 3x^3 - 36x + 20$ is the slope $\left(\dfrac{dy}{dx}\right)$ equal to (i) 2, (ii) 0 ?   (U.L.C.I.)

9. From first principles find $\dfrac{dy}{dx}$ if $y = x^2 + 2x$.

Write down $\dfrac{dy}{dx}$

   (i) when $y = 29x^{0\cdot7} + 5$,   (ii) when $y = \dfrac{3x^2 - 2}{x^3}$
   (U.L.C.I.)

10. The equation to a curve is $y = Kx^{\frac{1}{4}}$.   Find K so that $x = 8, y = 3$ is a point on the curve.   Find the gradient of the curve at this point.   (U.L.C.I.)

11. The equation of a curve is given by

$$y = \frac{x^3}{3} - 3x^2 + 5x + 4.$$

Find an expression which will give the slope of the curve at any point on it.

What are the co-ordinates of the points on the curve (i) where the curve is horizontal, (ii) and one point where it is inclined at 45°?   (U.L.C.I.)

12. The curve $y = \dfrac{a}{x} + bx^2$ passes through the point $x = 3$, $y = 16 \cdot 5$, and the value of $\dfrac{dy}{dx}$ at this point is (-1). Find the values of the constants a and b.   (U.L.C.I.)

13. Find from first principles the value of $\dfrac{dy}{dx}$ when $y = 3x^2$.

Find $\dfrac{dy}{dx}$ when :

$$(a)\ y = x + \frac{1}{x},\quad (b)\ y = A\!\left(\frac{l}{2} - x\right)\!\left(\frac{l}{2} + x\right).$$

(U.L.C.I.)

---

3. Repeated Differentiation

If $y = 3x^3 - 2x^2 + 1$ . . . . . . (1)

we have $\dfrac{dy}{dx} = 9x^2 - 4x$ . . . . (2)

A notation often used for $\dfrac{dy}{dx}$ is y_1; hence

$$y_1 = \frac{dy}{dx} = 9x^2 - 4x \quad . \quad . \quad . \quad . \quad . \quad (3)$$

Observe that y_1 is itself a function of x. Hence like y it too may be differentiated.

CH. 5]   DIFFERENTIATION OF FUNCTIONS   91

For two differentiations we use the notation $\frac{d^2y}{dx^2}$ or y_2. This is called the second derivative.

From (3) above we have :

$$y_2 = \frac{d^2y}{dx^2} = 18x - 4 \quad \cdots \cdots \quad (4)$$

Continuing from (4) we see that :

$$y_3 = \frac{d^3y}{dx^3} = 18 \text{ (a constant)}$$

and

$$y_4 = \frac{d^4y}{dx^4} = 0$$

as are all subsequent derivatives.

Example 1

$$y = 5x^2 + 3x + 4$$
$$y_1 = 10x + 3$$
$$y_2 = 10$$
$$y_3 = 0 = y_4, \text{ etc.}$$

Another notation for derivatives of $y = f(x)$ is $f'(x)$ for $\frac{dy}{dx}$, $f''(x)$ for $\frac{d^2y}{dx^2}$.

Example 2

If

$$f(x) = 3x^3 - 4x + 1$$
$$f'(x) = 9x^2 - 4$$
$$f''(x) = 18x.$$

EXERCISE 18

1. If $y = 3x^4 - 6x^2 + 2x - 1$, find y_1 and y_2.

2. Given $f(t) = \dfrac{3t^3 - 5t^2 + 2t - 3}{t}$, find $f''(t)$.

3. If $y = 3\theta^2 - 5\theta + 6$, find $\dfrac{d^2y}{d\theta^2}$.

4. Find which differential coefficient first vanishes if :

    (a) $y = 5x^4 - 3x^2 + 7x + 1$.

    (b) $y = \dfrac{3x^5 - 7x^4 + 3x^2}{2x^2}$.

5. If $f(x) = 3x^3 - 4x^2 + 3x - 6$, find the point on the curve where $f''(x) = 0$.

---

4. Function of a Function of x

Consider $y = (x^2 - 4)^6$

Putting $z = x^2 - 4$ . . . . (1)

then $y = z^6$ . . . . (2)

From (2) it is seen that y is a function of z. But from (1), z is a function of x.

y is thus seen to be a function of a variable, z, which is itself a function of x. From this point of view, y is said to be a function of a function of x, a cumbrous expression, which nevertheless must be noticed.

If we are asked to differentiate $(x^2 - 4)^6$, we observe that the independent variable is x, and putting

$$y = (x^2 - 4)^6, \text{ we must find } \frac{dy}{dx}.$$

Since $y = z^6$, $\dfrac{dy}{dz} = 6z^5 = 6(x^2 - 4)^5$, and $z = x^2 - 4$,

$\therefore$ $\dfrac{dz}{dx} = 2x$.

Now, $\dfrac{dy}{dx} = \dfrac{dy}{dz} \cdot \dfrac{dz}{dx}$ (see end of chapter for proof)

$$= 6(x^2 - 4)^5 \cdot 2x$$
$$= 12x(x^2 - 4)^5.$$

Example 2

$$y = (x^2 - 5x + 2)^3. \quad \text{We require } \frac{dy}{dx}.$$

Put
$$z = x^2 - 5x + 2$$

$$\therefore \frac{dz}{dx} = 2x - 5$$

$$y = z^3$$

and
$$\frac{dy}{dx} = \frac{dy}{dz} \cdot \frac{dz}{dx} = 3z^2 \cdot (2x - 5)$$
$$= 3(x^2 - 5x + 2)^2(2x - 5).$$

5. The Formal Aspect of Differentiation

There is no necessity for the substitution employed in the last paragraph if the formal aspect of differentiation is recognised.

Consider
$$\left. \begin{array}{l} y = x^n \\ \frac{dy}{dx} = nx^{n-1} \end{array} \right\} \quad \cdot \quad \cdot \quad \cdot \quad \cdot \quad \cdot \quad (1)$$

The formal meaning of (1) will be clear if we write :

$$\left. \begin{array}{l} y = (\quad)^n \\ \frac{dy}{d(\quad)} . = n(\quad)^{n-1} \end{array} \right\} \quad \cdot \quad \cdot \quad \cdot \quad \cdot \quad (2)$$

where any function of x may be written in the bracket. —*i.e.*, the " form " of (1) holds no matter what expression be put for x.

Hence if
$$y = (x^2 - 4)^6$$
$$\frac{dy}{dx} = \frac{dy}{d(\quad)} \cdot \frac{d(\quad)}{dx} = 6(x^2 - 4)^5 \cdot 2x.$$

With a little practice examples like the above may be done very readily, and the second step—putting in the brackets—may be omitted.

Example 3

$$y = \frac{1}{x^2 + a^2} = (x^2 + a^2)^{-1}$$

$$\frac{dy}{dx} = -1 . (x^2 + a^2)^{-2} . 2x$$

In the above

$$\frac{dy}{d(\quad)} = -1(x^2 + a^2)^{-2}$$

and

$$\frac{d(\quad)}{dx} = 2x.$$

EXERCISE 19

Differentiate the following functions of x :

(a) By first putting each bracket $= z$, finding $\frac{dz}{dx}$, and then using the equation

$$\frac{dy}{dx} = \frac{dy}{dz} . \frac{dz}{dx}.$$

(b) Without using the above substitution of z.

1. $(x^2 + x)^3$.
2. $(3x^2 - 5x + 6)^4$.
3. $(x^2 + 3)^5$.
4. $\dfrac{1}{(x^2 + 3x + 4)}$.
5. $\dfrac{1}{(x + 3)}$.
6. $\dfrac{1}{(x^2 + 3)^2}$.
7. $\dfrac{4}{(x^3 - 3x + 1)^4}$.
8. $(x^2 - 1\cdot3x + 4)^3$.
9. $\dfrac{1}{\sqrt{x^2 + 3}}$.
10. $\dfrac{4}{\sqrt[3]{2x^2 + x + 1}}$.

---

6. Differentiation of a Product

If $y = (x^2 + 4)^3 . (x + 2)^2$, it would be very tiresome to expand each bracket and then perform the multiplication before differentiating.

We now establish a formula which enables us to differentiate products such as this.

Let $y = u \cdot v$, where u and v are functions of x.

Let x increase to $x + h$, i.e., to $x + \Delta x$.

Then u and v become $(u + \Delta u)$ and $(v + \Delta v)$ respectively, whilst y becomes $y + \Delta y$.

Since $\qquad y = uv$ . . . . (1)

$$\therefore \quad y + \Delta y = (u + \Delta u)(v + \Delta v)$$
$$= uv + v\Delta u + u\Delta v + \Delta u \cdot \Delta v \quad . \quad (2)$$

Subtract (1) from (2) and get :

$$\Delta y = v\Delta u + u\Delta v + \Delta u \cdot \Delta v$$

$$\therefore \quad \frac{\Delta y}{\Delta x} = v\frac{\Delta u}{\Delta x} + u\frac{\Delta v}{\Delta x} + \frac{\Delta u}{\Delta x} \cdot \Delta v \quad . \quad . \quad . \quad (3)$$

Notice that the last term involves the product of $\frac{\Delta u}{\Delta x}$ and a differential Δv.

Now let $\Delta x \rightarrow 0$. Then $\Delta v \rightarrow 0$, and the last term on the R.H.S. of (3) $\rightarrow 0$, and (3) becomes $\frac{dy}{dx} = v\frac{du}{dx} + u\frac{dv}{dx}$.

$$\therefore \quad \boldsymbol{\frac{duv}{dx} = u\frac{dv}{dx} + v\frac{du}{dx}} \quad . \quad . \quad . \quad . \quad (4)$$

(4) must be remembered thus :

(d.c. product) = (first factor × d.c. second)
$\qquad\qquad\qquad\qquad$ + (second factor × d.c. first).

Either of the two factors of uv may be called the " first factor," since $uv = vu$.

Example 1

$$y = x^3(x^2 + 6x + 3)$$
$$\frac{dy}{dx} = 3x^2(x^2 + 6x + 3) + x^3(2x + 6) \quad . \quad (5)$$
$$= 5x^4 + 24x^3 + 9x^2.$$

Example 2

$$y = x^3 \cdot (x^2 + 4)^4$$
$$\frac{dy}{dx} = 3x^2(x^2 + 4)^4 + x^3 \cdot 4(x^2 + 4)^3 \cdot 2x \qquad (6)$$

$$\left[\text{N.B.} \quad \frac{d}{dx}(x^2 + 4)^4 = 4(x^2 + 4)^3 \cdot 2x \right]$$

Simplifying (6) we get :

$$\frac{dy}{dx} = x^2(x^2 + 4)^3\{3(x^2 + 4) + 8x^2\}$$
$$= x^2(x^2 + 4)^3(11x^2 + 12).$$

Example 3

$$y = \frac{2x^2}{(x + 5)}$$

Notice $\quad y = 2x^2 \times (x + 5)^{-1}$

$$\therefore \quad \frac{dy}{dx} = 4x \times (x + 5)^{-1} + (-1)(x + 5)^{-2} \times 2x^2$$

$$= \frac{4x}{x + 5} - \frac{2x^2}{(x + 5)^2}$$

This example shows how a quotient may be treated as a product.

EXERCISE 20

Differentiate the following products :

1. $x^2(x^2 + 3x + 6)$.   2. $x^{\frac{3}{2}}(x^2 + 5x - 2)$.

3. (i) $x^2(x^2 + 3x + 6)^2$, (ii) $x^5(x - 1)^4$.

4. (i) $3x^{-3}(x^2 + 2)^4$, (ii) $t^{-\frac{1}{2}}(t + 3)^3$.

5. (i) $x^4(x^2 + 3)^{-2}$, (ii) $2x^2(1 - x^2)^{-2}$, (iii) $3x(2 - x)^{-4}$.

6. (i) $\dfrac{x}{(x + 2)^2}$,   (ii) $\dfrac{3x^2}{1 - x}$,   (iii) $\dfrac{1}{x^2(x + 3)}$,

   (iv) $\dfrac{x^2 + x + 2}{(x + 1)^2}$,   (v) $\dfrac{t^2 + 3}{(1 + t + t^2)^2}$.

7. The Differential Coefficient of a Quotient

The formula for differentiating a quotient could be obtained from that for a product.

We will, however, get it directly.

Let $y = \dfrac{u}{v}$, where u and v are functions of x.

Let x change to $x + \Delta x$.   Then, as before, we get

$$y + \Delta y = \frac{u + \Delta u}{v + \Delta v}$$

$$\therefore \quad \Delta y = \frac{u + \Delta u}{v + \Delta v} - \frac{u}{v}$$

$$= \frac{v(u + \Delta u) - u(v + \Delta v)}{(v + \Delta v)(v)}$$

$$= \frac{v \Delta u - u \Delta v}{(v + \Delta v)v}$$

$$\therefore \quad \frac{\Delta y}{\Delta x} = \frac{v \dfrac{\Delta u}{\Delta x} - u \dfrac{\Delta v}{\Delta x}}{(v + \Delta v) \cdot v} \quad \cdots \cdots \quad (1)$$

Now let $\Delta x \longrightarrow 0$.   Then $(v + \Delta v) \longrightarrow v$

and (1) becomes $\dfrac{dy}{dx} = \dfrac{v \dfrac{du}{dx} - u \dfrac{dv}{du}}{v_2}$.

i.e., $$\frac{d}{dx}\left(\frac{u}{v}\right) = \frac{v \dfrac{du}{dx} - u \dfrac{dv}{dx}}{v^2} \quad \cdots \cdots \quad (2)$$

This formula should be remembered in words, thus :

(D.C. quotient) =
$$\frac{\text{(Denom.} \times \text{D.C. numerator)} - \text{(Numerator} \times \text{D.C. Denom.)}}{\text{(Denom.)}^2}$$

Example 1 $$y = \frac{x - a}{x + a}$$

$$\frac{dy}{dx} = \frac{(x + a) - (x - a)}{(x + a)^2}$$

$$= \frac{2a}{(x + a)^2}$$

Example 2

$$y = \frac{(a-x)^2}{a^2 + x^2}$$

$$\frac{dy}{dx} = \frac{(a^2 + x^2) \cdot 2(a-x) \cdot (-1) - (a-x)^2 \cdot 2x}{(a^2 + x^2)^2}$$

$$= \frac{-2(a-x)\{a^2 + x^2 + x(a-x)\}}{(a^2 + x^2)^2}$$

$$= \frac{-2(a-x)(a^2 + ax)}{(a^2 + x^2)^2}$$

$$= \frac{-2a(a^2 - x^2)}{(a^2 + x^2)^2}$$

EXERCISE 21

Differentiate the following quotients :

1. $\dfrac{x}{x+a}$.

2. $\dfrac{x^2 - a^2}{x^2 + a^2}$.

3. $\dfrac{x^2 + 2x + 2}{x+1}$.

4. $\dfrac{\sqrt{x}}{x+2}$.

5. $\dfrac{3x^2}{x+2}$.

6. $\dfrac{5x^2}{(x^2+1)^2}$.

7. $\sqrt{\dfrac{1+x}{1-x}}$.

8. $\sqrt[3]{\dfrac{5x^2+3}{x+2}}$.

---

8. Differentiation of an Implicit Function of x

If we consider the two equations :

$$y = 3x^2 + 2x + 1 \quad . \quad . \quad . \quad . \quad (1)$$

and $$\qquad x^2 + y^2 = 9 \quad . \quad . \quad . \quad . \quad . \quad . \quad (2)$$

we notice that in (1), the two variables x and y appear on opposite sides of the equation; they are not mixed together, as in equation (2).

In (1) y is said to be an explicit function of x.

In (2) y is an " implicit " function of x.

In the simple case considered above in (2) it is seen that we could write:

$$y^2 = 9 - x^2$$

i.e., $$y = \pm \sqrt{9 - x^2}$$

where y becomes an explicit function of x.

In other cases it may become tedious to express y explicitly in terms of x, yet we may require the value of $\frac{dy}{dx}$.

If $$z = y^2$$

$$\frac{dz}{dx} = \frac{dz}{dy} \cdot \frac{dy}{dx} = 2y \cdot \frac{dy}{dx}$$

i.e., $$\frac{d}{dx}(y^2) = 2y\frac{dy}{dx} \quad \cdots \quad \cdots \quad (3)$$

Similarly $$\frac{d}{dx}(y^3) = 3y^2 \cdot \frac{dy}{dx} \cdot \quad \cdots \quad \cdots \quad (4)$$

If we now differentiate (2) with respect to x, we get:

$$2x + 2y\frac{dy}{dx} = 0, \ \ i.e., \ \frac{dy}{dx} = -\frac{x}{y}$$

Now suppose we require $\frac{d}{dx}(x^2y^2)$, where y is regarded as some function of x.

Differentiating as a product, we get:

$$\frac{d}{dx}(x^2y^2) = x^2 \cdot 2y\frac{dy}{dx} + 2x \cdot y^2. \quad \cdots \quad (5)$$

Example

The point $(1, 1)$ is clearly on the circle whose equation is:

$$x^2 + y^2 + 2x + 4y - 8 = 0 \ . \quad \cdots \quad (6)$$

Find the gradient of the tangent at this point.

Differentiating (6) we get:

$$2x + 2y\frac{dy}{dx} + 2 + 4\frac{dy}{dx} = 0$$

i.e., $\dfrac{dy}{dx}(2y + 4) = -2x - 2 = -2(x + 1)$

$$\therefore \dfrac{dy}{dx} = -\dfrac{x + 1}{y + 2}.$$

Now put $x = 1$, $y = 1$, and we see that the required gradient is $-\frac{2}{3}$.

EXERCISE 22

Differentiate with respect to x :

1. $3x^{1\cdot2} - 4\sqrt{x} + \dfrac{3}{x^3}.$ 2. $(2x - 3)^3.$

3. $\sqrt{x - 4}.$ 4. $\dfrac{1}{(x + a)^2}.$

5. $\dfrac{5}{\sqrt{4x - 2}}.$ 6. $\sqrt{5 - 6x}.$

7. $(3 - x^2)^4.$ 8. $(3x^2 - 2x + 2)^4.$

9. $x\sqrt{x + a}.$ 10. $x^3(x + a)^3.$

11. $2x^5(x^2 + 2x + 3)^2.$ 12. $\sqrt[4]{(x^2 - a^2)^3}.$

13. $\dfrac{1}{\sqrt[3]{x^2 + x + 1}}.$ 14. $\dfrac{3x^2 + 2x + 1}{x + 2}.$

15. $\dfrac{x^3}{\sqrt{x + 1}}.$ 16. $\dfrac{2x^2 - 1}{x^2 + 3}.$

17. $\sqrt{\dfrac{3 - x}{2 + x}}.$

Find the gradients of the tangents at the points indicated on the following curves :

18. $y = 3x^2 - x + 1$ at $(1, 3)$ and $(2, 11)$.

19. $y = \dfrac{x^2}{x + 1}$ at $(2, \frac{4}{3})$ and $(1, \frac{1}{2})$.

Find $\dfrac{dy}{dx}$ from the following equations :

20. $x^2 + y^2 = 6.$
21. $x^2 + 3xy + 4 = 0.$
22. $x^2 + y^2 + 3x + 4y + 1 = 0.$

APPENDIX TO CHAPTER 5

1. To Show that the Sum of Two Limits = Limit of Their Sum

Suppose $\underset{\Delta x \to 0}{Lt} \dfrac{\Delta y}{\Delta x} = l_1$ and $\underset{\Delta x \to 0}{Lt} \dfrac{\Delta z}{\Delta x} = l_2$.

Then $\dfrac{\Delta y}{\Delta x} = l_1 + k_1$ and $\dfrac{\Delta z}{\Delta x} = l_2 + k_2$, where k_1 and k_2 both $\longrightarrow 0$, as $\Delta x \longrightarrow 0$.

Then
$$\underset{\Delta x \to 0}{Lt}\left(\frac{\Delta y}{\Delta x} + \frac{\Delta z}{\Delta x}\right) = Lt(l_1 + k_1 + l_2 + k_2)$$
$$= l_1 + l_2$$

which proves the proposition.

This can be extended to the sum of any finite number of functions.

2. To Show that the Limit of the Product of Two Functions = the Product of Their Limits

$$Lt\left(\frac{\Delta y}{\Delta x} \cdot \frac{\Delta z}{\Delta x}\right) = Lt(l_1 + k_1)(l_2 + k_2)$$
$$= Lt(l_1 l_2 + k_1 l_2 + k_2 l_1 + k_1 k_2)$$
$$= l_1 l_2 \text{ (since } k_1 \text{ and } k_2 \text{ both} \longrightarrow 0 \text{ as } \Delta x \longrightarrow 0)$$
$$= \text{product of the two limits.}$$

CHAPTER 6

DIFFERENTIATION REVERSED. INTEGRATION

1. In the previous chapter we were given certain functions of a variable, usually x, and we learned how to obtain the derivative or differential coefficient of the function.

In this chapter we learn how, in certain cases, to reverse the process.

We are given the derivative, and we try to find the original function.

2. If $y = f(x)$

$$\frac{dy}{dx} = \underset{h \to 0}{Lt} \frac{f(x + h) - f(x)}{h} = \underset{\Delta x \to 0}{Lt} \frac{\Delta y}{\Delta x}$$

Hence the relationship

$$\frac{dy}{dx} = \underset{\Delta x \to 0}{Lt} \frac{\Delta y}{\Delta x}$$

is always true, whilst the statement

$$\frac{dy}{dx} = \frac{\Delta y}{\Delta x}$$

becomes more nearly true, the closer Δx tends to zero.

Hence $\Delta y = \frac{dy}{dx} . \Delta x$ as $\Delta x \longrightarrow 0$, and in any case, when

Δx is small, Δy gives a close approximation to the change in y corresponding to the small change Δx in x.

From the relationship

$$\Delta y = \frac{dy}{dx} . \Delta x \quad . \quad . \quad . \quad . \quad (1)$$

which is widely used for the calculation of small corrections

where the ratio $\dfrac{\Delta y}{\Delta x} = \dfrac{dy}{dx}$

we see that $\frac{dy}{dx}$ is the coefficient of the " differential," Δx, and for this reason it is called a " differential coefficient."

We now learn to drop the Δ in (1) and write it :

$$dy = \frac{dy}{dx} \cdot dx \quad . \quad . \quad . \quad . \quad . \quad . \quad (2)$$

and we shall in future refer to dx and dy as the differentials of x and of y, respectively.   Each is a distinct quantity.

If we now differentiate both sides of the equation

$$y = x^4$$

we get :

$$\frac{dy}{dx} = 4x^3 \quad . \quad . \quad . \quad . \quad . \quad . \quad (3)$$

Hence from (2) :

$$dy = 4x^3 \cdot dx . \quad . \quad . \quad . \quad . \quad (4)$$

From (3) $4x^3$ is the differential coefficient of x^4 with respect to x, whilst from (4) dy or $4x^3 \cdot dx$ is the differential of x^4.

3. Reversing the process of differentiation is called integration, and is indicated by using the symbol $\int$, an old-fashioned s, in front of a differential.

Thus from

$$y = \frac{x^3}{3}$$

we get

$$dy = x^2 dx.$$

Reversing the process :

$$\int x^2 dx = \frac{x^3}{3} \quad . \quad . \quad . \quad . \quad (1)$$

Similarly if

$$y = \frac{x^{n+1}}{n+1}$$

$$dy = x^n dx$$

and

$$\int x^n dx = \frac{x^{n+1}}{n+1} . \quad . \quad . \quad . \quad (2)$$

$\frac{x^{n+1}}{n+1}$ is called an integral of $x^n dx$.

From (1) and (2) of this paragraph the rule for integrating any power of x is seen to be

"Increase the index by one, and divide by the increased index."

4. The Constant of Integration or the Arbitrary Constant

Starting with $$y = \frac{x^3}{3}$$

or with $$y = \frac{x^3}{3} + C$$

where C is any constant we get $dy = x^2 dx$ in both cases.

Hence $\int x^2 dx = \frac{x^3}{3} + C$. This is the most general form of the integral. We do not know the value of the constant, and for this reason it is sometimes termed the Arbitrary Constant, and *must* be added each time we integrate.

Example 1
$$\int x^{\frac{1}{2}} dx = \tfrac{2}{3} x^{\frac{3}{2}} + C$$

Example 2
$$\int x^{-1\cdot02} dx = - \frac{x^{-0\cdot02}}{0\cdot02} + C$$

Example 3
$$\int \frac{1}{x^4} \cdot dx = \int x^{-4} dx = - \frac{x^{-3}}{3} + C$$
$$= - \frac{1}{3x^3} + C$$

Example 4
$$\int \frac{dx}{\sqrt[4]{x^3}} = \int \frac{dx}{x^{\frac{3}{4}}}$$
$$= \int x^{-\frac{3}{4}} dx$$
$$= 4x^{\frac{1}{4}} + C$$

Notice that we can always test the accuracy of our integration by differentiating the integral. Take the last example

$$\frac{d}{dx}(4x^{\frac{1}{4}} + C) = x^{-\frac{3}{4}} = \frac{1}{\sqrt[4]{x^3}}$$

Determination of the Constant of Integration

The constant can be determined if a corresponding pair of values of x and y are known. The following example indicates the method.

Example 5

If $dy = x^{-3}dx$, and $y = 3$ when $x = 2$, express y in terms of x.

We have
$$dy = x^{-3}dx$$
$$\therefore \quad y = \int x^{-3}dx$$
$$= \frac{x^{-2}}{-2} + C$$
$$= -\frac{1}{2x^2} + C$$

Now put $x = 2$ and $y = 3$

We get
$$C = 3 + \tfrac{1}{8} = \tfrac{25}{8}$$

Hence
$$y = \tfrac{25}{8} - \frac{1}{2x^2}$$

5. The Integration of a Sum

The differential coefficient of a sum of separate functions is the sum of their differential coefficients. Hence, reversing the process, the integral of a sum of differentials will be the sum of their separate integrals.

Example 1

$$\int (x^3 + x^4)dx = \frac{x^4}{4} + \frac{x^5}{5} + C$$

We need add only one constant.

It is no use writing the integral as

$$\frac{x^4}{4} + C_1 + \frac{x^5}{5} + C_2$$

since the two constants combine into a single one.

Example 2

$$\int (x^2 - x^{-\frac{1}{2}} + x^{-3})dx = \frac{x^3}{3} - \frac{4}{3}x^{\frac{3}{4}} - \frac{x^{-2}}{2} + C$$

6. A constant coefficient may be taken outside the integration sign.

Thus $\int 4x^3 dx = 4\int x^3 dx = 4 \cdot \frac{x^4}{4} + C$, *i.e.*, $= x^4 + C$

Similarly $\int ax^n dx = a\int x^n dx = \frac{ax^{n+1}}{n+1} + C$

Example 1

$$\int (3x^2 - 4x + 2)dx = x^3 - 2x^2 + 2x + C$$

Example 2

$$\int (1 \cdot 3x^{2 \cdot 3} + 0 \cdot 5x^{0 \cdot 3})dx = \frac{1 \cdot 3}{3 \cdot 3}x^{3 \cdot 3} + \frac{0 \cdot 5}{1 \cdot 3}x^{1 \cdot 3} + C$$
$$= 0 \cdot 39x^{3 \cdot 3} + 0 \cdot 38x^{1 \cdot 3} + C$$

7. An Exception to the Rule for Integrating a Power of x

If we apply the rule for integrating a power of x to

$$\int \frac{dx}{x} = \int x^{-1} dx$$

we get $\frac{x^0}{0}$ *i.e.*, $\frac{1}{0}$, an expression that is meaningless.

The student must not infer that $\int \frac{dx}{x}$ is meaningless.

We shall later show that

$$\int \frac{dx}{x} = \log_e x + C$$

a result that should be noted.

EXERCISE 23

Integrate the following functions :

1. x^4.　　　　2. $x^{\frac{1}{2}}$.　　　　3. $x^{-\frac{3}{2}}$.　　　　4. $\dfrac{1}{x^5}$.

5. $3x^5$.　　　　6. $2x^{\frac{2}{3}}$.　　　　7. $5x^{-\frac{1}{4}}$.　　　　8. $\dfrac{4}{x^4}$.

9. $2x^{0\cdot6}$.　　10. $3\cdot2x^{1\cdot3}$.　　11. $\dfrac{2\cdot1}{x^{-3}}$.　　12. $\dfrac{0\cdot1}{x^{1\cdot1}}$.

13. $(x^2 + 3x)$.　　　　　14. $\left(x^{1\cdot3} - x^{0\cdot4} + \dfrac{1}{2x^2}\right)$.

15. $\left(3x^2 + 2x^{-3} + \dfrac{1}{x^4}\right)$.　　　16. $(3x^{0\cdot2} - 2\cdot1x^{1\cdot3})$.

17. If $dy = 3x^4dx$, express y in terms of x if $y = 4$ when $x = 1$.

18. If $ds = 3t^2dt$, express s in terms of t, given that $s = 4$ when $t = 2$.

19. Given that $ds = (2t^2 + 5)dt$, and that $s = 2$ when $t = 3$, express s as a function of t.

20. Integrate with respect to x :

(a) $\dfrac{1}{2x^3}$,　(b) $\sqrt{2} - 4x^{0\cdot25}$,　(c) $\left(x - \dfrac{1}{x^3}\right)^2$.　(N.C.)

21. Integrate (after simplifying where necessary) the following functions :

(a) $6x^{\frac{2}{3}}$, (b) $3 - 2x^{-0\cdot2}$, (c) $(x^3 - x^2)^2$, (d) $\dfrac{(x^2 - 1)(x^2 + 1)}{x^2}$

(U.L.C.I.)

22. Integrate (after simplifying where necessary) :

(a) $\dfrac{1}{2\sqrt{2x^3}}$,　　(b) $\pi - 5x^{-0\cdot5}$,　　(c) $1 - \tfrac{1}{3}x^2 - \dfrac{1}{2\sqrt{x}}$,

(d) $8x(x^{\frac{1}{2}} + x^{-\frac{1}{3}})^2$.　　　　(N.C.)

23. Integrate each of the following :

(a) $\displaystyle\int \sqrt[3]{t^3}dt$,　(b) $\displaystyle\int\left(\dfrac{6}{\sqrt{x}} + 2\right)dx$.　(U.L.C.I.)

8. The " Formal " Aspect of Integration

We have previously drawn attention to the importance of " form " in differentiation.

It is equally important in integration. In fact the student must be warned at the beginning of his study of integration that his success in evaluating integrals will depend largely on his ability to recognise their " form."

Consider
$$\int x^n dx = \frac{x^{n+1}}{n+1} + C$$

Under the sign of integration he will notice a power, the nth, of x, followed by the differential of x.

The " form " of this is evidently $\int (\qquad)^n d(\qquad)$, where the same function of x may be put in the brackets.

We have then

$$\int (\qquad)^n d(\qquad) = \frac{(\qquad)^{n+1}}{n+1} + C \quad . \quad . \quad (1)$$

where the same function of x is put in each bracket.

Example 1

$$I = \int (x-3)^2 dx . \quad . \quad . \quad . \quad . \quad (1)$$

Notice $dx = d(x-3)$, since the differential of the constant is zero.

$$\therefore \quad I = \int (x-3)^2 d(x-3)$$

$$= \int z^2 dz \qquad (z = \overline{x-3})$$

$$= \frac{z^3}{3} \quad \text{or} \quad \frac{(x-3)^3}{3} + C$$

If the student will observe the " form " of (1), he can write down the value of the integral immediately.

Example 2

$$I = \int 2(x^2 + 5)^3 x dx.$$

Notice $\qquad 2xdx = d(x^2)$ or $d(x^2 + 5)$.

$$\therefore \quad I = \int (x^2 + 5)^3 d(x^2 + 5)$$

i.e., $\qquad \int (\quad)^3 d(\quad) = \dfrac{(x^2 + 5)^4}{4} + C.$

Example 3

$$I = \int (x^2 + a)^3 \cdot x dx$$

In this case $\quad xdx = \tfrac{1}{2}d(x^2 + a)$

$$\therefore \quad I = \frac{1}{2}\int (x^2 + a)^3 d(x^2 + a)$$

$$= \frac{1}{2} \cdot \frac{(x^2 + a)^4}{4} + C$$

It is always possible to evaluate integrals similar to the preceding in the following way :

Example 4

Put $\qquad I = \int (x^3 + 2)^3 x^2 dx$

Let $\qquad z = x^3 + 2$

$$\therefore \quad dz = 3x^2 dx$$

i.e., $\qquad x^2 dx = \dfrac{dz}{3}$

$$\therefore \quad I = \int z^3 \cdot \frac{dz}{3} = \frac{1}{3}\int z^3 dz = \frac{z^4}{12} + C$$

i.e., $\qquad 1 = \dfrac{(x^3 + 2)^4}{12} + C$

The student should, however, try to see the " form " of the integral at once, and should learn to recognise the differentials xdx, x^2dx, x^3dx, etc., as $\tfrac{1}{2}d(x^2 + \text{constant})$, $\tfrac{1}{3}d(x^3 + c)$, etc.

Example 5

$$I = \int \frac{xdx}{\sqrt{x^2 + a^2}}$$
$$= \frac{1}{2}\int (x^2 + a^2)^{-\frac{1}{2}}d(x^2 + a^2)$$
$$= \frac{1}{2} \cdot \frac{(x^2 + a^2)^{\frac{1}{2}}}{\frac{1}{2}} + C$$
$$= \sqrt{x^2 + a^2} + C.$$

EXERCISE 24

Evaluate

1. $\int (x + 3)dx.$ 2. $\int (x + 4)^2 dx.$ 3. $\int (5 + x)^{-4} dx.$

4. $\int \frac{dx}{(x + 3)^2}.$ 5. $\int (x^2 + 3) \cdot 2xdx.$ 6. $\int (x^2 + 3)xdx.$

7. $\int (x^2 - 1)^3 \cdot xdx.$ 8. $\int (x^3 - 1)x^2 dx.$

9. $\int (x^3 + 3)^3 x^2 dx.$ 10. $\int \frac{2xdx}{(x^2 + 5)^3}.$

11. $\int \frac{xdx}{(x^2 + 5)^4}.$ 12. $\int \frac{3x^2 dx}{(x^3 - 2)^2}.$

13. $\int \frac{2xdx}{\sqrt{x^2 + 3}}.$ 14. $\int \frac{xdx}{\sqrt[3]{x^2 + a^2}}.$

15. $\int \frac{(2x + 1)dx}{(x^2 + x + 3)^2}.$ 16. $\int \frac{(3x^2 + 2x)dx}{(x^3 + x^2 + 1)^3}.$

CHAPTER 7

SOME APPLICATIONS OF THE CALCULUS.
MAXIMA AND MINIMA

1. Velocity and Acceleration

Suppose a body is moving in a straight line; for example, a train moving on a level track, a stone falling vertically, or a weight vibrating at the end of a spring.

We can get expressions for the velocity and acceleration in the following way :

FIG. 19.

Suppose OX is the line of motion, O being a fixed point P is the position of the moving body at time t, Q the position at $t + \Delta t$.

Let $OP = x$, $PQ = \Delta x$. We require the velocity and acceleration at P, *i.e.*, at any time t.

$\dfrac{\Delta x}{\Delta t}$ = average velocity over the distance PQ.

Now, as $\Delta t \longrightarrow 0$, $Q \longrightarrow P$, and the actual velocity at P is $Lt \dfrac{\Delta x}{\Delta t}$ or $\dfrac{dx}{dt}$.

Hence $\qquad v = \dfrac{dx}{dt}$ . . . . (1)

The relationship between acceleration and velocity is analogous to that between velocity and distance. We thus infer that :

Acceleration at P $\qquad = \dfrac{dv}{dt} = \dfrac{d^2x}{dt^2}$ . . . . (2)

Notice also that

$$\frac{dv}{dt} = \frac{dv}{dx} \cdot \frac{dx}{dt} = \frac{dv}{dx} \cdot v \text{ or } \frac{v\,dv}{dx} \qquad . \quad . \quad . \quad (3)$$

All the expressions in (1), (2) and (3) are widely used.

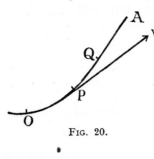

FIG. 20.

Should the body be moving in a curve, OA, let the length of the arc $OP = s$, where O is a fixed point on the curve. If $PQ = \Delta s$, we get by reasoning similar to that in the last paragraph, that velocity at P

$$= v = \frac{ds}{dt}$$

and tangential component of acceleration at P

$$= \frac{dv}{dt} = \frac{d^2s}{dt^2} = \frac{v\,dv}{ds}.$$

There is also a component along the normal at P.

Example 1

Suppose a body is moving in a straight line, and its distance x from a fixed point O in the line, at any time t, is given by

$$x = 3t^2 - 2t + 1 \quad . \quad . \quad . \quad . \quad . \quad (A)$$

Then

$$v = \frac{dx}{dt} = 6t - 2 \quad . \quad . \quad . \quad . \quad . \quad (1)$$

and

$$\frac{dv}{dt} = \frac{d^2x}{dt^2} = 6 \quad . \quad . \quad . \quad . \quad . \quad . \quad (2)$$

From (2) we infer that the body has a constant acceleration of 6 ft./sec.².

From (1) we deduce the velocity at any time.

Put $t = 3$, we get $\frac{dx}{dt} = 16$—i.e., $v = 16$ ft./sec., after moving for 3 secs.

Example 2

A body moving along a straight path passes a fixed point O *of the path with a velocity of 12 ft./sec., and t secs. later, when it is s ft. from* O, *its acceleration is given by* $\dfrac{d^2s}{dt^2} = 6t$. *Find the velocity of the body when* $t = 4$, *and its distance from* O *at that instant.*   (U.L.C.I.)

We have
$$\frac{d^2s}{dt^2} = \frac{dv}{dt} = 6t$$

$$\therefore \quad dv = 6t\,dt$$

and
$$v = 3t^2 + C \quad . \quad . \quad . \quad . \quad (1)$$

when $v = 12$, $t = 0$ if we measure time from the instant the body was at the point O of the path.

$$\therefore \qquad C = 12.$$

Hence, from (1)

$$v = 3t^2 + 12 \quad . \quad . \quad . \quad . \quad . \quad (2)$$

$$i.e., \quad \frac{ds}{dt} = 3t^2 + 12$$

$$\therefore \quad ds = (3t^2 + 12)dt$$

and
$$s = t^3 + 12t + C_1 \quad . \quad . \quad . \quad (3)$$

Now, when $t = 0$, the body was at the point O. Hence putting $s = 0$ and $t = 0$ in (3), we find $C_1 = 0$.

$$\therefore \quad s = t^3 + 12t \quad . \quad . \quad . \quad . \quad . \quad (4)$$

When $t = 4$, we get

$$v = 60 \text{ ft./sec. [from (2)]}$$

and
$$s = 112 \text{ ft. [from (4)]}$$

Example 3

If s is a function of t such that $\dfrac{d^2s}{dt^2}$ *is inversely proportional to* t^2, *and the value of* $\dfrac{ds}{dt}$ *is 5 when* $t = 1$, *and 7 when* $t = 3$, *express* $\dfrac{ds}{dt}$ *as a function of t.*   (N.C.)

We have $\dfrac{d^2s}{dt^2} = \dfrac{dv}{dt} = \dfrac{k}{t^2}.$

Integrating once,

$$v = \dfrac{ds}{dt} = \int \dfrac{k}{t^2}dt = -\dfrac{k}{t} + \mathrm{C} \quad . \quad . \quad . \quad . \quad (1)$$

Now put the given values in (1) we get

$$5 = -k + \mathrm{C}$$
$$7 = -\dfrac{k}{3} + \mathrm{C}.$$

These are two simultaneous equations for k and C. Solving, we find $k = 3$ and $\mathrm{C} = 8$.

Substituting in (1) $\dfrac{ds}{dt} = -\dfrac{3}{t} + 8.$

EXERCISE 25

1. A body moves in a straight line, and its distance s ft. from a fixed point O in the line is given by

$$s = 3t^2 - t + 2,$$

where t is the time in secs.

Find (1) How far the body was from O at zero time.
   (2) Its velocity six seconds later.
   (3) When its velocity vanishes.
   (4) Its acceleration.
   (5) Its average velocity from $t = 3$ to $t = 5$.

2. If s is a function of t such that $\dfrac{ds}{dt}$ is proportional to $\sqrt{t}$, and the value of s increases by 31 whilst the value of t increases from $+ 4$ to $+ 12\frac{1}{4}$, find the increase in the value of s whilst the value of t increases from $12\frac{1}{4}$ to 25. Find also the average rate of increase of s with respect to t for the interval $t = \frac{1}{4}$ to $t = 4$.   (N.C.)

3. If $s = 8 + 108t - t^3$, where s and t have the same meaning as in question (1), find (a) the velocity, (b) the acceleration, (c) when and where the body stops and reverses the direction of motion.

4. If $s = t^3 + 2t^2 + 4t - 10$, plot a velocity time graph for the interval $t = 1$ to $t = 4$. From the graph, find the acceleration at time $t = 2\cdot5$. Compare the value you obtain with the value calculated from the given equation.

5. At time t secs. a body has moved x ft. along its path from a fixed point in it. Find the average speed in each interval, and the approximate acceleration at each instant.

t . .	0	0·1	0·2	0·3	0·4	0·5	0·6
x . .	0	4	8·175	12·558	17·187	22·094	27·306

(B.E.)

6. x and t are the distance in miles and the time in hours of a train from a railway station. Plot on squared paper and state why it is that the slope of the curve shows the speed. Where is the speed (1) greatest, (2) least?

x . .	0	0·12	0·5	1·52	2·5	2·92	3·05	3·05	3·17	3·50	3·82
t . .	0	0·05	0·10	0·15	0·20	0·25	0·30	0·35	0·40	0·45	0·50

(B.E.)

7. The distance covered s (ft.) in time t secs. is given by

$$s = 200t - 16t^2.$$

Find the velocity at $t = 1, 2, 3, 4, 5$ and 6 secs. Plot velocity vertically against time horizontally. From this velocity time curve find the acceleration by a graphic construction.   (U.E.I.)

3. Maxima and Minima

It is often important to know what the maximum or minimum value of a given function of x is, and where such a value occurs. For instance, we may wish to know where the maximum binding moment occurs in a loaded beam, and what is its value.

The determination of maximum and minimum values

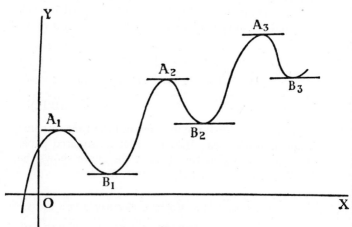

FIG. 21.

of a function of one variable is a simple exercise in differentiation.

The curve above is one drawn merely for illustration. Suppose its equation is $y = f(x)$. At the points marked, we observe that the curve turns. Hence, these points are called " turning points." At each of these points the tangent is parallel to the x-axis; therefore its gradient is

zero; *i.e.*, at every turning point $\dfrac{dy}{dx} = 0.$

Example

Find the turning points on the curve

$$y = \frac{x^3}{3} - \frac{5x^2}{2} + 6x - 4 \quad . \quad . \quad . \quad (1)$$

We have

$$\frac{dy}{dx} = x^2 - 5x + 6$$
$$= (x - 3)(x - 2)$$

∴ for turning points

$$(x - 3)(x - 2) = 0$$

i.e., $x = 3$ or 2.

Put $x = 3$ in (1) above.

We get $y = 9 - \frac{4.5}{2} + 18 - 4$
               $= \frac{1}{2}$.

Now put $x = 2$ in (1)

               $y = \frac{8}{3} - 10 + 12 - 4$
               $= \frac{2}{3}$.

Hence $(3, \frac{1}{2})$ and $(2, \frac{2}{3})$ are the co-ordinates of the turning points.

4. Referring to Fig. 21, the ordinates at A_1, A_2, A_3 are maxima, those at B_1 and B_2 are minima.

Definition :

A maximum value of a given function of x is one that is greater than the values immediately before and immediately after it.

Similarly, a minimum value of a function is one less than the values immediately before and immediately after it.

It will be seen from the figure that the minimum at B_2 is greater than the maximum at A_1. The word " immediately " is therefore important in the above definitions.

Another inference may be made from the figure—viz., that maxima and minima occur alternately.

Hence, if we know that there are two turning points on a curve, and that one of them has a minimum ordinate, the other ordinate must be a maximum.

5. To Distinguish a Maximum from a Minimum

There are two very simple ways of distinguishing a maximum from a minimum.

First Method.

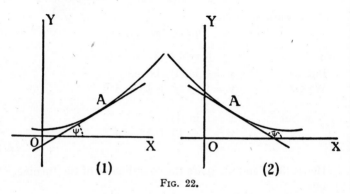

FIG. 22.

It will be recalled that $\frac{dy}{dx}$ is the gradient of the tangent to the curve $y = f(x)$, at the point (x, y).

i.e., $$\frac{dy}{dx} = \tan \psi,$$

where A is any point (x, y) on the curve.

In Fig. 22 (1) $\frac{dy}{dx}$ is $+$ because ψ is acute.

In Fig. 22 (2) $\frac{dy}{dx}$ is $-$, because ψ is obtuse.

Notice that in Fig. 22 (1), as the value of x increases, that of y also increases, and the curve slopes upwards from left to right, whereas in Fig. 22 (2), as the abscissa increases—*i.e.*

moves from left to right—the ordinate y decreases, and the curve slopes downwards.

No matter how the curve be drawn, it will be found that when $\frac{dy}{dx}$ is positive, y increases as x increases, and when $\frac{dy}{dx}$ is negative, y decreases as x increases.

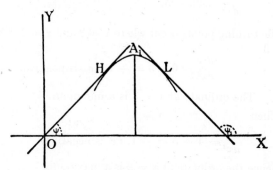

FIG. 23.

Consider the turning-point A_1, illustrated in Fig. 23.

Notice that as we pass from the left to the right of a maximum, ψ changes from acute to obtuse—*i.e.*, $\frac{dy}{dx}$ changes from positive to negative.

This means that $\frac{dy}{dx}$ is itself decreasing as x increases, and that therefore *its* differential coefficient is negative—*i.e.*, at a maximum $\frac{d^2y}{dx^2}$ is negative.

Similarly at a minimum, $\frac{d^2y}{dx^2}$ is positive.

The results of this paragraph should be remembered.

Taking the previous example :

$$y = \frac{x^3}{3} - \frac{5x^2}{2} + 6x - 4$$

$$\frac{dy}{dx} = x^2 - 5x + 6 = (x - 3)(x - 2)$$

$$\frac{d^2y}{dx^2} = 2x - 5.$$

The turning points occur where $x = 3$ and $x = 2$. When $x = 3$

$$\frac{d^2y}{dx^2} = 6 - 5 = + 1, \; i.e., \text{ is positive.}$$

$\therefore$ The ordinate at $x = 3$ is a minimum.

When $x = 2$

$$\frac{d^2y}{dx^2} = 4 - 5 = - 1, \; i.e. \text{ is negative.}$$

Hence the ordinate at $x = 2$ is a maximum.

We found the maximum value of the function was $\frac{2}{3}$, whilst the minimum value was $\frac{1}{2}$.

Summary :

(1) To find turning points on $y = f(x)$.

Solve $\frac{dy}{dx} = 0.$

The roots of this equation give the abscissæ of the turning points.

(2) Substitute each root in the expression for $\frac{d^2y}{dx^2}$.

A negative result indicates a maximum. A positive result indicates a minimum.

(3) To find the maximum and minimum values of the ordinates, we must substitute the appropriate value of x in the original equation.

6. *A second method* which distinguishes maxima from minima can be employed which does not use any differential coefficient except the first.

It was seen that as we pass through a maximum from left to right, $\frac{dy}{dx}$ changes sign from positive to negative, whilst when we pass through a minimum, the change is from $-$ to $+$.

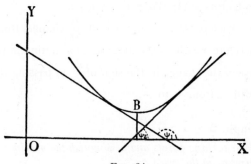

FIG. 24.

The change through the minimum is shown in Fig. 24, where as we pass through B from the immediate left to the immediate right, ψ_1 is obtuse, *i.e.*, $\frac{dy}{dx}$ is negative, whilst ψ_2 is acute, *i.e.*, $\frac{dy}{dx}$ is positive.

We take the example previously used to show how the above ideas are applied.

Example 1

$$y = \frac{x^3}{3} - \frac{5x^2}{2} + 6x - 4$$

$$\frac{dy}{dx} = x^2 - 5x + 6 = (x - 3)(x - 2) \quad . \quad . \quad (1)$$

The turning points are at $x = 3$ and $x = 2$.

The abscissa of a point immediately to the left of $x = 3$ is $x = 3 - h$, where h is very small.

Now, putting $(3 - h)$ for x in (1), the first factor becomes $(- h)$ and the second $(1 - h)$. Since h is very small, the signs of these two factors are $(-)(+)$, and the product is negative.

Similarly, taking the point immediately to the right of $x = 3$, i.e., putting $3 + h$ for x, we see that the signs of the two factors in (1) above are $(+)(+)$.

Hence when passing through $x = 3$, $\frac{dy}{dx}$ changes from $-$ to $+$; therefore $x = 3$, is the abscissa of a minimum point.

Similarly the change in the sign of $\frac{dy}{dx}$ in passing through $x = 2$ will be from $+$ to $-$.

Example 2

Find the turning points and distinguish the maximum from the minimum on the curve

$$y = \frac{2x^3}{3} - \frac{5x^2}{2} + 2x - 3 \quad . \quad . \quad . \quad . \quad (1)$$

We have
$$\frac{dy}{dx} = 2x^2 - 5x + 2$$
$$= (2x - 1)(x - 2) \quad . \quad . \quad . \quad (2)$$

The abscissæ of the turning points are $x = \frac{1}{2}, x = 2$.

Suppose x is just less than $\frac{1}{2}$, the signs of the factors in (2) above are clearly

$$(-)(-), \text{ i.e., } \frac{dy}{dx} \text{ is } +.$$

If x is just greater than $\frac{1}{2}$ the signs are $(+)(-)$

$$\therefore \quad \frac{dy}{dx} \text{ is } (-).$$

Hence the change in $\frac{dy}{dx}$ is from $+$ to $-$.

We infer $x = \frac{1}{2}$ is the abscissa of a maximum.

Since maxima and minima occur alternately, $x = 2$ is the abscissa of a minimum.

The values of the maximum and minimum ordinates can be found by putting $x = \frac{1}{2}$, and $x = 2$ in (1) above, and will be found to be $- 2\frac{13}{24}$ and $- 3\frac{2}{3}$ respectively.

Example 3

Given the equation $y = x(12 - 2x)^2$, determine the values of x for which y is a maximum or minimum, and the value of y corresponding to each of the two values of x so determined.

(U.L.C.I.)

We have, $y = x(12 - 2x)^2$ . . . . (1)

$$\frac{dy}{dx} = 2x(12 - 2x)(- 2) + (12 - 2x)^2$$

$$= (12 - 2x)(12 - 6x)$$

$$= 12(6 - x)(2 - x) \quad . \quad . \quad . \quad . \quad . \quad (2)$$

From (2) $\frac{dy}{dx} = 0$ when $x = 6$ and when $x = 2$

Putting $x = (6 - h)$ in (2), $\frac{dy}{dx}$ is $- ve$.

Putting $x = (6 + h)$ in (2), $\frac{dy}{dx}$ is $+ ve$

∴ $x = 6$ is the abscissa of a minimum

and $x = 2$ that of a maximum.

Substituting these values in (1)

        $y = 0$ is the minimum value

and $y = 128$ is the maximum value.

Example 4

The total surface area of a solid cylinder of diameter x ins. is S sq. ins. Obtain formulæ in terms of x and S for the height and volume of the cylinder.

If S *is constant, prove that when the volume of this cylinder is a maximum,* $x = \sqrt{\dfrac{2S}{3\pi}}$ *and that the area of its curved surface is two-thirds of* S.   (N.C.)

Let h = the height and V = the volume of the cylinder.

Then   S = the cylindrical surface + two ends

$$= \pi x h + 2 \cdot \pi \cdot \frac{x^2}{4} \quad . \quad . \quad . \quad . \quad . \quad (1)$$

∴ Solving (1) for h, we get :

$$h = \frac{1}{\pi x}\left(S - \frac{\pi x^2}{2}\right)$$

$$= \frac{S}{\pi x} - \frac{x}{2} \quad . \quad . \quad . \quad . \quad (2)$$

Similarly,

$$V = \frac{\pi x^2}{4} \cdot h$$

$$= \frac{\pi x^2}{4}\left(\frac{S}{\pi x} - \frac{x}{2}\right) \text{ using (2) above}$$

$$= \frac{xS}{4} - \frac{\pi x^3}{8} \quad . \quad . \quad . \quad . \quad (3)$$

Differentiating (3) with respect to x, we get :

$$\frac{dV}{dx} = \frac{S}{4} - \frac{3\pi x^2}{8} \quad . \quad . \quad . \quad . \quad (4)$$

Equating $\dfrac{dV}{dx}$ to zero gives :

$$\frac{S}{4} = \frac{3\pi x^2}{8}$$

$$i.e.,\ x^2 = \frac{2S}{3\pi}.$$

i.e., $x = \sqrt{\dfrac{2S}{3\pi}}$, rejecting the negative value of the square root.

From (4) $\dfrac{d^2V}{dx^2} = -\dfrac{6\pi x}{8}$. Hence the value found for x gives a maximum value of V.

The area of the curved surface is πxh.

$$= \pi x\left(\frac{S}{\pi x} - \frac{x}{2}\right), \text{ using (2)}$$

$$= S - \frac{\pi x^2}{2}$$

$$= S - \frac{\pi}{2}\left(\sqrt{\frac{2S}{3\pi}}\right)^2, \text{ using the value found for } x$$

$$= S - \frac{S}{3}$$

$$= \frac{2S}{3}.$$

Example 5

Given that $\dfrac{ds}{dt} = 4\cdot8 - 3\cdot2t$, *and that* $s = 5$ *when* $t = 0\cdot5$, *express s as a function of t and find :*

    (i) *the other value of t when* $s = 5$,
    (ii) *the maximum value of s* (N.C.)

From $\qquad\qquad \dfrac{ds}{dt} = 4\cdot8 - 3\cdot2t \quad . \quad . \quad . \quad . \quad (1)$

we get, by integration, $s = 4\cdot8t - 1\cdot6t^2 + C$.

Put $s = 5$, $t = 0\cdot5$, and find $C = 3$.

$$\therefore \quad s = 4\cdot8t - 1\cdot6t^2 + 3 \quad . \quad . \quad . \quad . \quad (2)$$

When $s = 5$, we have the quadratic equation

$$1\cdot6t^2 - 4\cdot8t + 2 = 0.$$

The sum of the roots of this equation is $\dfrac{4\cdot8}{1\cdot6}$, *i.e.*, **3**.

Since one root is $0\cdot5$, the other is $2\cdot5$.

From (1) $\qquad \dfrac{ds}{dt} = 4{\cdot}8 - 3{\cdot}2t$

$\qquad\qquad\qquad\qquad = 0$ for a turning point.

$\therefore$ at this point $\qquad t = \dfrac{4{\cdot}8}{3{\cdot}2} = \dfrac{3}{2}.$

Since $\dfrac{d^2s}{dt^2} = -3{\cdot}2$ (by differentiating (1)) this value of t gives a maximum value of s.

Substituting in (2), the maximum is given by

$$s = 4{\cdot}8 \times \tfrac{3}{2} - 1{\cdot}6 \times \tfrac{9}{4} + 3$$
$$= 7{\cdot}2 - 3{\cdot}6 + 3$$
$$= 6{\cdot}6.$$

EXERCISE 26

1. Find the maximum and minimum ordinates of the following curves :

(i) $y = \dfrac{x^3}{3} - \dfrac{x^2}{2} - 2x + 4,$

(ii) $y = x^3 - 6x^2 + 12,$

(iii) $y = x^3 + x^2 - x + 4.$

2. A sphere has a radius of 1 ft. Find the volume of the greatest cylinder which can be cut from it.

3. What is the volume of the largest cone whose slant side is 8 ins. long?

4. Explain how differentiation enables us to find the maximum or minimum value of a function.

The energy available in a certain water supply is given by the equation

$$E = 3(1732V - 0{\cdot}602V^3).$$

Determine the value of V which makes E a maximum and calculate this value of E.   (U.L.C.I.)

5. A metal tank for a liquid motor starter has to be constructed on a square base to contain 8 cu. ft. of electrolyte. Calculate the dimensions of this tank so that the surface contact between the tank and liquid may be a minimum.   (U.L.C.I.)

6. A piece of wire is cut into two parts. One part is bent into the form of an equilateral triangle, and the other into that of a square. It is desired that the sum of the areas of these two figures should be a minimum. If the wire was originally 10 ins. long, find the point at which it must be cut.   (U.L.C.I.)

7. Show how the sign of the gradient of the graph of the function $\left(\dfrac{x^2}{8} + \dfrac{2}{x}\right)$ changes as the graph passes through the point at which its gradient is zero.   (N.C.)

8. Draw the graph of $y = x^2 - 5x + 7$. Find graphically the slopes of the curve where $x = 1\cdot5$ and $x = -2$.

Show by the calculus that the values of the slopes found are correct.

Determine the minimum value of y and the value of x where it occurs.   (U.E.I.)

9. The curve $y = \dfrac{a}{x} + bx^2$ passes through the point given by $x = 3$, $y = 16\cdot5$, and the value of $\dfrac{dy}{dx}$ at this point is (-1). Find (i) the values of the constants a and b, (ii) the minimum ordinate of the given curve for positive values of x.   (U.L.C.I.)

10. A right triangular prism whose ends are equilateral triangles is to be made of aluminium. If the total surface area is to be 90 sq. ins., find the dimensions of the prism which will give the greatest volume.   (U.L.C.I.)

11. For what value or values of x is the value of the function $x^2(5x - 4)(x - 2)$, (i) a maximum, (ii) a minimum? Sketch the graph of the function for values of x from $-0\cdot2$ to 2.   (N.C.)

12. Prove that the turning values of the function $a(x^3 - 9x^2 + 15x) + b$, where a and b are constants occur when $x = 1$ and $x = 5$.

If this function has turning values of $+ 4$ and $- 2$ when x has the values $+ 1$ and $+ 5$ respectively, find a and b and calculate the values of the function when x equals $- 1$, $+ 3$, and $+ 7$.   (N.C.)

13. In estimating the cost of an electric cable the following equation was obtained :

$$y = (2x + 1) + \frac{1}{2x + 1}.$$

Determine the values of x which make y a maximum or minimum.   (U.L.C.I.)

14. The section of an open gutter is made of thin material, and is to be a rectangle of area 40 sq. ins. If the base is x ins. wide, express the perimeter of the section in terms of x. Hence find the dimensions of the section if its perimeter is to be a minimum.   (U.L.C.I.)

15. (a) Find the turning point on the curve

$$y = 2x^2 - 6x + 10.$$

State whether it is a maximum or a minimum.

(b) If $H = pV$ and $p = 3 - \frac{1}{2}V$, find the maximum value of H.   (U.L.C.I.)

16. A gas holder is a flat-topped cylinder without a bottom. Find the dimensions of a gas holder to hold 1 million cu. ft. of gas if the area of the metal plate used in its construction is a minimum.   (U.L.C.I.)

---

7. Calculation of Small Corrections

Most of the following formulæ, and many others, will be familiar :

$A = \frac{1}{2}bh$ (area of a triangle).

$V = \frac{4}{3}\pi r^3$ (vol. of sphere)

$$T = 2\pi\sqrt{\frac{l}{g}} \text{ (time of oscillation of a simple pendulum)}$$

$pv = C$ (Boyle's law).

The data employed in the formulæ are usually the results of measurements whose accuracy can only be vouched for between certain limits. It will thus be clear that results dependent on such data will be erroneous, and it is frequently necessary to calculate the proportionate error or the percentage error.

Example 1

Suppose the radius of a sphere is taken as 4 ins. subject to an error of 0·01 in. What is the approximate error in the volume? Find also the proportionate error and the percentage error.

$$V = \tfrac{4}{3}\pi r^3$$
$$dV = 4\pi r^2 dr \text{ (notice the use of differentials)}$$
$$= 4\pi \cdot 4^2 \cdot (0\cdot01)$$
$$= 0\cdot64\pi \text{ cub. ins.}$$

The relative error $= \dfrac{\text{Calculated error}}{\text{Calculated volume}}$

$$= \frac{0\cdot64\pi}{\tfrac{4}{3}\cdot\pi\cdot4^3}$$
$$= \frac{3 \times 0\cdot64}{4^4}$$
$$= 0\cdot0075.$$

The percentage error $=$ relative error $\times$ 100
$$= 0\cdot75$$

Example 2

A hollow cylindrical vessel was ordered whose height was to be 8 ins. and diameter 10 ins. It held the correct amount of liquid, but the radius of the base was $\frac{1}{10}$ in. too great. What was the height?

$$\text{Vol} = \pi r^2 h = \pi \cdot 25 \cdot 8 = 200\pi \cdot \text{cub. ins.}$$

$$\therefore \quad h = \frac{200}{r^2}$$

$$\therefore \quad dh = -\frac{400}{r^3} \cdot dr.$$

i.e.,
$$dh = -\frac{400}{5^3} \times 0 \cdot 1$$

$$= -\tfrac{8}{25}.$$

Hence the decrease in height was $\tfrac{8}{25}$ in. and the approximate height was $7\tfrac{17}{25}$ ins.

Notice in the above that if the radius was found to be $\tfrac{1}{10}$ in. too small instead of too large, we should have taken $dr = -0 \cdot 1$ in. and then

$$dh = -\frac{400}{5^3} \times (-0 \cdot 1)$$

$$= +\tfrac{8}{25} \text{ in.}$$

Example 3

A standard type of question on the simple pendulum is the following.

Given the formula $t = 2\pi\sqrt{\dfrac{l}{g}}$, find the % change in t if the length is decreased by 1%.

Notice that 2π and g are constants, and we can write :

$$t = k \cdot l^{\frac{1}{2}} \left(\text{where } k = \frac{2\pi}{\sqrt{g}}\right) \quad \cdots \quad (1)$$

Hence $dt = \tfrac{1}{2}kl^{-\frac{1}{2}}dl$

Now $dl = -\dfrac{l}{100}$

$$\therefore \quad dt = -\tfrac{1}{2} \cdot kl^{-\frac{1}{2}} \cdot \frac{l}{100} = -\frac{k}{200} \cdot l^{\frac{1}{2}} = -\frac{t}{200} \text{ from (1)}$$

Hence the percentage change

$$= \frac{dt}{t} \times 100 = -\tfrac{1}{2}.$$

EXERCISE 27

1. If the side of an equilateral triangle can be measured accurately to 0·01 in., find the possible error in the area when its sides are 20 ins.

2. Find the possible error in the area of a square whose side is 20 ins., assuming the same accuracy of measurements as in Example 1.

3. The diameter of a circular disc can be measured accurately to $\frac{1}{50}$ in. Find the error in estimating the area of a disc of 8 ins. diameter.

4. A cylindrical steel bar has to be made from a given volume of metal. Its diameter should be 8 ins. and its length 30 ins. If the diameter is found to be $\frac{1}{50}$ in. too small, find the difference in length.

5. Suppose that the pressure and volume of a gas are connected by the relation

$$pv = C \text{ (a constant).}$$

At a given instant $p = 14$ lb./sq. in. and $v = 20$ cu. ft.
find v (1) when $p = 14\cdot1$ lb./sq. in.
       (2) when $p = 13\cdot98$ lb./ sq. in.
Also   (3) find p when $v = 20\cdot2$ cub. ft.

6. The formula $t = 2\pi\sqrt{\dfrac{l}{g}}$ gives the time of oscillation of a simple pendulum of length l. Find the change in the time of oscillation when the length l is increased by 2%.

7. The area of a triangle ABC is Δ, where $\Delta = \frac{1}{2}bc \sin A$.

If A and c are measured correctly, but there is an error of 2% in the measurement of b, find the relative error in the calculated area.

8. If x and y are the sides of a rectangle of constant area A, we get $xy = A$. If the side x is slightly altered to $x + dx$, show that the correction to be applied to y is

$$-y\frac{dx}{x}.$$

9. If h is the hypotenuse of a right-angled triangle and x and y the other two sides we have $h^2 = x^2 + y^2$, and get by differentiation

$$2h \, . \, dh = 2x \, . \, dx + 2y \, . \, dy \quad . \quad . \quad . \quad . \quad (1)$$

If when $x = 8$ ins. and $y = 6$ ins., both sides receive an increment of 0·02 in., find from (1) above the increase in the hypotenuse.

---

8. Rates

A velocity and an acceleration are examples previously met with of " rates." The underlying idea in most rates is that of " change per unit time."

Example 1

Suppose the radius of a circular ripple on a pond is increasing at $\frac{1}{10}$ ft./sec. At what rate is the area increasing when the radius of the circle is 10 ft.?

Let A be the area, and r the radius at any time. Then

$$A = \pi r^2 \quad . \quad . \quad . \quad . \quad . \quad . \quad (1)$$

and

$$\frac{dr}{dt} = \frac{1}{10} \text{ (given)} \quad . \quad . \quad . \quad . \quad (2)$$

We require $\dfrac{dA}{dt}$

$$\frac{dA}{dt} = \frac{dA}{dr} \cdot \frac{dr}{dt}$$

From (1)

$$\frac{dA}{dr} = 2\pi r$$

and

$$\frac{dr}{dt} = \frac{1}{10}$$

$$\therefore \quad \frac{dA}{dt} = 2\pi r \cdot \frac{1}{10} = \frac{\pi r}{5}.$$

This result gives the rate of growth for any radius, r. To answer the question put $r = 10$.

We get $$\frac{dA}{dt} = \frac{\pi \cdot 10}{5} = 2\pi \text{ sq. ft. per sec.}$$

Example 2

The adiabatic law for the expansion of air is $pv^{1\cdot4} = k$. At a given time, $p = 100$ lb. per sq. in. and $v = 20$ cu. ft. Find at what rate the pressure is changing, if, at the given time, the volume is decreasing at 2 cu. ft. per sec.

$$pv^{1\cdot4} = k$$
$$\therefore \quad p = \frac{k}{v^{1\cdot4}} \quad \cdots \cdots \quad (1)$$

We are given

$$\frac{dv}{dt} = -2 \text{ cu. ft./sec.} \quad \cdots \quad (2)$$

Now $$\frac{dp}{dt} = \frac{dp}{dv} \cdot \frac{dv}{dt}$$

and from (1) $$\frac{dp}{dv} = -\frac{k \times 1\cdot4}{v^{2\cdot4}}$$

Hence

$$\frac{dp}{dt} = -\frac{k \times 1\cdot4}{v^{2\cdot4}} \times (-2)$$
$$= \frac{k \times 2\cdot8 \times p}{pv^{1\cdot4} \times v}.$$

(Notice the multiplication of numerator and denominator by p.)

$$= \frac{2\cdot8 \times p}{v}.$$

Now put $p = 100$ and $v = 20$. This gives

$$\frac{dp}{dt} = \frac{2\cdot8 \times 100}{20} = 14 \text{ lb./sq. in. per sec.}$$

EXERCISE 28

1. The radius of a sphere is increasing at the rate of $\frac{1}{10}$ in. per sec. At what rate is the volume increasing when the radius is 6 ins.?

2. If $y = 3x + x^2$, and $\frac{dx}{dt} = 2$, find $\frac{dy}{dt}$ when $x = 4$.

3. Find the rate at which the volume of a cone is increasing when the radius of its base is 4 ins., given that its height is constant and equal to 6 ins., whilst the radius of the base increases at the rate of 0·3 in. per sec.

4. An inverted conical vessel with its axis vertical has water running into it at a constant rate. Show that the height H at which the water stands after a time t is

$$\mathrm{H} = c\sqrt[3]{t},$$

where c is a constant. Prove that the rate of increase of H at any particular height is inversely proportional to the square of the height. (U.L.C.I.)

5. A rod AB, 15 ft. long, slides in slots along two bars OX, OY, at right angles and fixed. A moves along OX at the rate of 0·2 ft. per sec. At what rate is B moving along OY when OA = 6 ft.?

6. Coal is pouring steadily into a symmetrical bunker of wedge shape whose inverted apex angle is 40° and whose length is 5 ft. at the rate of 10 cu. ft. per sec. Find by calculus the rate at which the depth of the coal in the bunker increases. (U.E.I.)

7. A weight is being lifted by means of a rope passing over a pulley 25 ft. above the ground. The rope is 50 ft. long. A man holds the other end of the rope at a height of 5 ft. and walks away at 10 ft./sec. How rapidly does the weight start to ascend?

8. A water cistern has the form of an inverted cone, radius 3 ft. and height 10 ft. At what rate is the water pouring into the cistern when its height in the cistern is 4 ft. and rising at the rate of 2 in./sec.?

CHAPTER 8

TRIGONOMETRY

1. Measurement of Angles

The figure below, which we shall refer to as the " angle generator," consists of the usual axes XOX_1, YOY_1 at right angles to each other, and a movable radius OP.

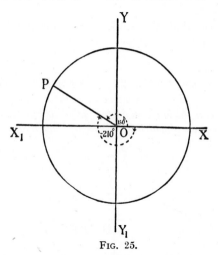

FIG. 25.

The amount of turning which OP undergoes in passing from the position OX to its present position is called the angle POX.

If OP turns anti-clockwise, the angle POX is positive; if clockwise, negative.

Thus OP will occupy the same position on the generator if POX = 150° or − 210°.

We observe, further, that we can generate positive or negative angles of any size, though the greatest angle we can picture on the generator is one of 360° or four right angles.

In generating an angle of 390°, OP would occupy the same position as in generating an angle of 30°.

Angles will be measured in degrees or in radians, a radian being the angle subtended at the centre of a circle by an arc equal in length to the radius. Observe in this definition that the radius must be bent to coincide with the arc.

The value of 1 radian in degrees, minutes and seconds is 57° 17′ 44″, approx.

We assume that the student can convert degrees to radians, or radians to degrees. (See Vol. I and Vol. II.)

Example

A thin rod whose length is 25 ins. is bent into the form of an arc of a circle. The distance between the ends of the rod is 20 ins. If φ is the angle in degrees subtended by the rod at the centre of the circle of which it forms part show that

$$sin \frac{\phi}{2} = \frac{\pi\phi}{450} \qquad \text{(U.L.C.I.)}$$

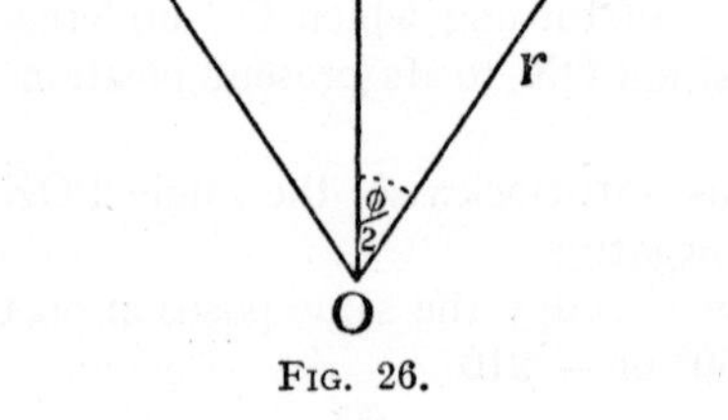

Fig. 26.

Suppose that O is the centre of the circle.

OA is the radius $= r$, say.

ODB bisects the arc, the chord AC, and the angle AOC $(= \phi)$.

Then arc AB $= 12\frac{1}{2}$ ins. and AD $= 10$ ins.

(1) Express $\dfrac{\phi}{2}$ in radian measure, thus: let $\dfrac{\phi^{\circ}}{2} = \alpha$ radians.

Then
$$\frac{\phi}{360} = \frac{\alpha}{\pi}$$

i.e.,
$$\alpha = \frac{\pi\phi}{360} = \frac{12\frac{1}{2}}{r}$$

i.e.,
$$\frac{25}{2r} = \frac{\pi\phi}{360} \quad . \quad . \quad . \quad . \quad (1)$$

From the figure $\quad r\sin\dfrac{\phi}{2} = 10 \quad . \quad . \quad . \quad . \quad . \quad (2)$

Substitute for r in (1) and get the result.

2. The Trigonometrical Ratios of Angles of Any Magnitude

Let XOP be any angle.　The radius OP is shown (Fig. 27) in each of the four quadrants.

Drop PM perpendicular to the x-axis.

The triangle MOP will be referred to always as the " defining triangle," since its sides are used to define the trigonometrical ratios of the angle XOP.

Each side of this triangle will be named thus : OP is the hypotenuse—denoted by " h " the initial letter.

PM is the ordinate (or opposite), denoted by " o."

OM is the abscissa (or adjacent) denoted by " a."

The terms ordinate and abscissa are quite familiar from our graphic work.

For them the rule of signs, as in graphs, holds whilst OP or h is always positive.

The appropriate signs are placed on each figure.

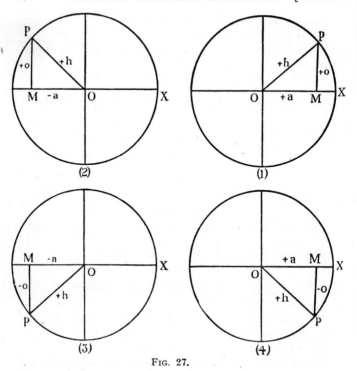

Fig. 27.

In every case let XOP = θ.
The equations of definition are :

$$\sin \theta = \frac{\text{ordinate}}{\text{hypotenuse}} = \frac{o}{h}$$

$$\cos \theta = \frac{\text{abscissa}}{\text{hypotenuse}} = \frac{a}{h}$$

$$\tan \theta = \frac{\text{ordinate}}{\text{abscissa}} = \frac{o}{a}$$

The signs of these ratios vary with the quadrant in which OP stops. Anyone familiar with graphs will have no difficulty in seeing that the signs to be given to the ratios are those in the following table.

	1st Quadrant.	2nd Quadrant.	3rd Quadrant.	4th Quadrant.
sin . . .	+	+	−	−
cos . . .	+	−	−	+
tan . . .	+	−	+	−
positive . .	All	sin	tan	cos

The words in the bottom row may assist the student in remembering which ratios are positive in the various quadrants.

In addition to the three ratios given, we must know also their **reciprocals**.

The reciprocal of $\sin \theta$ is *cosec* $\theta \left(= \dfrac{\text{hypotenuse}}{\text{ordinate}} \right)$, of $\cos \theta$ is *sec* θ, and of $\tan \theta$ is *cot* θ.

The abbreviations are those of cosecant θ, secant θ, and cotangent θ respectively.

Hence for all angles

$$\left. \begin{array}{l} \sin \theta \,.\, \text{cosec } \theta = 1 \\ \cos \theta \,.\, \sec \theta = 1 \\ \tan \theta \cot \theta = 1 \end{array} \right\} \quad . \quad . \quad . \quad . \quad \textbf{(1)}$$

Notice also that $\tan \theta = \dfrac{o}{a} = \dfrac{\frac{o}{h}}{\frac{a}{h}} = \dfrac{\sin \theta}{\cos \theta} \quad . \quad . \quad . \quad \textbf{(2)}$

And $\qquad \therefore \quad \cot \theta = \dfrac{\cos \theta}{\sin \theta} \quad . \quad . \quad . \quad . \quad . \quad \textbf{(3)}$

Further, in each of the four figures—*i.e.*, for all values of θ

$$o^2 + a^2 = h^2 \quad . \quad . \quad . \quad . \quad . \quad (4)$$

Dividing both sides of (4) by h^2, we get :

$$\frac{o^2}{h^2} + \frac{a^2}{h^2} = 1$$

i.e., $\qquad\qquad \sin^2\theta + \cos^2\theta = 1 \quad . \quad . \quad . \quad (5)$

Similarly, dividing (4) by o^2 and a^2 in succession

we get $\qquad 1 + \cot^2\theta = \operatorname{cosec}^2\theta \quad . \quad . \quad . \quad . \quad (6)$

and $\qquad \tan^2\theta + 1 = \sec^2) \quad . \quad . \quad . \quad . \quad (7)$

The values of the trigonometrical ratios of certain angles are given below.

	0°	30°	45°	60°	90°
sin	0	$\frac{1}{2}$	$\frac{1}{\sqrt{2}}$	$\frac{\sqrt{3}}{2}$	1
cos	1	$\frac{\sqrt{3}}{2}$	$\frac{1}{\sqrt{2}}$	$\frac{1}{2}$	0
tan	0	$\frac{1}{\sqrt{3}}$	1	$\sqrt{3}$	∞
cosec	∞	2	$\sqrt{2}$	$\frac{2}{\sqrt{3}}$	1
sec	1	$\frac{2}{\sqrt{3}}$	$\sqrt{2}$	2	∞
cot	∞	$\sqrt{3}$	1	$\frac{1}{\sqrt{3}}$	0

3. Graphs of the Trigonometrical Functions

The following facts assist us in drawing the graphs of the trigonometrical functions :

1. sin θ and cos θ are never numerically greater than unity.   Both have values between ± 1, or ± 1.

2. Their reciprocals cosec θ and sec θ are never numerically less than unity.

3. tan θ and cot θ have values ranging from − ∞ to + ∞.

4. We need to calculate the values of any of the functions only in the range from θ = 0 to θ = 90° $\left(\text{or } \dfrac{\pi}{2}\right)$.

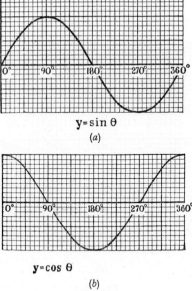

y = sin θ

(a)

y = cos θ

(b)

Fig. 28.

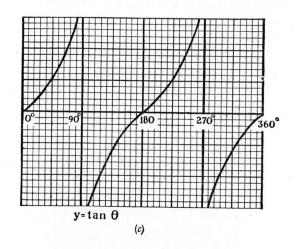

$y = \tan \theta$

(c)

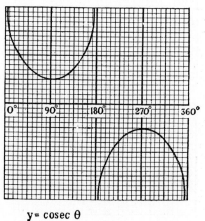

$y = \operatorname{cosec} \theta$

(d)

FIG. 28.

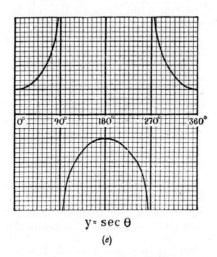

$y = \sec \theta$

(e)

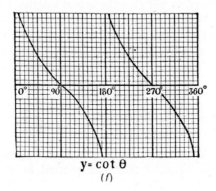

$y = \cot \theta$

(f)

FIG. 28.

4. If we are given the value of one trigonometrical ratio of an angle, we can write down all the rest by using the following method.

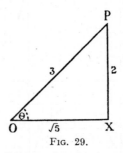

Fig. 29.

Given $\sin \theta = \frac{2}{3}$, find $\tan \theta$, $\cos \theta$, and $\cot \theta$.

Sketch any right-angled triangle POX. Mark the angle θ, and put numbers on the appropriate sides; in the above case, since $\dfrac{PX}{OP} = \dfrac{2}{3}$, put 2 on side PX and 3 on OP. These numbers do not give the actual lengths, but merely the ratio between them.

By Pythagoras' theorem, $OX = \sqrt{5}$.

Then we can write down any ratio of the angle θ.

Thus

$$\tan \theta = \frac{2}{\sqrt{5}} = \frac{2\sqrt{5}}{5}$$

$$\cos \theta = \frac{\sqrt{5}}{3} \text{ and } \cot \theta = \frac{\sqrt{5}}{2}$$

Similarly if we are asked to express every trigonometrical ratio of θ in terms of $\tan \theta$, we proceed in exactly the same way.

Put $\tan \theta = a$

i.e., $\tan \theta = \dfrac{a}{1}$

The triangle is sketched.   Since the value of tan θ is a, we let BC = a, and AB = 1.

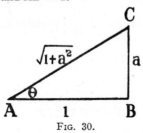

FIG. 30.

By calculation   AC = $\sqrt{1 + a^2}$

We can now express every trigonometrical ratio of θ in terms of a—i.e., in terms of tan θ.

Thus $\sin \theta = \dfrac{a}{\sqrt{1 + a^2}} = \dfrac{\tan \theta}{\sqrt{1 + \tan^2 \theta}}$

5. The Inverse Notation

If $\cos \theta = a,$

we write : $\theta = \cos^{-1} a.$

Any equation such as this must be read by the student thus :
" θ is the angle whose cosine is a."

Thus $\cos^{-1} \frac{1}{2}$ means the angle whose cosine is $\frac{1}{2}$—i.e., 60° or $\dfrac{\pi}{3}$.

Similarly $\tan^{-1} 1$ is the angle whose tangent is 1—i.e., 45° or $\dfrac{\pi}{4}$.

Further,

$$\sin^{-1} \frac{\sqrt{3}}{2} + \cos^{-1} \frac{1}{\sqrt{2}} = 60° + 45°$$
$$= 105°$$

and is thus the sum of two angles.

Sin^{-1} x and (sin x)$^{-1}$ must then be clearly differentiated. Sin^{-1}x is the angle whose sine is x; but

$$(\sin x)^{-1} = \frac{1}{\sin x} = \operatorname{cosec} x,$$

and means the reciprocal of sin x, just as $x^{-1} = \dfrac{1}{x}$, the reciprocal of x.

EXERCISE 29

1. State the values of the following, using tables where necessary :

   (i) sin 124°, (ii) cos 130°, (iii) tan (− 320°),

   (iv) cosec 348°, (v) sec (− 290°), (vi) cos $\dfrac{\pi}{6}$,

   (vii) sin $\dfrac{3\pi}{7}$, (viii) tan $\dfrac{7\pi}{8}$.

2. Given that sec θ = $\frac{3}{2}$, find cot θ and sin θ.

3. If tan A = 3, find all the other trigonometrical ratios of A.

4. If θ = cos^{-1} $\frac{1}{3}$, find sin θ and tan θ.

5. Show that sin$^{-1}\dfrac{\sqrt{3}}{2}$ + cos^{-1} $\dfrac{\sqrt{3}}{2}$ = 90°.

6. Express the following angles in circular measure :

   (i) 30°, (ii) 45°, (iii) 60°, (iv) 120°, (v) 228°.

7. Express the following angles in degrees :

   (i) $\dfrac{\pi}{5}$, (ii) $\dfrac{3\pi}{8}$, (iii) $\dfrac{\pi}{7}$, (iv) $\dfrac{\theta}{3}$, (v) $\dfrac{2}{3}$ radians.

8. Show that cos^{-1} $\dfrac{1}{\sqrt{2}}$ + sin^{-1} $\dfrac{1}{2}$ = 75°.

9. Show that sin^{-1} 1 + cos^{-1} 1 = $\dfrac{\pi}{2}$.

10. The following formula is developed in connection with a high-pressure transmission line

$$E_s{}^2 = (E_R \cos \phi + RI)^2 + (E_R \sin \phi + X \cdot I)^2$$

Where E_s is the sending end voltage and E_R the receiving end voltage. Find E_R given that $E_s = 8{,}000$, $\cos \phi = 0{\cdot}8$, $R = 8{\cdot}5$, $X = 6{\cdot}5$, and $I = 200$.   (U.E.I.)

---

5. It will have been noticed that as θ completes the range from $0°$ to $360°$, or from 0 to 2π, $\sin \theta$ takes every possible value. If OP continues to revolve, $\sin \theta$ repeats the previous values.

Now $\sin \theta$ satisfies our definition of a function of θ, since when θ is given a value, $\sin \theta$ takes a value.

It is called a periodic function of θ whose period is $360°$ or 2π radians, because each time θ is increased by 2π, $\sin \theta$ has the same value as before.

Thus $\sin \theta = \sin (\theta + 2\pi)$
Similarly $\cos \theta = \cos (\theta + 2\pi)$

But note $\tan \theta = \tan (\theta + \pi)$, showing that the period of $\tan \theta$ is π.

Now let OP start from OX, and turn in the positive sense at the rate of 3 radians per sec. In t secs., $XOP = 3t$ radians and $\sin XOP = \sin 3t$.

No matter what value t may have

$$\sin 3t = \sin (3t + 2\pi)$$
$$= \sin \left[3\!\left(t + \frac{2\pi}{3}\right) \right].$$

Notice that the sine has the same value at times " t " and $t + \dfrac{2\pi}{3}$. In this case $\sin 3t$ is a periodic function of t, whose period is $\dfrac{2\pi}{3}$.

Generally, since

$$\sin nx = \sin (nx + 2\pi)$$
$$= \sin n\left(x + \frac{2\pi}{n}\right)$$

the period of $\sin nx$ is $\frac{2\pi}{n}$.

Similarly we find that the period of $\cos k\theta$ is $\frac{2\pi}{k}$,

since

$$\cos k\theta = \cos (k\theta + 2\pi)$$
$$= \cos k\left(\theta + \frac{2\pi}{k}\right)$$

showing that $\cos k\theta$ has the same value for angles θ and $\left(\theta + \frac{2\pi}{k}\right)$.

The addition of a constant to the angle does not affect its period.

$$\text{Thus } \sin (3x + 4) = \sin (3x + 4 + 2\pi)$$
$$= \sin \left\{3\left(x + \frac{2\pi}{3}\right) + 4\right\}$$

showing that the period is $\frac{2\pi}{3}$.

Now consider $3 \sin 2x + 4 \cos 4x$. The period of $\sin 2x$ is $\frac{2\pi}{2}$—*i.e.*, π—that of $\cos 4x$ is $\frac{2\pi}{4}$—*i.e.*, $\frac{\pi}{2}$.

Hence the expression $3 \sin 2x + 4 \cos 4x$ will have the same value for angles x, $x + \pi$, $x + 2\pi$, etc.—*i.e.*, its period is π.

6. The Solution of Trigonometrical Equations

Fig. 31 (1) Shows two angles XOP, XOP_1 whose sines are equal.

If $XOP = \theta$, $XOP_1 = \pi - \theta$

and $\sin \theta = \dfrac{MP}{OP} = \dfrac{M_1P_1}{OP_1} = \sin (\pi - \theta)$.

Hence between 0 and 2π there are two angles whose sines have the same value.

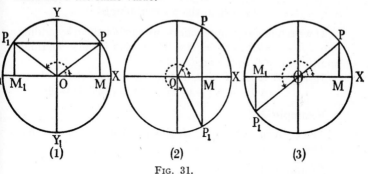

FIG. 31.

We know that $\sin 60° = \dfrac{\sqrt{3}}{2} = 0.866$. If we try to solve $\sin x° = \dfrac{\sqrt{3}}{2}$, we infer at once that *one* value of x is 60°. There is, however, another value—viz., the supplement of 60°. Hence there are two solutions giving angles between 0° and 360°—viz., 60° and 120°.

The number of solutions is infinite, since we can increase either of the above angles by any integral multiple of 360°.

Usually we are interested only in those values of x between 0° and 360°.

Example 1

Solve $\sin 3x° = \frac{1}{2}$.

$\qquad\qquad \sin 3x° = \sin 30° = \sin 150°$.

$\qquad\qquad \therefore \ 3x = 30° \text{ or } 150°$

i.e., $x = 10° \text{ or } 50°$.

Example 2

Solve $\sin 5x = 0.3972$.

We have, $\sin 5x = \sin 23° \ 24'$ (from the tables)

$\qquad\qquad\qquad = \sin 156° \ 36'$ (using the supplement)

$$\therefore \quad 5x = 23° 24' \text{ or } 156° 36' \quad . \quad . \quad . \quad . \quad (1)$$
$$\therefore \quad x = 4° 41' \text{ or } 31° 19' \quad . \quad . \quad . \quad . \quad (2)$$
correct to the nearest minute.

If we require any more values, we can get them by adding multiples of 360° to the angles (1), or what is the same thing multiples of 72° to the angles (2).

In Fig. 31 (2) XOP = θ, and we see at once that
$$\cos \theta = \cos (- \theta) \text{ or } \cos \theta = \cos (360 - \theta).$$

Example 3

Thus, given $\cos \theta = \frac{1}{2}$, we infer at once that $\theta = 60°$ or 300°.

Example 4

If
$$\cos 4x = 0.2974$$
$$= \cos 72° 42' \text{ (from tables)}$$
$$= \cos (360° - 72° 42')$$
$$= \cos 287° 18'$$
$$\therefore \quad 4x° = 72° 42' \text{ or } 287° 18'$$
i.e., $\qquad x = 18° 10.5' \text{ or } 71° 49 5'.$

In Fig. 31 (3) if XOP = θ and XOP$_1$ = $\pi + \theta$,
$$\tan \theta = \tan (\pi + \theta).$$

Example 5

$$\text{Solve } \tan x° = \frac{1}{\sqrt{3}}.$$
$$\tan x° = \frac{1}{\sqrt{3}} = \tan 30°$$
$$x = 30° \text{ or } (180 + 30)°$$
$$= 30° \text{ or } 210°$$

7. To Express the Trigonometrical Ratios of Negative Angles in Terms of those of the Corresponding Positive Angle

Suppose XOP = θ and XOP$_1$ = $- \theta$.

Notice that the defining triangles for each angle are

congruent. They have a common side OM. The signs to be placed on abscissæ and ordinates are shown. We get:

$$\sin \theta = \frac{MP}{OP} = -\frac{MP_1}{OP_1} = -\sin(-\theta)$$

$$\cos \theta = \frac{OM}{OP} = \frac{OM}{OP_1} = \cos(-\theta)$$

$$\tan \theta = \frac{MP}{OM} = -\frac{MP_1}{OM} = -\tan(-\theta)$$

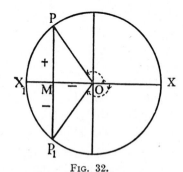

FIG. 32.

Hence
$$\left.\begin{aligned}\sin(-\theta) &= -\sin\theta\\ \cos(-\theta) &= \cos\theta\\ \tan(-\theta) &= -\tan\theta\end{aligned}\right\}$$

Taking the reciprocals of these, we have:

$$\left.\begin{aligned}\operatorname{cosec}(-\theta) &= -\operatorname{cosec}\theta\\ \sec(-\theta) &= \sec\theta\\ \tan(-\theta) &= -\tan\theta\end{aligned}\right\}$$

EXERCISE 30

1. Explain what is meant by saying that the trigonometric functions of θ, $\sin\theta$, $\cos\theta$ and $\tan\theta$ are periodic. State their periods.

2. If t represents time in seconds measured from some

fixed instant, find the number of seconds that has elapsed before $\sin 2t$ again reaches the value it had at time t.

3. Find the periods of (i) $\sin 3t$, (ii) $\cos 4t$, (iii) $\tan 3t$, (iv) $\cos (5x + 4)$, (v) $\sin (ax + \alpha)$, (vi) $3 \sin 5x + 4 \cos 2x$, (vii) $2 \cos 3x - \sin 4x$.

4. Write down the values of the trigonometrical ratios of $(90 + A)$ in terms of those of A.

5. Solve the following trigonometrical equations, giving in each case two values of the angle between $0°$ and $360°$ which satisfies it :

$\qquad$ (1) $\sin 2x = \frac{1}{2}$.
$\qquad$ (2) $\cos 3x = \dfrac{\sqrt{3}}{2}$

$\qquad$ (3) $\tan 2\theta = 1$.
$\qquad$ (4) $\sin 5x = 0\cdot 3621$.
$\qquad$ (5) $\tan 3\theta = 2$.
$\qquad$ (6) $\cos 3x = \cos 60°$.

6. Express $5 - 5 \cos \theta - 3 \sin^2 \theta = 0$ as a quadratic equation in $\cos \theta$, and find all the values of θ between $0°$ and $360°$ which satisfy it.

7. Use the relation $\sec^2 \theta = 1 + \tan^2 \theta$ to find all the values of θ between $0°$ and $360°$ which satisfy the equation

$$\tan^2 \theta - \sec \theta - 5 = 0.$$

8. Solve $14 - 11 \sin \theta - 12 \cos^2 \theta = 0$, for values of θ between $0°$ and $360°$.

9. Find the periods of

$\qquad$ (1) $\sin (3t + 2)$.
$\qquad$ (2) $\cos (5t + 3)$
$\qquad$ (3) $\sin (2t + \alpha)$.
$\qquad$ (4) $\tan (4t + \beta)$.
$\qquad$ (5) $\sin (ax + \alpha) + \cos (3ax + \beta)$.

10. Express the following in terms of the trigonometrical ratios of the corresponding positive angle :

      (1) $\sin(-20°)$.
      (2) $\cos(-60°)$.
      (3) $\tan(-42°)$.
      (4) $\sec(-130°)$.

CHAPTER 9

COMPOUND ANGLES

1. Projections

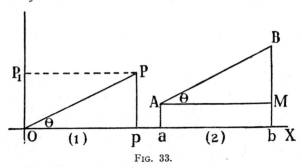

Fig. 33.

AB is any segment of a straight line. It may be considered to have two senses—viz., AB and BA, and we have AB = − BA.

If Aa, Bb are perpendicular to any line OX, then ab is the orthogonal projection of AB on OX.

If OP is equal and parallel to AB, and Pp is drawn perpendicular to OX, then Op = ab. Hence "equal and parallel straight lines have equal projections on any other straight line."

If AM is parallel to OX, we have AM = ab = AB cos θ.

Further, notice that $Op_1 = pP = MB = AB \sin \theta$.

Hence, the projections of any line AB which makes an angle θ with OX are

$$\left. \begin{array}{l} \text{AB cos } \theta \text{ on the } x\text{-axis} \\ \text{AB sin } \theta \text{ on the } y\text{-axis} \end{array} \right\} \quad \cdots \quad (1)$$

and

also $\qquad AB^2 = AM^2 + BM^2.$

154

Hence if we know the lengths, AM and BM, of the projections of AB on two straight lines at right angles, we can find the length of AB.

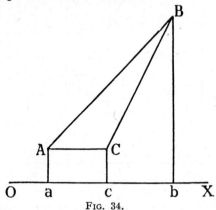

FIG. 34.

Let ABC be any triangle; drop the perpendiculars Aa, Bb, Cc on OX.

Now notice from the above figure that

$$ab = ac + cb,$$

i.e., the projection of AB = the sum of the projections of the two straight lines joining A to B.

By drawing any figure, the student will see that the projection of AB = sum of the projections of all the straight lines joining A to B in any way. It is not even necessary to keep to the plane of the paper.

The above property of projections is often stated thus:

The sum of the projections of the sides of any closed polygon, on any straight line is zero.

In the case of the triangle above, we have

$$ac + cb + ba = 0,$$

since $ba = - ab.$

3. Let OP make θ with OX, and let PR be perpendicular to OP.

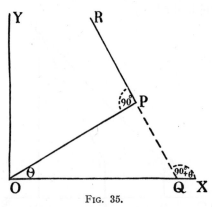

FIG. 35.

Then PR makes $90° + θ$ with OX, as can readily be seen by imagining RP produced backwards to Q

$$\angle XQP = θ + 90°.$$

Hence the projection of PR on OX is, by using a previous result,

$$PR \cos (90 + θ).$$

But $\cos (θ + 90) = - \sin θ.$

∴ the projection of PR on OX $= - PR \sin θ.$

The projection of OP on the X-axis $= OP \cos θ$⎱
and the projection of OP on the Y-axis $= OP \sin θ$⎰

Similarly the projection of PR on the Y-axis is

$$PR \sin(90 + θ) = PR \cos θ.$$

Example

Suppose AB = 3 ins. and BC = 2 ins., and that AB is inclined at 14° to OX, whilst BC makes 30° with AB, as shown in Fig. 36.

We require the length of the projection of AC on OX.

The projection could be readily found by a drawing to scale, but we are interested in calculating it from the diagram.

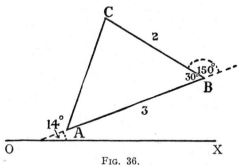

FIG. 36.

The projection of AC = proj. of AB + proj. of BC
$$= 3 \cos 14° + 2 \cos 164° \quad . \quad (1)$$

[Notice that BC makes 150° with AB, and hence 164° with OX.]

(1) becomes
$$3 \cos 14° - 2 \cos 16°$$
$$= 3 \times 0·9703 - 2 \times 0·9613$$
$$= 2·9109 - 1·9226$$
$$= 0·9883 \text{ ins.}$$

4. To find cos (A + B) and sin (A + B)

In Fig. 37 suppose $\angle XOQ = A$ and $\angle QOP = B$.

Let PR be $\perp$ to OQ.

Then the projection of OP on OX = the projection of OR on OX + the projection of RP on OX.

i.e., OP cos (A + B) = OR cos A + RP cos (A + 90°)
$$= \text{OR} \cos A - \text{RP} \sin A \quad . \quad . \quad (1)$$

Now OR = OP cos B and RP = OP sin B.

Substituting for OR and RP in (1), we get :

OP cos (A + B) = OP cos A cos B — OP sin A sin B.

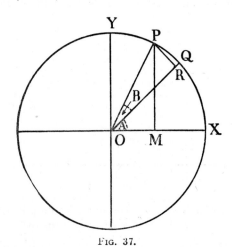

FIG. 37.

Hence, cancelling OP,

$$\cos (A + B) = \cos A \cos B - \sin A \sin B \quad . \quad (2)$$

For sin (A + B), project OP on OY. We get :

$$\text{OP} \sin (A + B) = \text{OR} \sin A + \text{RP} \sin (A + 90°)$$
$$= \text{OR} \sin A + \text{RP} \cos A$$

Substitute for OR and RP as before, and get :

OP sin (A + B) = OP sin A cos B + OP cos A sin B.

Now divide throughout by OP, and

$$\sin (A + B) = \sin A \cos B + \cos A \sin B \quad . \quad (3)$$

The figure in the preceding proof has been drawn for two positive angles whose sum falls in the first quadrant, but the proof is quite general for all angles.

Now take cos $(A + B) = \cos A \cos B - \sin A \sin B$ and write $(-B)$ for $+ B$.

We get:

$$\cos (A - B) = \cos A \cos (-B) - \sin A \sin (-B)$$

i.e., $\cos (A - B) = \cos A \cos B + \sin A \sin B$. (4)

since $\cos (-B) = \cos B$

and $\sin (-B) = -\sin B$

Similarly writing $-B$ for $+B$ in (3) we get:

$$\sin (A - B) = \sin A \cos (-B) + \cos A \sin (-B)$$

i.e., $\sin (A - B) = \sin A \cos B - \cos A \sin B$ . . (5)

The four formulæ (2), (3), (4), (5) are collected here for reference, and should be well known.

$$\left. \begin{aligned} \sin (A + B) &= \sin A \cos B + \cos A \sin B \\ \sin (A - B) &= \sin A \cos B - \cos A \sin B \end{aligned} \right\}$$

$$\left. \begin{aligned} \cos (A + B) &= \cos A \cos B - \sin A \sin B \\ \cos (A - B) &= \cos A \cos B + \sin A \sin B \end{aligned} \right\}$$

Example

Find, without using tables, sin 75°.

$$\sin 75° = \sin (45 + 30)° = \sin 45° \cos 30° + \cos 45° \sin 30°$$

$$= \frac{1}{\sqrt{2}} \cdot \frac{\sqrt{3}}{2} + \frac{1}{\sqrt{2}} \cdot \frac{1}{2}$$

$$= \frac{\sqrt{3} + 1}{2\sqrt{2}}.$$

5. Consider the two equations

$$r \sin \alpha = 2 \quad . \quad . \quad . \quad . \quad . \quad (1)$$
$$r \cos \alpha = 3 \quad . \quad . \quad . \quad . \quad . \quad (2)$$

Squaring both sides, then adding, we get:

$$r^2 (\sin^2 \alpha + \cos^2 \alpha) = 13$$

i.e., $r^2 = 13$, since $\sin^2 \alpha + \cos^2 \alpha = 1$.

Taking the positive square root for r, this gives :
$$r = \sqrt{13} = 3.61.$$

Now divide (1) by (2) we get :
$$\tan \alpha = \tfrac{2}{3} = 0.6666 \ldots$$
$$\therefore \quad \alpha = 33° \, 41' \text{ from the tables.}$$

This method of finding r and α illustrated above is important.

Example 1

Express $3 \sin x + 2 \cos x$ in the form $r \sin (x + \alpha)$, where r and α are determinate.

Expanding $\sin (x + \alpha)$ we get :
$$3 \sin x + 2 \cos x = r \sin x \cos \alpha + r \cos x \sin \alpha$$
$$= r \cos \alpha \, . \sin x + r \sin a \, . \cos x$$

This will be true if $r \cos \alpha = 3$ and $r \sin \alpha = 2$.
We have found values for r and α above.
Hence :
$$3 \sin x + 2 \cos x = \sqrt{13} \sin (x + 33° \, 41').$$

Example 2

Express $3 \sin nx + 4 \cos nx$ in the form $R \sin (nx + \alpha)$ where R and α are independent of x.

Find the value of x between $0°$ and $360°$ for which
$$3 \sin \frac{x}{2} + 4 \cos \frac{x}{2} = 2. \qquad \text{(N.C.)}$$

We must have
$$3 \sin nx + 4 \cos nx = R \sin (nx + \alpha)$$
$$= R (\sin nx \cos \alpha + \cos nx \sin \alpha)$$
$$= R \cos \alpha \, . \sin nx + R \sin \alpha \cos nx.$$

Hence we put :
$$R \cos \alpha = 3 \quad . \quad . \quad . \quad . \quad . \quad (1)$$
and
$$R \sin \alpha = 4 \quad . \quad . \quad . \quad . \quad . \quad (2)$$

Solving (1) and (2) in the way shown, it follows that :

$R^2 = 25$, $\therefore$ R = 5 (taking the + square root) and dividing (2) by (1)

$$\tan \alpha = \tfrac{4}{3} = 1 \cdot 3333$$
$$\therefore \quad \alpha = 53° \ 8' \text{ (from the tables).}$$

So that :

$$3 \sin nx + 4 \cos nx = 5 \sin (nx + 53° \ 8') \quad . \quad (3)$$

To solve

$$3 \sin \frac{x}{2} + 4 \cos \frac{x}{2} = 2 \quad . \quad . \quad . \quad . \quad (4)$$

notice that the left-hand side of (4) is the same as that of (3) if we put $n = \tfrac{1}{2}$.

$$\therefore \quad 5 \sin \left(\frac{x}{2} + 53° \ 8' \right) = 2$$

or $$\sin \left(\frac{x}{2} + 53° \ 8' \right) = \frac{2}{5} = 0 \cdot 4.$$

From the tables, $\quad \sin 23° \ 35' = 0 \cdot 4$
Hence, also, $\quad \sin (180 - 23° \ 35') = 0 \cdot 4.$

$$\therefore \quad \frac{x}{2} + 53° \ 8' = 23° \ 35' \text{ or } 156° \ 25'$$

$$\therefore \quad \quad \quad \frac{x}{2} = -29° \ 33' \text{ or } 103° \ 17'$$

$$\therefore \quad \quad \quad x = -59° \ 6' \text{ or } 206° \ 34'$$

$x = -59° \ 6'$ is the value asked for.

Written positively $x = (360° - 59° \ 6') = 300° \ 54'$.

EXERCISE 31

1. A man walks for 3·2 miles in a direction 13° N. of E., and then 5·4 miles in a direction 27° N. of E. How far due E. has he travelled ? and due N ?

2. ABC is a triangle whose side AB is inclined at **13°** to the horizontal OX.

If AB = 7 ins., BC = 5 ins., and the angle ABC = 63°, find

(1) the projection of AC on OX.

(2) its projection on a perpendicular to OX.

Hence deduce the length of AC.

3. Solve for r and α

$$(1) \quad \begin{matrix} r \cos \alpha = 2 \\ r \sin \alpha = 1 \end{matrix} \Bigg\}$$

$$(2) \quad \begin{matrix} r \sin \alpha = 3 \\ r \cos \alpha = 5 \end{matrix} \Bigg\}$$

Then put $2 \sin x + \cos x$ in the form $r \sin (x + \alpha)$ and $5 \cos x + 3 \sin x$ in the form $r \cos (x + \alpha)$.

4. Find all the values of x between 0° and 360° for which

$$4 \cdot 37 \cos 3x + 3 \cdot 84 \sin 3x = 5 \cdot 73.$$

(U.L.C.I.)

5. (a) Write out the formulæ for sin (A + B), sin (A — B), cos (A + B), and cos (A — B). Prove any one of them.

(b) Use the formulæ to find the value of sin 75° and of tan 15°. (U.L.C.I.)

6. Show $\sin \theta + \sin (\theta + 120) + \sin (\theta + 240) = 0$.

(U.L.C.I.)

7. By expanding $\sin (\theta + 90)$ and $\cos (\theta + 90)$ or otherwise, show

$$\sin (\theta + 90) = \cos \theta \text{ and } \cos (\theta + 90) = - \sin \theta.$$

(U.L.C.I.)

8. Find, without using the calculus, the maximum value of $2 \cos x + 3 \sin x$.

9. Two straight rods OA, OB of lengths 3 ft. and 2 ft. respectively, are rigidly joined at O so that $\angle AOB = 30°$. Initially OA lies along a horizontal line OX, and B is above OX. If the rods rotate about O in a vertical plane, with a

uniform angular velocity of 4 radians/sec., find an expression for the length of the projection on OX of the join BA at time t secs. Deduce the maximum value of this projection and the smallest value of t which gives it. (U.L.C.I.)

10. Show that

$$\cos (A + B) . \cos (A - B) = \cos^2 A - \sin^2 B = \cos^2 B - \sin^2 A.$$

11. Find x in degrees approximately if

$$3 \sin x + 2 \cos x = 3{\cdot}4$$

For what value of x is $3 \sin x + 2 \cos x$ a maximum?
(B.E.)

12. Find A and α so that $20 \sin \theta + 41 \cos \theta$ may equal $A \sin (\theta + \alpha)$ for all values of θ.

Deduce the values of θ between $0°$ and $360°$ for which the given expression has (1) a maximum value, (2) a minimum value, (3) zero value, (3) the value 43·4. (U.L.C.I.)

13. Put the expression $3 \sin x + \sqrt{2} \cos (x + 45)$ in the form $A \sin (x + \alpha)$, where A and α are known.

6. $\tan (A + B) = \dfrac{\sin (A + B)}{\cos (A + B)}$

$$= \dfrac{\sin A \cos B + \cos A \sin B}{\cos A \cos B - \sin A \sin B}$$

$$= \dfrac{\cos A \cos B \left[\dfrac{\sin A}{\cos A} + \dfrac{\sin B}{\cos B} \right]}{\cos A \cos B \left[1 - \dfrac{\sin A}{\cos A} \cdot \dfrac{\sin B}{\cos B} \right]}$$

i.e., $\tan (A + B) = \dfrac{\tan A + \tan B}{1 - \tan A \tan B}$

Changing the sign of B, we get :

$$\tan (A - B) = \dfrac{\tan A - \tan B}{1 + \tan A \tan B}$$

Example

An object which is six feet high stands on the top of a tower. At a place on the same horizontal plane as the foot of the tower and 40 ft. away from it, the object subtends an angle of 5°. Find the height of the tower.   (U.L.C.I.)

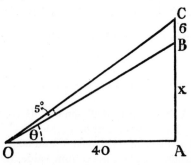

FIG. 38.

AB is the tower, BC the object, O the point at which BC subtends an angle of 5°.

$$OA = 40 \text{ ft.} \qquad BC = 6 \text{ ft.}$$

Let $AB = x$ ft. and $\angle BOA = \theta°$.

Then $\dfrac{x}{40} = \tan \theta$

and $\dfrac{x + 6}{40} = \tan (\theta + 5)° = \dfrac{\tan \theta + \tan 5°}{1 - \tan \theta \cdot \tan 5°}$

$\therefore \quad \dfrac{x + 6}{40} = \dfrac{\dfrac{x}{40} + a}{1 - \dfrac{ax}{40}}$ $\left(\begin{array}{c} a \text{ is put for } \tan 5°\text{—}i.e., \\ a = 0\cdot 0875 \end{array} \right)$

i.e., $\dfrac{x + 6}{40} = \dfrac{x + 40a}{40 - ax}.$

$\therefore \quad (x + 6)(40 - ax) = 40(x + 40a)$

i.e., $40x + 240 - ax^2 - 6ax = 40x + 1600a$

giving $\qquad ax^2 + 6ax + 1600a - 240 = 0$

i.e., $\qquad x^2 + 6x + 1600 - \dfrac{240}{a} = 0$ . . . (1)

$$\frac{240}{a} = \frac{240}{0 \cdot 0875} = \frac{2400}{\frac{7}{8}} = 2743 \text{ (nearly).}$$

Hence (1) becomes

$$x^2 + 6x - 1143 = 0$$
$$x = \frac{-6 \pm \sqrt{36 + 4 \times 1143}}{2}$$

The value of x required is

$$\frac{-6 + \sqrt{36 + 4572}}{2}$$
$$= \frac{-6 + 68}{2} \text{ to the nearest ft.}$$
$$= 31 \, ft.$$

7. Double Angle Formulæ

Writing A for B in $\sin (A + B)$, we get :

$$\sin (A + A) = \sin A \cos A + \cos A \sin A$$

i.e., $\qquad \mathbf{\sin 2A = 2 \sin A \cos A}$ . . . . . (1)

or $\qquad \sin (\text{angle}) = 2 \sin (\tfrac{1}{2} \text{ angle}) \cos (\tfrac{1}{2} \text{ angle})$

Similarly

$$\cos (A + A) = \cos A \,.\, \cos A - \sin A \sin A$$

i.e., $\qquad \mathbf{\cos 2A = \cos^2 A - \sin^2 A}$ . . . . . (2)

This gives the form

$$\cos (\text{angle}) = \cos^2 (\tfrac{1}{2} \text{ angle}) - \sin^2 (\tfrac{1}{2} \text{ angle})$$ . .

In (2), put $1 - \cos^2 A$ for $\sin^2 A$; then :

$$\cos 2A = \cos^2 A - (1 - \cos^2 A)$$

i.e., $\qquad \mathbf{\cos 2A = 2 \cos^2 A - 1}$ . . . . . . (3)

Similarly, putting $(1 - \sin^2 A)$ for $\cos^2 A$ in (2) we get :

$$\mathbf{\cos 2A = 1 - 2 \sin^2 A}$$ . . . . (4)

(1), (2), (3), and (4) are important formulæ.

Example 1

Given $\cos 30° = \dfrac{\sqrt{3}}{2}$, find $\cos 15°$.

$$\cos 30° = 2\cos^2 15° - 1$$

i.e., $$2\cos^2 15° = 1 + \frac{\sqrt{3}}{2} = 1.866$$

$$\therefore \quad \cos^2 15° = 0.933$$

and taking the square root, we get :

$$\cos 15° = 0.966.$$

Example 2

Given $\sin A = \frac{1}{5}$, find by calculation, $\sin 2A$ and $\cos 2A$.

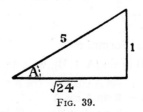

Fig. 39.

We are given $\sin A = \frac{1}{5}$. Sketch the usual triangle containing the angle A, and we find the third side is $\sqrt{24}$.

Now
$$\sin 2A = 2\sin A \,.\, \cos A$$
$$= 2 \times \tfrac{1}{5} \times \frac{\sqrt{24}}{5}$$
$$= \frac{2\sqrt{24}}{25}.$$

$$\cos 2A = 1 - 2\sin^2 A$$
$$= 1 - 2 \times \tfrac{1}{25}$$
$$= \tfrac{23}{25}.$$

8. Since $\tan (A + B) = \dfrac{\tan A + \tan B}{1 - \tan A \tan B}$

putting A for B, we get:

$$\tan 2A = \frac{2 \tan A}{1 - \tan^2 A}$$

Example 1
Given cos A = $\frac{1}{3}$, find tan 2A.

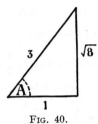

FIG. 40.

Since cos A = $\frac{1}{3}$, the third side of the triangle is $\sqrt{8}$.

$$\tan 2A = \frac{2 \tan A}{1 - \tan^2 A} = \frac{2\sqrt{8}}{1 - 8} = -\frac{2\sqrt{8}}{7} = -\frac{4\sqrt{2}}{7}$$

Similarly if we are given any trigonometrical ratio of the angle A, we can calculate from the double angle formulæ all the trigonometrical ratios of the angle 2A.

Example 2
The values of the crank angle θ for which the velocity of the piston of a certain engine is a maximum are obtained from the equation cos θ + $\frac{2}{15}$ cos 2θ = 0. Find the two solutions of this equation between 0° and 360°. (U.L.C.I.)

We have cos θ + $\frac{2}{15}$ (2 cos² θ − 1) = 0 by substituting for cos 2θ.

Rewriting the equation, we get:

$$4 \cos^2 \theta + 15 \cos \theta - 2 = 0$$

$$\therefore \quad \cos \theta = \frac{-15 \pm \sqrt{15^2 + 32}}{8}$$

$$= \frac{-15 \pm 16 \cdot 03}{8}$$

$$= 0 \cdot 1288 \text{ (other value rejected as it > unity)}.$$

$\therefore$ From the tables $\theta = 82° 36'$ or $360° - 82° 36'$ *i.e.*, $277° 24'$.

9. Half-Angle Formulæ

It will now be clear since

$$\sin 2A = 2 \sin A . \cos A$$

that

$$\sin A = 2 \sin \frac{A}{2} . \cos \frac{A}{2}$$

for

$$\sin A = \sin \left(2 . \frac{A}{2}\right)$$

Similarly we get the other " half-angle formulæ "

viz.,

$$\cos A = \cos^2 \frac{A}{2} - \sin^2 \frac{A}{2}$$
$$= 1 - 2 \sin^2 \frac{A}{2}$$
$$= 2 \cos^2 \frac{A}{2} - 1$$

and

$$tan A = \frac{2 \, tan \frac{A}{2}}{1 - tan^2 \frac{A}{2}}$$

It will be observed that the formulæ above have the same form as those of pars. 7 and 8.

10. The following very important formulæ will now be proved :

$$\sin S + \sin T = 2 \sin \frac{S + T}{2} . \cos \frac{S - T}{2} \quad . \quad (1)$$

$$\sin S - \sin T = 2 \cos \frac{S + T}{2} . \sin \frac{S - T}{2} \quad . \quad (2)$$

$$\cos S + \cos T = 2 \cos \frac{S + T}{2} . \cos \frac{S - T}{2} \quad . \quad (3)$$

$$\cos T - \cos S = 2 \sin \frac{S + T}{2} . \sin \frac{S - T}{2} \quad . \quad (4)$$

In the above T is the smaller angle.

$\therefore \cos T > \cos S$. In (4) we change the order to keep the left-hand side positive.

The above formulæ should be remembered in words. Thus (2) is " *The difference between two sines is equal to twice cos (semi-sum) . sin (semi-difference).*"

(1), (3), and (4) can be translated into similar forms.

11. Proofs of the Formulæ

$$\sin (A + B) = \sin A \cos B + \cos A \sin B$$
$$\sin (A - B) = \sin A \cos B - \cos A \sin B$$

Now add and subtract these : we get

$$\sin (A + B) + \sin (A - B) = 2 \sin A \cos B \quad . \quad . \quad (5)$$
$$\sin (A + B) - \sin (A - B) = 2 \cos A \sin B \quad . \quad . \quad (6)$$

Put $\qquad\qquad A + B = S$
and $\qquad\qquad A - B = T$

adding, $\qquad 2A = S + T \qquad \therefore A = \dfrac{S + T}{2}$

Subtracting $\qquad 2B = S - T \qquad \therefore B = \dfrac{S - T}{2}$

Hence (5) becomes :

$$\sin S + \sin T = 2 \sin \frac{S + T}{2} . \cos \frac{S - T}{2}$$

and (6)

$$\sin S - \sin T = 2 \cos \frac{S + T}{2} . \sin \frac{S - T}{2}$$

These are the formulæ (1) and (2).
To prove (3) and (4) we have :

$$\cos (A + B) = \cos A \cos B - \sin A \sin B$$
$$\cos (A - B) = \cos A \cos B + \sin A \sin B.$$

adding

$$\cos (A + B) + \cos (A - B) = 2 \cos A \cos B \quad . \quad (7)$$

i.e., $\cos S + \cos T = 2 \cos \dfrac{S + T}{2} \cos \dfrac{S - T}{2}$. This is (3).

Subtracting, we get

$$\cos (A - B) - \cos (A + B) = 2 \sin A \sin B \quad . \quad . \quad (8)$$

i.e., $\cos T - \cos S = 2 \sin \dfrac{S+T}{2} \sin \dfrac{S-T}{2}$. This is (4).

12. Formulæ (5) to (8) of the last paragraph should be noted. Remember the " form " of these results.

Take (5) :

$$2 \sin A \cos B = \sin (A + B) + \sin (A - B).$$

It enables us to express the product $2 \sin A \cos B$ as the sum of two trigonometrical ratios.

This transformation is useful when we come to deal with the integration of trigonometrical functions.

Example

$$2 \sin 3x \cos 2x = \sin 5x + \sin x$$
$$2 \sin 33° \cos 12° = \sin 45° + \sin 21°$$

Similarly from (7) we get :

$$2 \cos A \cos B = \cos (A + B) + \cos (A - B)$$

Thus $\cos 4x \cos 3x = \frac{1}{2}[\cos 7x + \cos x]$

and $\cos 51° \cos 31° = \frac{1}{2}[\cos 82° + \cos 20°]$

From (8) we have :

$$2 \sin A \sin B = \cos (A - B) - \cos (A + B)$$

Hence $2 \sin 3\theta \sin \theta = \cos 2\theta - \cos 4\theta$

Similarly from (6)

$$2 \cos 5\alpha . \sin 2\alpha = \sin 7\alpha - \sin 3\alpha$$

EXERCISE 32

1. (*a*) Write out the formulæ for $\sin 2\theta$ and $\cos 2\theta$ in terms of $\sin \theta$ and $\cos \theta$. Use these formulæ to show that

$$\tan 2\theta = \frac{2 \tan \theta}{1 - \tan^2 \theta}$$

If $\tan 2\theta = 2$ find without the use of tables the values of $\tan \theta$.   (U.L.C.I.)

2. If $\tan 2A = \dfrac{2 \cdot 5}{1 \cdot 375 - b}$ and $\tan A = 2b$

Calculate :

     (i) the value of b,

     (ii) the least positive value of the angle A to the nearest degree.   (U.E.I.)

3. Write out the value of $\cos 2\theta$ in terms of $\cos \theta$.

Hence solve $5 \cos 2\theta - 13 \cos \theta + 9 = 0$, giving all the solutions between $0°$ and $360°$.   (U.L.C.I.)

4. Assuming the formulæ for the sine of the sum and of the difference of two angles, show that :

$$\sin A + \sin B = 2 \sin \frac{A + B}{2} \cos \frac{A - B}{2}$$

Express in factors $\sin 3A + \sin A$. Find the value of $\sin 75° + \sin 15°$ using the above formula.   (U.L.C.I.)

5. Find, without using tables, $\tan B$ if

$$\tan (A + B) = 3 \cdot 81 \text{ and } \tan A = 2.$$

6. Express as sums or differences of two trigonometrical ratios :

     (1) $\sin 32° \cos 18°$.   (2) $\cos 53° \sin 37°$.

     (3) $2 \cos 44° \cos 38°$.   (4) $2 \sin 38° \sin 42°$.

     (5) $2 \sin (2\theta + \alpha) \sin (2\theta - \alpha)$.

7. Express as products :

     (1) $\sin 3x + \sin 2x$.   (2) $\sin 48° + \sin 36°$.

     (4) $\cos 51° + \cos 29°$.   (4) $\cos (x + h) - \cos x$.

8. If $y = mx + c$ and $y = m_1 x + b$ are the equations of two straight lines, and θ is the angle between them, show that :

$$\tan \theta = \frac{m_1 - m}{1 + m_1 m}.$$

9. Find $\cos 3\theta$ in terms of $\cos \theta$ and $\sin 3\theta$ in terms of $\sin \theta$. Hence deduce the values of $\cos^3 \theta$ and $\sin^3 \theta$.

10. Solve $4 \cos \theta + \cos 2\theta = 0$.

CHAPTER 10

1. Formulæ Connected with any Triangle. The Solution of Problems, including the Solution of Triangles

1. In dealing with any triangle the capital letters A, B, C stand for the measures of the angles, while the small letters *a, b, c* denote the measures of the sides opposite these angles.

2. The Sine Rule

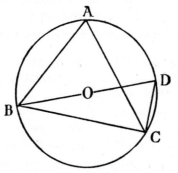

Fig. 41.

Let O be the centre of the circumscribed circle of the triangle ABC; let R = radius of this circle.

Draw the diameter BOD, and join CD.

Then   ∠BDC = ∠BAC (angles in the same segment).

Also   ∠BCD = 90° (angle in a semi-circle).

$$\therefore \quad \frac{BC}{BD} = \sin D = \sin A$$

i.e., $\qquad \dfrac{a}{2R} = \sin A$

or $\qquad \dfrac{a}{\sin A} = 2R.$

Similarly we can prove $\dfrac{b}{\sin B} = 2R = \dfrac{c}{\sin C}.$

Hence :

$$\frac{a}{\sin A} = \frac{b}{\sin B} = \frac{c}{\sin C} = 2R \quad . \quad . \quad . \quad (1)$$

(1) is sometimes called the sine rule, and shows that the sides of any triangle are proportional to the sines of the opposite angles.

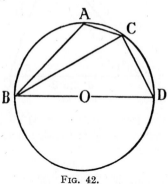

Fig. 42.

If the angle A is obtuse, perform the same construction as in Fig. 41.

ABCD is a cyclic quadrilateral, and $\angle A + \angle D = 180^{\circ}$ *i.e.,* A and D are supplementary.

$$\therefore \quad \sin A = \sin D$$

as before $\qquad \dfrac{BC}{BD} = \sin D = \sin A$

i.e.,
$$\frac{a}{2R} = \sin A$$

giving
$$\frac{a}{\sin A} = 2R.$$

If we know two angles and one side of a triangle, we can now find by calculation the other two sides and the third angle.

Example
Given $a = 26 \cdot 2$ ins., $B = 38° 41'$, $C = 53°$, find b and c.

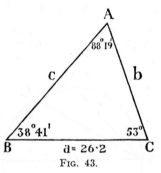

Fig. 43.

The angle $A = 180° - (53° + 38° 41') = 88° 19'$.

Put in the angles, and letter the sketch as shown.   Using the sine rule we get :

$$\frac{c}{\sin 53°} = \frac{26 \cdot 2}{\sin 88° 19'}$$

i.e.,
$$c = \frac{\sin 53° \times 26 \cdot 2}{\sin 88° 19'}$$

$\log c = \log \sin 53° + \log 26 \cdot 2 - \log \sin 88° 19'$

$\qquad\quad = 1 \cdot 3208$

$\therefore \quad c = 20 \cdot 9$ ins.

sin 53	$\bar{1} \cdot 9023$
26·2	$1 \cdot 4183$
	$1 \cdot 3206$
sin 88° 19'	$\bar{1} \cdot 9998$
	$1 \cdot 3208$

Similarly

$$\frac{b}{\sin 38° \, 41'} = \frac{26·2}{\sin 88° \, 19'}$$

$$\therefore \quad b = \frac{\sin 38° \, 41' \times 26·2}{\sin 88° \, 19'}$$

$$\therefore \quad \log b = 1·2143$$

and
$$b = 16·4 \text{ ins.}$$

	log
sin 38° 41'	$\bar{1}$·7958
26·2	1·4183
	1·2141
sin 88° 19'	$\bar{1}$·9998
	1·2143

The Solution of Problems in Heights and Distances

Example 1

In the sketch below, ABC *is a wireless mast and* EDC *is the ground level. To find* AC *observations were taken from* D *and* E *to points* A *and* B *on the mast. The point* C *was not accessible. Determine the length* AC. (U.L.C.I.)

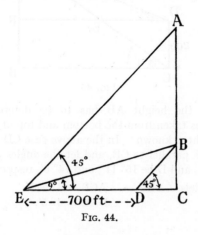

Fig. 44.

Since $\angle C = 90°$ and $\angle AEC = 45°$ $\therefore$ $\angle A = 45°$
and $AC = EC.$

If $BC = x$ ft.   Then DC is x ft
    $\therefore$ $EC = AC = (700 + x)$ ft.

Now $\dfrac{BC}{EC} = \dfrac{x}{700 + x} = \tan 9° = 0\cdot 1584$

$$x = 0\cdot 1584\,(700 + x)$$
$$= 110\cdot 88 + 0\cdot 1584x$$
$$x(1 - 0\cdot 1584) = 110\cdot 88$$
$$x = \frac{110\cdot 88}{0\cdot 8416} = 132 \text{ ft. (nearly)}$$
$$\therefore\quad AC = 832 \text{ ft.}$$

Examples (2) and (3) below are standard and illustrate useful methods of solving problems.

Example 2

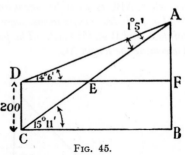

FIG. 45.

Suppose the height AB has to be determined from observations taken from the bottom and top of a tower CD whose height is known.   In the above case CD = 200 ft.

Draw DF parallel to CB, and let the angles of elevation of A from C and D be 15° 11', and 14° 6', respectively.

By parallels $\angle AEF = \angle ACB = 15° \, 11'$.
Hence $\angle DAE = 1° \, 5'$.

Start the solution by comparing the unknown height AB with the known one CD.

$$\frac{AB}{CD} = \frac{AB}{AC} \cdot \frac{AC}{CD} \qquad \cdots \cdots \cdots \quad (1)$$

$$\frac{AB}{AC} = \sin 15^\circ \, 11'$$

and

$$\frac{AC}{CD} = \frac{\sin (90^\circ + 14^\circ \, 6')}{\sin 1^\circ \, 5'} = \frac{\cos 14^\circ \, 6'}{\sin 1^\circ \, 5'}$$

Substituting in (1) we get :

$$\frac{AB}{CD} = \frac{\sin 15^\circ \, 11' . \times \cos 14^\circ \, 6'}{\sin 1^\circ \, 5'}$$

$$\therefore \quad AB = \frac{200 \times \sin 15^\circ \, 11' \times \cos 14^\circ \, 6'}{\sin 1^\circ \, 5'}$$

$$\log AB = 3\cdot4292$$

and $\therefore$ AB = 2686 ft.

Number	log
200	2·3010
sin 15° 11′	$\bar{1}$·4181
cos 14° 6′	$\bar{1}$·9867
	1·7058
sin 1° 5′	$\bar{2}$·2766
	3·4292

Example 3

At a point A due south of a chimney-stack, the angle of elevation of the stack is 55°. From B due west of A, such that AB = 300 ft., the elevation of the stack is 33°. Find the height of the stack and its horizontal distance from A

(U.E.I.)

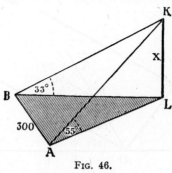

FIG. 46.

M

KL is the stack, and the points B, L, A are on the ground. Since A is south of L, $\angle LAB = 90°$.

Let $\qquad KL = x$ ft.

Then $\qquad LA = x \cot 55°$

and $\qquad LB = x \cot 33°$

By Pythagoras' Theorem,

$$LB^2 = LA^2 + BA^2$$

i.e., $\qquad LB^2 - LA^2 = BA^2$

giving $\qquad x^2(\cot^2 33° - \cot^2 55°) = 300^2.$

$$\therefore \quad x^2 = \frac{300^2}{\cot^2 33° - \cot^2 55°}$$

$$\therefore \quad x = \frac{300}{\sqrt{(\cot 33° + \cot 55°)(\cot 33° - \cot 55°)}}$$

i.e., $\qquad x = \frac{300}{\sqrt{2 \cdot 2401 \times 0 \cdot 8397}}$

$$= 219 \text{ ft.}$$

Also $LA = LK \cot 55°$

$$= 219 \times 0 \cdot 7002$$

$$= 153 \text{ ft.}$$

Example 4

A hillside, which may be considered a plane inclined at $13\frac{1}{2}°$ to the horizontal, is traversed by a straight path which

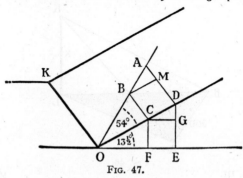

Fig. 47.

*makes 54° with a line of greatest slope. Find the distance
between two points on the path whose levels differ by 100 ft.*

(N.C.)

OD is a line of greatest slope, OBA the path on the hillside, EOK is the horizontal plane through the base of the
hill. A and B are the points whose levels differ by 100 ft.

CG is parallel to OE, and OD is at right angles to OK.

Then   DG = 100

∴   CD = 100 cosec $13\frac{1}{2}°$

= BM, where BM is parallel to CD.

∴   BA = BM sec 54°

= 100 cosec $13\frac{1}{2}°$ sec 54°

= 729 ft.

3. The Cosine Formulæ

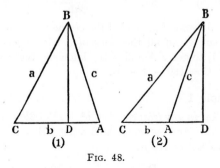

Fig. 48.

Fig. 48 (1) is an acute-angled triangle.

Fig. 48 (2) is an obtuse-angled triangle, with ∠A obtuse.

By well-known geometrical theorems, we have : if BD
is drawn perpendicular to CA,

In (1) $BC^2 = AB^2 + AC^2 - 2AC \cdot AD$ . . (1)
In (2) $BC^2 = AB^2 + AC^2 + 2AC \cdot AD$ . . (2)
In (1) $AD = c \cdot \cos A$
In (2) $AD = AB \cos BAD = - c \cos A$

$\therefore$ From (1) $a^2 = b^2 + c^2 - 2bc \cos A$
and from (2) $a^2 = b^2 + c^2 - 2bc \cos A$ $\Big\}$.   .   (3)

Hence whether the triangle is acute or obtuse angled we get the same formula.

Similarly $b^2 = c^2 + a^2 - 2ca \cos B$.   .   .   (4)
and $c^2 = a^2 + b^2 - 2ab \cos C$.   .   .   (5)

Notice the cyclic order of the letters.

From these formulæ, if we know two sides and the included angle of any triangle, we can find the third side.

From (3) we get $\cos A = \dfrac{b^2 + c^2 - a^2}{2bc}$.   .   .   (6)

From (4) $\cos B = \dfrac{c^2 + a^2 - b^2}{2ca}$.   .   .   (7)

and from (5) $\cos C = \dfrac{a^2 + b^2 - c^2}{2ab}$.   .   .   (8)

These are sometimes called the cosine formulæ.

If we are given all the sides of a triangle, we can use (6) and (7) to get $\angle A$ and $\angle B$; knowing these we find C at once; $C = 180 - A - B$.

Example 1

Show that in any triangle $a^2 = b^2 + c^2 - 2bc \cos A$. In a triangle ABC find the angle ACB when AB = 92 ft., BC = 50 ft., and CA = 110 ft.   (U.L.C.I).

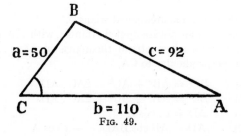

FIG. 49.

Letter the triangle as in the figure.

The first part of the question is answered in the text.
The angle required in the second part is C

$$\cos C = \frac{a^2 + b^2 - c^2}{2ab}$$

$$= \frac{50^2 + 110^2 - 92^2}{2 \times 50 \times 110}$$

$$= \frac{2500 + 12100 - 8464}{100 \times 110}$$

$$= \frac{6 \cdot 136}{11}$$

$$= 0 \cdot 5578.$$

Hence C = 56° 6′ from the tables.

Example 2

*P and Q are points on a straight coast line Q being 5·3 miles
E. of P.   A ship starting from P steams 4 miles in a direction
65½ north of east.*

Calculate :

      (i) *the distance the ship is now from the coast line,*

      (ii) *the ship's bearing from Q.*   (N.C.)

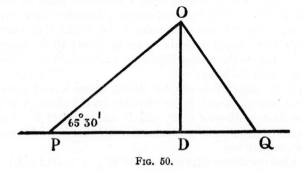

Fig. 50.

Let O be the present position of the ship, and OD the perpendicular from O on the coast line PQ.

Then $\qquad$ PO = 4, $\quad$ PQ = 5·3.

$$OD = OP \sin 65\tfrac{1}{2}° = 4 \times 0·91 = 3·64 \text{ miles.}$$

Also PD $= OP \cos 65\tfrac{1}{2}° = 4 \times 0·4147$

$\qquad\qquad\qquad\quad = 1·66$ miles (correct to two places).

$\qquad \therefore \quad$ DQ = PQ − PD

$\qquad\qquad\qquad = 5·3 − 1·66$

$\qquad\qquad\qquad = 3·64$ mls.

Hence $\qquad \tan OQD = \dfrac{OD}{DQ} = \dfrac{3·64}{3·64} = 1$

$\qquad \therefore \quad$ OQD = 45°

and the ship's bearing from Q is 45° west of north, *i.e.* N. 45° W.

Notice that if we required the distance QO, we could find it at once since $OQ^2 = PQ^2 + PO^2 − 2PQ \cdot PO \cos 65\tfrac{1}{2}°$

EXERCISE 33

1. (*a*) If ABC is an acute-angled triangle, deduce the formula for cos A in terms of the sides.

(*b*) A weight was hung from a horizontal beam by two chains 8 ft. and 9 ft. long, respectively, the ends of the chains being fastened to the same point of the weight, their other ends being fastened to the beam at points 10 ft. apart. Determine to the nearest degree the angles which the chains make with the beam. $\qquad$ (U.L.C.I.)

2. An object P is situated 345 ft. above a level plane. Two persons, A and B, are standing on the plane, A in a direction south-west of P, and B due south of P. The angles of elevation of P as observed at A and B are 34° and 26°, respectively

Find the distance between A and B. $\qquad$ (U.L.C.I.)

3. Prove that in any triangle ABC

$$\frac{a}{\sin A} = \frac{b}{\sin B} = \frac{c}{\sin C} = D,$$

where D is the diameter of the circle through A, B, and C.

A rod whose cross-section is a triangle having sides 1 in., 1·93 in., and 1·93 ins., respectively, can just be driven lengthwise into a cylindrical tube. Find the internal diameter of the tube.   (U.L.C.I.)

4. One panel of a girder consists of four bars forming a parallelogram of sides 3 ft. and 4 ft., respectively, and a fifth bar 3 ft. 6 ins. long is a diagonal. Find the length of the remaining diagonal and find the angles between adjacent sides of the parallelogram.   (U.L.C.I.)

5. The lengths of the sides of a triangle are 5·6 ins., 5 ins., and 3·4 ins. Find the angles.   (N.C.)

6. OB and OC are two straight lines at right angles in a horizontal plane. OB = 50 ins. and OC = 120 ins., whilst A is 73·86 ins. vertically above O. Calculate the angle between the planes ABC and OBC.   (N.C.)

7. Two angles of a triangle are 53° 18′ and 70° 13′. The greatest side of the triangle is 22·3 ft. long. Find the other two sides and the third angle.

8. The angles of elevation of a chimney are 11° 20′ from A and 14° 35′ from B where AB = 55 yds. Find the height of the chimney, if the line AB passes through its base.

9. A weight hangs from the junction of two ropes 2·4 ft. and 2·8 ft. long, respectively, the other ends being attached one to each of two small hooks fixed 3 ft. apart on the under side of a horizontal beam. Find the angle between the ropes and the depth of the junction of the ropes below the beam.   (U.L.C.I.)

10. Four rods, AB = 18 ins., BC = 21 ins., CD = 20 ins. and DA = 24 ins., are jointed to form a plane quadrilateral

ABCD. A fifth rod joining A to C keeps the frame rigid with the angle BCD = 90°. Find by calculation the length of this fifth rod.   (U.L.C.I.)

11. The angle of elevation of the top of a hill is 10° 13′, and on walking 2000 ft. up an incline of 6° 50′, it is found to be 14° 12′. Find the height of the hill.

12. X and Y are two points on a straight shore 1200 ft. apart, Y lying due E. of X. The bearings of a buoy are 28° N. of E. from X and 51° N. of W. from Y. How far is the buoy from the shore?

13. Observations are taken from the bottom and from the top of a tower 200 ft. high, to find the height of a hill.

From the bottom of the tower the angle of elevation of the summit is 14° 30′, and from the top it is 13° 25′. Find the height of the hill.

14. The distance between two buildings is 60 ft. The angular depression of the top of the first when viewed from the second is 30°. If the second building is 150 ft. high, find the height of the first.

15. A building is 130 ft. high. The angles of elevation of the top viewed from two points A and B are 27° 38′ and 44°. Find the distance AB, where AB is perpendicular to the face of the building.

16. A man stands 50 ft., away from the wall of a building in which there is a window directly opposite to him. If the angles of elevation of the bottom and top of the window are 22° 13′ and 27° 18′, find the length of the window.

17. AB is the diameter of a circle whose radius is 20 ins. AC is a chord of length 32 ins. Find :

   (1) the length of CB,
   (2) the length of the perpendicular from C to AB.

18. Find the angles of a parallelogram if two adjacent sides are 12 ins. and 15 ins. long, whilst one diagonal is 17 ins. long.

4. An objection to the cosine formulæ is that they are not adapted to logarithmic calculation.

They can, however, be adapted in the following way :

$$\cos A = 1 - 2 \sin^2 \frac{A}{2} = \frac{b^2 + c^2 - a^2}{2bc}$$

$$\therefore \quad 2 \sin^2 \frac{A}{2} = 1 - \left(\frac{b^2 + c^2 - a^2}{2bc}\right)$$

$$= \frac{2bc - (b^2 + c^2 - a^2)}{2bc}$$

$$= \frac{a^2 - (b - c)^2}{2bc}$$

$$\therefore \quad \sin^2 \frac{A}{2} = \frac{a^2 - (b - c)^2}{4bc}$$

$$= \frac{(a - b + c)(a + b - c)}{4bc}$$

$$= \frac{(a + b + c - 2b)(a + b + c - 2c)}{4bc}.$$

The sum of the sides of a triangle is usually denoted by $2s$, so that s is the semi-sum

$$i.e., \quad a + b + c = 2s.$$

Hence

$$\sin^2 \frac{A}{2} = \frac{(2s - 2b)(2s - 2c)}{4bc}$$

Giving

$$\sin \frac{A}{2} = \sqrt{\frac{(s - b)(s - c)}{bc}} \quad . \quad . \quad . \quad . \quad (1)$$

Similarly

$$\cos A = 2 \cos^2 \frac{A}{2} - 1 = \frac{b^2 + c^2 - a^2}{2bc}$$

$$\therefore \quad 2 \cos^2 \frac{A}{2} = 1 + \left(\frac{b^2 + c^2 - a^2}{2bc}\right)$$

$$= \frac{(b + c)^2 - a^2}{2bc}$$

$$= \frac{(b + c - a)(b + c + a)}{2bc}$$

$$\therefore \quad \cos^2 \frac{A}{2} = \frac{2s(2s-2a)}{4bc}$$

and $$\cos \frac{A}{2} = \sqrt{\frac{s(s-a)}{bc}} \quad . \quad . \quad . \quad . \quad (2)$$

Now divide (1) by (2) and get

$$\tan \frac{A}{2} = \sqrt{\frac{(s-b)(s-c)}{s(s-a)}} \quad . \quad . \quad . \quad (3)$$

In a similar way we may prove that:

$$\tan \frac{B}{2} = \sqrt{\frac{(s-c)(s-a)}{s(s-b)}} \quad . \quad . \quad . \quad . \quad (4)$$

and $$\tan \frac{C}{2} = \sqrt{\frac{(s-a)(s-b)}{s(s-c)}} \quad . \quad . \quad . \quad (5)$$

These formulæ are readily remembered if the cyclic order of the letters a, b, and c is observed.

Further, when we have found the necessary logarithms for calculating $\tan \frac{A}{2}$, we use them for finding $\tan \frac{B}{2}$.

Area of a Triangle

We can now find an important formula for the area of a triangle.

$$\text{Area} = \tfrac{1}{2}bc \sin A$$
$$= \tfrac{1}{2}bc \cdot 2 \sin \frac{A}{2} \cdot \cos \frac{A}{2}$$
$$= bc \sqrt{\frac{(s-b)(s-c)}{bc}} \cdot \sqrt{\frac{s(s-a)}{bc}}$$

i.e. $$\text{Area} = \sqrt{s(s-a)(s-b)(s-c)}.$$

where a, b, and c are the sides and s is their semi-sum.

Example

Let the lengths of the sides be 48·3 ft., 31·6 ft., and 62·4 ft.

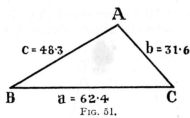

FIG. 51.

$$a = 62·4 \qquad\qquad \therefore \quad s = 71·15$$
$$b = 31·6 \qquad\qquad s - a = 8·75$$
$$c = 48·3 \qquad\qquad s - b = 39·55$$
$$\overline{\qquad\qquad\qquad} \qquad s - c = 22·85$$
$$2s = 142·3$$

$$\tan \frac{A}{2} = \sqrt{\frac{39·55 \times 22·85}{71·15 \times 8·75}}$$

	log
39·55	1·5971
22·85	1·3589
	2·9560
71·15	1·8522
8·75	0·9420
	2·7942
	0·1618

$$\log \tan \frac{A}{2} = 0·0809$$

$$\therefore \quad \frac{A}{2} = 50° \ 18' \ 20''$$

$$A = 100° \ 37' \text{ to the nearest minute}$$

$$\tan \frac{B}{2} = \sqrt{\frac{22·85 \times 8·75}{71·15 \times 39·55}}$$

Giving $\quad \dfrac{B}{2} = 14° \ 56'$

Hence $\qquad\qquad B = 29° \ 52'$

and $\qquad\qquad\qquad C = 49° \ 31'$

The area of the triangle $= \sqrt{(71·15 \times 8·75 \times 39·55 \times 22·85)}$
$$= 750 \text{ sq. ft. to three figures}$$

The formulæ of this paragraph are much easier to work with when the lengths of the three sides contain three or four figures.

5. We now establish a formula which enables us to find the other two angles of a triangle when we know two sides and the included angle.

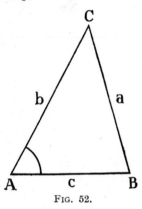

Fig. 52.

Suppose that we are given A, b, and c, we could find a, as we have done previously from the formula

$$a^2 = b^2 + c^2 - 2bc \cos A.$$

This gives us a tiresome calculation when the lengths of the sides contain three or four figures.

Since $\angle A$ is known, B + C is known. We now find a formula which gives us (B − C).

Knowing (B + C) and (B − C), we readily find B and C. a can then be found by using the sine rule.

To prove

$$\tan \frac{B-C}{2} = \frac{b-c}{b+c} \cdot \cot \frac{A}{2} \quad . \quad . \quad (1)$$

Put $$\frac{a}{\sin A} = \frac{b}{\sin B} = \frac{c}{\sin C} = k$$

then $a = k \sin A$, $b = k \sin B$ and $c = k \sin C$.

Hence
$$\frac{b-c}{b+c} = \frac{k(\sin B - \sin C)}{k(\sin B + \sin C)}$$

$$= \frac{2 \cos \dfrac{B+C}{2} \sin \dfrac{B-C}{2}}{2 \sin \dfrac{B+C}{2} \cos \dfrac{B-C}{2}}$$

$$= \cot \frac{B+C}{2} . \tan \frac{B-C}{2}$$

$$= \tan \frac{A}{2} . \tan \frac{B-C}{2} \quad . \quad . \quad . \quad (2)$$

since $\dfrac{A}{2}$ and $\dfrac{B+C}{2}$ are complementary angles

and
$$\therefore \quad \tan \frac{A}{2} = \cot \frac{B+C}{2}$$

Hence from (2), dividing both sides by $\tan \dfrac{A}{2}$

$$\tan \frac{B-C}{2} = \frac{b-c}{b+c} \cot \frac{A}{2}$$

Similarly
$$\tan \frac{C-A}{2} = \frac{c-a}{c+a} \cot \frac{B}{2} \quad . \quad . \quad . \quad (3)$$

and
$$\tan \frac{B-A}{2} = \frac{b-a}{b+a} \cot \frac{C}{2} \quad . \quad . \quad . \quad (4)$$

Example

Given $A = 71° 9'$, $b = 43.2$ *ft.*, *and* $c = 31.7$ *ft, find the other three parts of the triangle.*

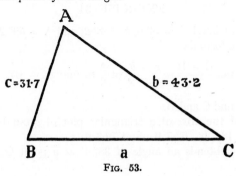

Fig. 53.

Sketch a figure. Notice that since $b > c$, $\angle B > \angle C$.

$$\tan \frac{B - C}{2} = \frac{43 \cdot 2 - 31 \cdot 7}{43 \cdot 2 + 31 \cdot 7} \cot \frac{71° \ 9'}{2}$$

$$= \frac{11 \cdot 5}{74 \cdot 9} \cot 35° \ 34\tfrac{1}{2}'$$

	Number	log
$\log \tan \dfrac{B - C}{2} = \bar{1} \cdot 3315$	11·5	1·0607
	cot 35° 34½′	0·1453
$\therefore \ \dfrac{B - C}{2} = 12° \ 7'$		1·2060
$\therefore \ B - C = 24° \ 14'$	74·9	1·8745
also $\qquad B + C = 108° \ 51'$		$\bar{1} \cdot 3315$

from which $\quad 2B = 133° \ 5'$, and $\therefore \ B = 66° \ 32 \cdot 5'$
and $\qquad\qquad 2C = 84° \ 37'$ and $\therefore \ C = 42° 18 \cdot 5'$

To get a, we have

		log
	43·2	1·6355
$\dfrac{a}{\sin 71° \ 9'} = \dfrac{43 \cdot 2}{\sin 66° \ 32 \cdot 5'}$	sin 71° 9′	$\bar{1} \cdot 9760$
		1·6115
$\therefore \ a = \dfrac{43 \cdot 2 \sin 71° \ 9'}{\sin 66° \ 32 \cdot 5'}$	sin 66° 32·5′	$\bar{1} \cdot 9625$
$a = 44 \cdot 6$ ft.		1·6490

EXERCISE 34

1. In a triangle $b = 39 \cdot 6$, $c = 43 \cdot 2$, and A = 58° 24′. Use the formula

$$\tan \frac{C - B}{2} = \frac{c - b}{c + b} \cot \frac{A}{2} \text{ to find (C - B).}$$

Hence find C and B.

2. Find the area of a triangular plot of ground whose sides are 48·3 ft., 62·7 ft., and 79·3 ft.

3. AB subtends an angle of 38° 4′ at a point O, where

OA = 37·3 ft. and OB = 49·3 ft.   Find the length of AB, and the angles at A and B.

4. Find the greatest angle of the triangle in question 2.

5. Find the angles of a parallelogram two of whose sides are 5·93 ins. and 6·45 ins. long, whilst a diagonal has a length 7·32 ins.

Find the area of the parallelogram.

CHAPTER 11

Differentiation and Integration of Trigonometrical Functions, with Some Applications

1. The differentiation of both sin θ and cos θ depends on the following limit, viz.

$$\underset{\theta \to 0}{\mathbf{L}t} \ \frac{\sin \theta}{\theta} = 1$$

It is established thus :

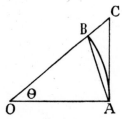

FIG. 54.

O is the centre of a circle, radius a.

Let ∠AOB = θ (radians).

AC is the tangent to the circle at A, cutting OB produced at C.

Then area of △AOB = $\frac{1}{2}a^2 \sin \theta$, and of △AOC = $\frac{1}{2}$OA . AC = $\frac{1}{2}a^2 \tan \theta$.

Also,   △AOB < sector AOB < △AOC.

i.e., $\frac{1}{2}a^2 \sin \theta < \frac{1}{2}a^2 \theta < \frac{1}{2}a^2 \tan \theta$.

     ∴   sin θ < θ < tan θ

or dividing by sin θ,

$$1 < \frac{\theta}{\sin \theta} < \sec \theta.$$

Hence $\dfrac{\theta}{\sin \theta}$ always lies between 1 and sec θ.

As $\theta \longrightarrow 0$, sec $\theta \longrightarrow 1$, $\quad \therefore \quad \dfrac{\theta}{\sin \theta} \longrightarrow 1$

or inverting $$\underset{\theta \to 0}{Lt}\ \dfrac{\sin \theta}{\theta} = 1$$

It should be observed that θ is in radians, and that the angle must be the same in both numerator and denominator. It is not sufficient that both be small.

Thus $$\underset{\theta \to 0}{Lt}\ \dfrac{\sin 2\theta}{\theta} = \underset{\theta \to 0}{Lt}\ 2 \cdot \dfrac{\sin 2\theta}{2\theta}$$
$$= 2.$$

2. To Find the Derivative of sin θ, with respect to θ.

The student should recall two results :

(1) that if $y = f(x)$,
$$\dfrac{dy}{dx} = \underset{h \to 0}{Lt}\ \dfrac{f(x + h) - f(x)}{h}$$

and (2) $\sin S - \sin T = 2 \cos \dfrac{S + T}{2} \cdot \sin \dfrac{S - T}{2}$ (see page 168).

Put $y = \sin \theta$

then $$\dfrac{dy}{d\theta} = \underset{h \to 0}{Lt}\ \dfrac{\sin (\theta + h) - \sin \theta}{h}$$

$$= Lt\ \dfrac{2 \cos \left(\theta + \dfrac{h}{2}\right) \sin \left(\dfrac{h}{2}\right)}{h}$$

$$= Lt \cos \left(\theta + \dfrac{h}{2}\right) \cdot \dfrac{\sin \dfrac{h}{2}}{\dfrac{h}{2}} \quad \cdot \quad \cdot \quad \cdot \quad \cdot \quad (1)$$

Now let $h \longrightarrow 0$; $\cos\left(\theta + \dfrac{h}{2}\right) \longrightarrow \cos\theta$, and $\dfrac{\sin\dfrac{h}{2}}{\dfrac{h}{2}} \longrightarrow 1$

$$\therefore \quad \frac{dy}{d\theta} = \cos\theta \quad \cdot \quad \cdot \quad \cdot \quad \cdot \quad \cdot \quad (2)$$

Hence if
$$y = \sin\theta$$
$$\frac{dy}{d\theta} = \cos\theta$$

i.e.,
$$\frac{d(\sin\theta)}{d\theta} = \cos\theta$$

The " form " of this result is important

$$y = \sin(\quad)$$
$$\frac{dy}{d(\quad)} = \cos(\quad) \binom{\text{any expression may be put}}{\text{in the bracket.}}$$

Thus, suppose $y = \sin 3\theta$.   (Put 3θ in the bracket.)

then
$$\frac{dy}{d(3\theta)} = \cos 3\theta$$

But
$$\frac{dy}{d\theta} = \frac{dy}{d(3\theta)} \cdot \frac{d(3\theta)}{d\theta} = \cos 3\theta \cdot 3 = 3\cos 3\theta.$$

Similarly if $y = \sin a\theta$
$$\frac{dy}{d\theta} = \frac{dy}{d(a\theta)} \cdot \frac{d(a\theta)}{d\theta} = a\cos a\theta.$$

Example 1
$$z = \sin\frac{t}{2}.   \text{(Here, } a = \tfrac{1}{2}\text{)}$$
$$\frac{dz}{dt} = \frac{1}{2}\cos\frac{t}{2}$$

Example 2
$$y = 5\sin 4x$$
$$\frac{dy}{dx} = 20\cos 4x$$

Example 3

$$y = \tfrac{1}{4} \sin \tfrac{1}{3} t$$

$$\frac{dy}{dt} = \frac{1}{12} \cos \frac{1}{3} t$$

Example 4

$$y = \sin\left(t + \frac{\pi}{6}\right)$$

$$\frac{dy}{dt} = \cos\left(t + \frac{\pi}{6}\right)$$

Example 5

$$y = \sin\left(2ft + \alpha\right) \text{ where } \alpha \text{ is constant}$$

$$\frac{dy}{dt} = 2f \cos\left(2ft + \alpha\right).$$

3. To Find the Differential Coefficient of cos θ, with respect to θ.

Let $\quad\quad\quad\quad y = \cos \theta$

then $\quad\quad \dfrac{dy}{d\theta} = \underset{h \to 0}{\mathrm{Lt}} \dfrac{\cos\left(\theta + h\right) - \cos \theta}{h}$

$$= - \underset{h \to 0}{\mathrm{Lt}}\ 2 \sin\left(\theta + \frac{h}{2}\right) \frac{\sin \dfrac{h}{2}}{h}$$

$$= - \underset{h \to 0}{\mathrm{Lt}}\ \sin\left(\theta + \frac{h}{2}\right) \frac{\sin \dfrac{h}{2}}{\dfrac{h}{2}}$$

$$= - \sin \theta.$$

Thus if $\quad\quad\quad\quad y = \cos \theta$

$$\frac{dy}{d\theta} = - \sin \theta$$

i.e., $\quad\quad\quad \dfrac{d \cos \theta}{d\theta} = - \sin \theta$

or in form $\quad\quad\quad y = \cos \text{(any angle)}$

$$\frac{dy}{d \text{(angle)}} = - \sin \text{(angle)}.$$

If
$$y = \cos 3\theta$$
$$\frac{dy}{d\theta} = \frac{dy}{d(3\theta)} \cdot \frac{d(3\theta)}{d\theta} = -3 \sin 3\theta$$

And generally, as with $\sin \theta$,

if
$$y = a \cos (b\theta + c)$$
$$\frac{dy}{d\theta} = -ab \sin (b\theta + c).$$

Example 1
$$y = \frac{1}{2} \cos \frac{t}{3}$$
$$\frac{dy}{dt} = -\frac{1}{6} \sin \frac{t}{3}.$$

Example 2
$$y = 5 \cos \left(3t + \frac{\pi}{6}\right)$$
$$\frac{dy}{dt} = -15 \sin \left(3t + \frac{\pi}{6}\right).$$

EXERCISE 35

Differentiate with respect to the appropriate variable :

1. $\sin t$.

2. $\sin 4t$.

3. $\sin \frac{t}{3}$.

4. $\sin \pi t$.

5. $\sin nt$.

6. $3 \sin 2t$.

7. $\frac{1}{2} \sin \frac{t}{3}$.

8. $\frac{2}{\pi} \sin \pi t$.

9. $a \sin bt$.

10. $5 \sin (\theta + \alpha)$.

11. $3 \sin (\theta + \pi)$.

12. $a \sin \left(\theta - \frac{\pi}{3}\right)$.

13. $5 \sin \left(3\theta - \frac{\pi}{5}\right)$.

14. $\frac{1}{2} \sin \left(\frac{1}{2}\theta + \frac{\pi}{3}\right)$.

15. $a \sin (2ft + n\pi)$.

16. $\cos 3x$.

17. $\cos \frac{x}{5}$.

18. $\cos \pi x$.

19. $5 \cos 3\theta$.

20. $3 \cos (5\theta + \alpha)$.   21. $4 \cos \left(3\theta + \dfrac{\pi}{4}\right)$.

22. $\dfrac{1}{2} \cos (k\theta + \alpha)$.   23. $a \cos (2nx + k\pi)$.

4. The differential coefficients of $\tan \theta$, $\operatorname{cosec} \theta$, $\sec \theta$ and $\cot \theta$ are all easily obtained from those for $\sin \theta$ and $\cos \theta$ if we use the formula for differentiating a quotient.

Thus if $\qquad y = \tan \theta$

i.e., $\qquad\qquad y = \dfrac{\sin \theta}{\cos \theta}$

$$\therefore \quad \frac{dy}{d\theta} = \frac{\cos \theta \,.\, \cos \theta - \sin \theta \,.\, (-\sin \theta)}{\cos^2 \theta}$$

$$= \frac{\cos^2 \theta + \sin^2 \theta}{\cos^2 \theta}$$

$$= \frac{1}{\cos^2 \theta}$$

$$= \sec^2 \theta$$

Hence $\dfrac{\boldsymbol{d}}{\boldsymbol{d}\theta}(\tan \theta) = \boldsymbol{\sec^2 \theta}$

If $\qquad\qquad y = \tan 5\theta$

$$\frac{dy}{d\theta} = 5 \sec^2 5\theta.$$

5. If $\qquad\qquad y = \operatorname{cosec} \theta$

$$y = \frac{1}{\sin \theta}$$

$$\frac{dy}{d\theta} = \frac{-\cos \theta}{\sin^2 \theta}$$

$$= -\frac{1}{\sin \theta} \cdot \frac{\cos \theta}{\sin \theta}$$

$$= -\operatorname{cosec} \theta \,.\, \cot \theta.$$

i.e. $\quad \dfrac{\boldsymbol{d}}{\boldsymbol{d}\theta} (\boldsymbol{\operatorname{cosec}} \,\theta) = -\boldsymbol{\operatorname{cosec}} \,\theta \, \boldsymbol{\cot} \,\theta$

The student can now prove that

$$\frac{d}{d\theta} \sec \theta = \sec \theta \tan \theta$$

and

$$\frac{d}{d\theta} \cot \theta = - \operatorname{cosec}^2 \theta.$$

6. The differentiation of the trigonometric functions has been performed on the supposition that the angles are measured in radians.

If the angles are given in degrees, we must convert to radians and then differentiate.

Example 1

If

$$y = \sin x^\circ$$

$$y = \sin \frac{\pi x}{180}$$

$$\therefore \quad \frac{dy}{dx} = \frac{\pi}{180} \cos \frac{\pi x}{180}$$

$$= \frac{\pi}{180} \cdot \cos x^\circ.$$

Example 2

$$z = \cos 3t^\circ$$

$$= \cos \frac{\pi t}{60}$$

$$\therefore \quad \frac{dz}{dt} = - \frac{\pi}{60} \sin \frac{\pi t}{60}$$

$$= - \frac{\pi}{60} \sin 3t^\circ.$$

EXERCISE 36

Differentiate the following functions :

1. $\tan \theta$.   2. $\sec x$.   3. $\operatorname{cosec} z$.

4. $\cot y$.   5. $\tan 3\theta$.   6. $\sec \frac{\theta}{2}$.

7. cosec $3x$.   8. $3 \cot 4\theta$.   9. $5 \sec \left(2\theta + \dfrac{\pi}{2}\right)$.

10. $3 \tan(\theta + \pi)$.   11. $\sin 3x°$.   12. $3 \cos \tfrac{1}{2}x°$.

13. $2 \tan x°$.

7. Products and Quotients

Example 1

$$y = x^3 \sin x$$
$$\frac{dy}{dx} = 3x^2 \sin x + x^3 \cos x.$$

Example 2

$$y = 3x^4 \cos 2x$$
$$\frac{dy}{dx} = 3[4x^3 \cos 2x - 2x^4 \sin 2x] \quad \cdot \quad \cdot \quad \cdot \quad \textbf{(1)}$$
$$\left(\text{Notice } \frac{d}{dx}(\cos 2x) = -2 \sin 2x\right)$$

(1) may be written

$$\frac{dy}{dx} = 6x^3(2 \cos 2x - x \sin 2x).$$

Example 3

$$z = \frac{3 \sin 5t}{t^3} \quad \cdot \quad \cdot \quad \cdot \quad \cdot \quad \cdot \quad \cdot \quad \cdot \quad \textbf{(2)}$$
$$\frac{dz}{dt} = \frac{3[5t^3 \cos 5t - 3t^2 \sin 5t]}{t^6}$$
$$= \frac{3}{t^4}(5t \cos 5t - 3 \sin 5t).$$

Notice that (2) may be differentiated as a product, thus:

$$z = 3 \sin 5t \,.\, t^{-3}$$
$$\frac{dz}{dt} = 3[5 \cos 5t \,.\, t^{-3} - 3t^{-4} \sin 5t]$$
$$= \frac{3}{t^4}(5t \cos 5t - 3 \sin 5t).$$

8. The Differentiation of Powers of the Trigonometrical Functions

Example 1

Suppose
$$y = \sin^2 x$$
$$= u^2 \text{ (where } u = \sin x)$$
$$\frac{dy}{du} = 2u \text{ and } \frac{du}{dx} = \cos x.$$
$$\therefore \frac{dy}{dx} = \frac{dy}{du} \cdot \frac{du}{dx} = 2u \cdot \cos x$$
$$= 2 \sin x \cos x$$
$$= \sin 2x.$$

If the formal aspect of differentiation has been grasped, the substitution of u for $\sin x$ will be unnecessary.

If
$$y = \sin^2 x$$
$$\frac{dy}{dx} = \frac{dy}{d(\sin x)} \cdot \frac{d(\sin x)}{dx}$$
$$= 2 \sin x \cdot \cos x$$
$$= \sin 2x.$$

Example 2

Similarly if
$$y = \cos^3 2x$$
$$\frac{dy}{dx} = \frac{dy}{d(\cos 2x)} \cdot \frac{d(\cos 2x)}{d(2x)} \cdot \frac{d(2x)}{dx}$$
$$= 3 \cos^2 2x \cdot (- \sin 2x) \cdot 2$$
$$= - 6 \cos^2 2x \cdot \sin 2x.$$

EXERCISE 37

Differentiate the following products and quotients :

1. $x^2 \sin x.$

2. $2x^3 \sin x.$

3. $x^4 \sin 2x.$

4. $2x^6 \cos 3x.$

5. $\dfrac{\sin 2x}{x^2}.$

6. $\dfrac{3 \cos 4x}{x^4}.$

7. $\sin \theta \cos 2\theta.$

8. $3 \sin 2\theta \cos 4\theta.$

9. $\dfrac{\sin \theta}{\cos 2\theta}.$

10. $4 \sin 3\theta \cdot \cos 4\theta.$

11. $\sin 2\pi t \cdot \cos \pi t.$

Differentiate the following :

12. $\sin^2 x$.   13. $3 \sin^3 x$.   14. $\cos^3 \theta$.

15. $5 \cos^2 3\theta$.   16. $2 \sin^3 4x$.   17. $\dfrac{\cos^2 x}{\sin x}$.

18. $2 \cos^3 x - 3 \sin^2 2x$.

9. Applications

Example 1

Suppose two sides of a triangle are measured accurately, but there is a small error in the included angle. Find the relative error in the calculated area.

The area of a triangle is given by

$$x = \tfrac{1}{2}bc \sin A \quad . \quad . \quad . \quad . \quad (1)$$

$$\therefore \quad \frac{dx}{dA} = \frac{1}{2}bc \cos A$$

or

$$dx = \tfrac{1}{2}bc \cos A \cdot dA.$$

Hence the relative error $= \dfrac{dx}{x} = \dfrac{\text{error}}{\text{calculated area}}$

$$= \cot A \cdot dA \quad . \quad . \quad . \quad (2)$$

In the above work the angle must be in circular measure.

Thus, suppose $A = 35° 25'$, and suppose there is an error of $5'$ in A.

$$5' = \frac{5\pi}{60 \times 180} \text{ radians}$$

$$= \frac{\pi}{2160} \text{ radians} \quad . \quad . \quad . \quad . \quad (3)$$

From (2) and (3), the relative error

$$= \cot 35° 25' \times \frac{\pi}{2160} \text{ (approx.)}$$

$$= 0 \cdot 00205.$$

The % error $=$ relative error $\times 100$

$$= 0 \cdot 205$$

$$= \tfrac{1}{5}\%.$$

Example 2

Maxima and Minima.

Find the turning points on the curve

$$y = 2 \sin \theta + \cos \theta \quad . \quad . \quad . \quad . \quad (1)$$

and distinguish the maxima from the minima.

We have

$$\frac{dy}{d\theta} = 2 \cos \theta - \sin \theta.$$

∴ Turning points are given by

$$2 \cos \theta - \sin \theta = 0$$

i.e., $\qquad\qquad 2 \cos \theta = \sin \theta$

or $\qquad\qquad\qquad \tan \theta = 2.$

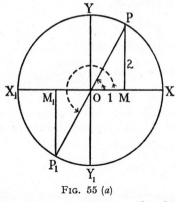

Fig. 55 (a)

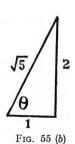

Fig. 55 (b)

Now observe that between 0° and 360° there are two angles XOP and XOP$_1$ whose tangent is 2, XOP in the first quadrant and XOP$_1$ extending to the third quadrant.

Both sin XOP and cos XOP are positive, whilst both sin XOP$_1$ and cos XOP$_1$ are negative. Fig. 55 (a).

The + values substituted in (1) give the maximum ordinates, the — values the minimum. See Fig. 55 (b) for the values.

The maximum values of y are $\dfrac{4}{\sqrt{5}} + \dfrac{1}{\sqrt{5}} = \sqrt{5}$.

The minimum values of y are $- \dfrac{4}{\sqrt{5}} - \dfrac{1}{\sqrt{5}} = - \sqrt{5}$.

It is to be observed that examples similar to the preceding one can be done in the following way.

If $\qquad\qquad y = 2 \sin \theta + \cos \theta$ . . . . (2)

Put $\qquad\qquad\qquad r \cos \alpha = 2$

$\qquad\qquad\qquad\qquad r \sin \alpha = 1$

$\qquad\qquad \therefore \quad r^2 = 5 \text{---} i.e., r = \sqrt{5}.$

and $\qquad\qquad\qquad \tan \alpha = \tfrac{1}{2}.$

From (2)

$\qquad\qquad \therefore \quad y = \sqrt{5} \sin (\theta + \alpha)$ . . . . (3)

The maximum value of the sin of any angle is unity, and the minimum $- 1$.

Hence the maximum value of y is $\sqrt{5}$, the minimum $- \sqrt{5}$. The corresponding values of θ are easily found.

Example 3

Show there is a turning-point at $x = \dfrac{\pi}{3}$ *on the curve*

$$y = \sin x + \cos x \sin x$$

Is the point on the curve a maximum or minimum?

(U.L.C.I.)

We have $\qquad y = \sin x + \dfrac{\sin 2x}{2}$ . . . . . (1)

$\qquad \therefore \quad \dfrac{dy}{dx} = \cos x + \cos 2x$ . . . . . (2)

Putting $\qquad \cos x + \cos 2x = 0,$

we get $\qquad \cos 2x = - \cos x = \cos (\pi - x).$

Hence $\qquad 2x = \pi - x$

i.e., $\qquad\qquad 3x = \pi$

and $\qquad\qquad x = \dfrac{\pi}{3} = 60°.$

Differentiating (2) we get :

$$\frac{d^2y}{dx^2} = -\sin x - 2 \sin 2x$$

If $\quad x = \dfrac{\pi}{3}, \quad \dfrac{d^2y}{dx^2}$ is negative. (Hence y is a maximum.)

From (1) (putting $x = 60°$)

$$y = \frac{\sqrt{3}}{2} + \frac{\sqrt{3}}{4} = \frac{3\sqrt{3}}{4}$$

$\therefore$ The point $\left(\dfrac{\pi}{3}, \dfrac{3\sqrt{3}}{4}\right)$ is a maximum point.

10. Simple Harmonic Motion

Suppose a point P describes a circle of radius a with uniform angular velocity w. Let PM be the perpendicular on the horizontal diameter XOX_1, where O is the centre. The foot of the ordinate, M, is said to move with simple harmonic motion—*i.e.*, with S.H.M.

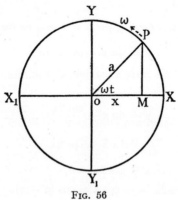

Fig. 56

Suppose P was at X when $t = 0$—*i.e.*, at zero time.

In t secs., $\angle \text{XOP} = wt$.

Let $\text{OM} = x$

Then $x = a \cos wt$ . . . . . . (1)

$$\frac{dx}{dt} = -aw \sin wt \quad . \quad . \quad . \quad (2)$$

$$\frac{d^2x}{dt^2} = -aw^2 \cos wt$$

$$= -w^2 x \quad . \quad . \quad . \quad . \quad (3)$$

From (3) notice that the acceleration of M, $\frac{d^2x}{dt^2}$, varies as the distance of M from O.

The negative sign shows that this acceleration is directed towards O.

Observe equation (2).   This gives the velocity

$$\frac{dx}{dt} = -w \, . \, a \sin wt$$

$$= -w \, . \, \text{MP}$$

$$= -wy \text{ if we put MP} = y.$$

Hence if a point moves in a straight line with an acceleration always directed to a fixed point in the line, and varying as the distance from that point, it is said to have S.H.M. This is the formal definition.

The motion is an oscillation along XOX_1.

The distance OX (or OX_1) is called the amplitude of the motion, and is equal to the radius of the circle.

The time of a complete oscillation is the time taken by P to describe the circle, and

$$= \frac{2\pi}{w}$$

where w is measured in rad./sec.

This is called the periodic time.   It is independent of the radius of the circle—*i.e.*, of the amplitude, and varies with *w*, only.

Example 1

Show in a S.H.M. the acceleration is proportional to the displacement from mid-position.

A cylindrical spiral spring supports a weight of 35 lbs. and is made to vibrate vertically. The stiffness of the spring is such that a weight of 10 lbs. would stretch it 1 in. Show that the motion is S.H.M. and find the periodic time.

Fig. 57.

Let AB be the natural length, and BO the extension when 35 lb. hangs at rest.

Then BO = 3·5 ins., and from Hooke's Law, using absolute units,

$$\text{Tension} = 35g \text{ (poundals)} = \frac{\lambda}{\text{AB}} \cdot \frac{3 \cdot 5}{12}$$

i.e.,
$$35g = \frac{\lambda}{\text{AB}} \cdot \frac{7}{24} \quad \cdot \quad \cdot \quad \cdot \quad \cdot \quad (1)$$

Let *x* ft. be the distance below O, at any time *t* after the weight has been pulled down. Then

$$35 \frac{d^2x}{dt^2} = - \frac{\lambda}{AB} \cdot x$$

$$\frac{d^2x}{dt^2} = - \frac{\lambda}{35AB} \cdot x \cdot = - w^2 x \quad . \quad . \quad (2)$$

where $w^2 = \frac{\lambda}{35AB} = \frac{24g}{7}$ from (1).

∴ from (2) the motion is S.H.M. and the periodic time

$$= \frac{2\pi}{w} = 2\pi \sqrt{\frac{7}{24g}}$$

$$= 0 \cdot 6 \text{ sec.}$$

Example 2

A particle is known to have S.H.M. about a fixed point O. When 2 ft. from O its velocity is 12 ft./sec. and its acceleration 4 ft./sec.². What is the amplitude?

This example may be very simply done by using Fig. 56. From the question we get that :

$$4 = 2w^2$$

$$\therefore \quad w = \sqrt{2}.$$

Hence (refer to Fig. 56), in the triangle OPM :

$$OM = 2, \quad MP = \frac{12}{\sqrt{2}}$$

$$\therefore \quad OP^2 = 4 + \tfrac{144}{2} = 76$$

$$\therefore \quad OP = \sqrt{76}.$$

EXERCISE 38

1. Obtain approximate values for

    (*a*) cos 60° 1′, (*b*) tan 45° 1′, (*c*) sin 29° 59′.

2. In a triangle ABC, $a = 40$ ft., B = 72°, A = 40°. Find the error in calculating b, if there is an error of 10′ in measuring B.

3. Given that $i = k \tan \theta$, where k is constant find the error in i, due to a small error in reading θ.

Find the percentage error in the current i, due to an error of 30' when θ is taken as 45°.

4. The angle of elevation of a chimney is observed from a point 100 ft. from its base as 63° 13' subject to an error of 5'. Calculate the error in the height.

5. Find the turning points in the following curves and state which are maxima :

(1) $y = \sin \theta + \cos \theta.$ (2) $y = \sin 2x + \cos x.$
(3) $y = \cos 2x + \sin x.$ (4) $y = \sin^3 \theta.$

6. If $T = c \cos x \sin^2 x$, where T is the turning effect of a boat's rudder and x the angle it makes with the keel, find for what value of x the rudder is most effective.

7. The lift of a valve moving with S.H.M. is $\frac{3}{16}$ in., and the total time occupied by the opening and closing of the valve is $\frac{1}{20}$ sec.

Find the accelerating forces at the ends of the stroke of the valve per lb. weight of the valve.   (U.L.C.I.)

8. A cylindrical spiral spring supports a weight of 20 lb. and is set vibrating. If a force of 15 lbs. is necessary to stretch it 1 in., find the period of vibration.

(U.L.C.I.)

9. In an S.H.M. along a straight line show the acceleration at any point is directly proportional to the distance of the point from the mid-point of the motion.

If a piston move with S.H.M., and has a stroke of 2 ft., find the force necessary to overcome the inertia of the reciprocating parts at the ends of the stroke, and also when the crank has turned through 45° from either dead centre. The reciprocating parts weigh 500 lb. and the crank-shaft makes 120 revs. per minute.   (U.E.I.)

10. What is meant by S.H.M. ?

A spring increases 1 in. in length when a load of 21 lb. is

attached to it. If a weight of 56 lb. is attached to this spring, drawn below its position of rest and then released, how many vibrations per minute will it make ?   (U.E.I.)

11. A point in a mechanism moves in a straight path, and its distance s ins. from a fixed point O of the path is given by $s = 4 \sin t + 2 \cdot 5 \cos t$, where t secs. is the time measured from a fixed instant. Find the velocity and acceleration when $t = \dfrac{\pi}{6}$ and find the maximum displacement from O.   (U.L.C.I.)

11. Integration of the Circular Functions

We have found that if $y = \sin \theta$

$$\frac{dy}{d\theta} = \cos \theta$$

i.e., $$dy = \cos \theta \,.\, d\theta.$$

Reversing the process we get :

$$\int \cos \theta d\theta = \sin \theta + C \quad . \quad . \quad . \quad . \quad . \quad (1)$$

Similarly

$$\int \sin \theta \,.\, d\theta = - \cos \theta + C \quad . \quad . \quad . \quad . \quad (2)$$

It is essential that the formal aspect of these integrations should be grasped.

Thus (1) becomes :

$$\int \cos \text{ (any angle) } d \text{ (angle) } = \sin \text{ (angle) } + C$$

Suppose we require $\int \sin 3\theta \,.\, d\theta$.

To get this in correct " form," we have :

$$\int \sin 3\theta \,.\, d\theta = \tfrac{1}{3} \int \sin 3\theta \,.\, d(3\theta)$$
$$= - \frac{\cos 3\theta}{3} + C.$$

Observe that constants may be taken outside the integral sign.

Generalising, we get :

$$\int \cos a\theta d\theta = \frac{1}{a} \int \cos a\theta \, . \, d(a\theta) = \frac{\sin a\theta}{a} + C \quad . \quad . \quad (3)$$

and

$$\int \sin b\theta \, . \, d\theta = \frac{1}{b} \int \sin b\theta \, . \, d(b\theta) = -\frac{\cos b\theta}{b} + C \quad . \quad (4)$$

Once we know these integrals we need not go through the process of putting them in " form."

Example 1

$$\int \sin 5x dx = -\frac{\cos 5x}{5} + C$$

Example 2

$$\int 3 \cos 4\theta \, . \, d\theta = \tfrac{3}{4} \sin 4\theta + C.$$

Example 3

$$\int \sin \left(\theta + \frac{\pi}{3}\right) d\theta = -\cos \left(\theta + \frac{\pi}{3}\right) + C.$$

Notice that the " form " of the integrand is correct. [Integrand = expression to be integrated.]

Example 4

$$\int \sin \left(2kt + \frac{\pi}{6}\right) dt = -\frac{1}{2k} \cos \left(2kt + \frac{\pi}{6}\right) + C.$$

EXERCISE 39

Integrate the following :

1. $\cos \theta$.
2. $\sin \theta$.
3. $\sin 3\theta$.
4. $3 \sin 2\theta$.
5. $2 \cos 4\theta$.
6. $\cos \tfrac{1}{2}\theta$.
7. $\dfrac{3}{4} \sin \dfrac{2\theta}{3}$.
8. $3 \sin 2\theta - 4 \cos 5\theta$.
9. $\sin (\theta + \alpha)$.
10. $\cos \left(3\theta + \dfrac{\pi}{7}\right)$.
11. $2 \sin \left(\dfrac{\pi}{5} - \theta\right)$.
12. $3 \cos \left(\alpha - \dfrac{\theta}{2}\right)$.

CHAPTER 12

THE DEFINITE INTEGRAL. MEAN VALUES. SIMPSON'S RULE

1. It will be recalled that if

$$y = f(x)$$
$$\frac{dy}{dx} = f'(x)$$

or, using the differential notation :

$$dy = f'x \cdot dx$$

Reversing the process we get :

$$\int f'(x) \cdot dx = f(x) + C \quad . \quad . \quad . \quad (1)$$

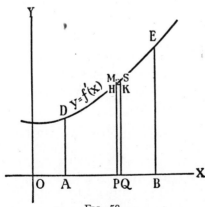

Fig. 58.

Let us suppose that the equation of the curve DSE, Fig. 58, is $y = f'(x)$

If $OA = a$, $AD = f'(a)$.

Let $OP = x$ and $PQ = \Delta x$.

Complete the rectangles PQKH and PQSM.

It will be seen that the area PQSH lies between the areas of the rectangles PQKH and PQSM.

The rectangle HKSM has an area HK × KS and as Δx, or PQ, $\longrightarrow 0$, this area will vanish, since it is the product of two infinitesimals.

We shall then take the rectangle PQKH and the figure PQSH as being equal in area when $\Delta x \longrightarrow 0$.

Let the area   APHD $= z$

Then   PQSH $= \Delta z$

i.e., $\Delta z = f'(x) \cdot \Delta x$ as $\Delta x \longrightarrow 0$

i.e., $Lt \cdot \dfrac{\Delta z}{\Delta x} = f'(x)$.   .   .   .   .   (2)

We infer from (2) that z is a function of x whose differential coefficient is $f'(x)$;

$$\therefore \quad z = \int f'(x) \cdot dx = f(x) + C \quad . \quad . \quad . \quad (3)$$

subject to the condition that $z = 0$ when $x = a$, since the area APHD vanishes when $x = a$. From (3) we get, on substituting these values for z and x,

$$0 = f(a) + C,$$

i.e., $C = -f(a)$.

Hence from (3) we get that the area APHD is given by

$$z = f(x) - f(a) . \quad . \quad . \quad . \quad . \quad (4)$$

If $OB = b$ the area ABED is given by $f(b) - f(a)$, which is obtained from (4) by putting b for x—i.e., by supposing that P moves up to coincidence with B.

The results may be summarised thus :

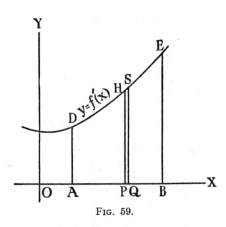

Fig. 59.

To find the area ABED between the curve, $y = f'(x)$
the x-axis and two ordinates at $x = a$, and $x = b$, first find
$\int f'(x) \cdot dx = f(x)$ (do not put in a constant).

Then put $x = b$ and get $f(b)$.
Next put $x = a$ and get $f(a)$.
The area is given by $f(b) - f(a)$.
The notation for this result is

$$\int_a^b f'(x)dx = \left[f(x) \right]_a^b = f(b) - f(a).$$

2. The integral $\int_a^b f'(x)dx$ is called a definite integral;
a and b are called its limits, a being the lower limit, b the
upper limit. Notice that the word limit as used above
merely means a boundary.

The integral $\int_a^b f'(x)dx = f(b) - f(a)$ is called definite, since its value is definite, in contrast with that of

$$\int f'(x)dx = f(x) + c,$$

which contains the constant of integration.

3. We have seen that the definite integral can be interpreted as an area.

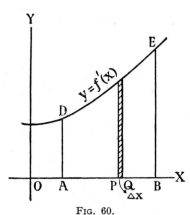

FIG. 60.

If ABED represents the area, it may be regarded as the sum of elementary areas like the one shaded in Fig. 60.

i.e., $\int_a^b f'(x) \cdot dx$ may be read thus :

" Find the sum of the rectangles like $f'(x) \cdot dx$ as x increases from a to b." The integral sign $\int$ may be regarded as a letter s, the initial letter of the word sum.

Without reference to areas the integral $\int_a^b f'(x)dx$ is best translated by the words " Sum the infinitesimals like $f'(x)dx$, as x increases from a to b."

Example 1

Find the area between the curve $y = x^3$, the x-axis and the ordinates at $x = 2$ and $x = 4$.

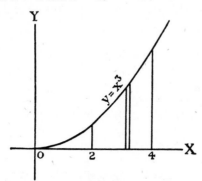

FIG. 61.

The required area $= \displaystyle\int_2^4 x^3\,dx = \left[\dfrac{x^4}{4}\right]_2^4 = 64 - 4$

$$= 60 \text{ square units.}$$

Example 2

Find the area between one arch of the curve $y = \sin\theta$ and the x-axis.

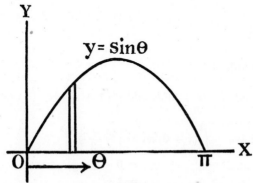

FIG. 62.

We see first that $y = 0$, when $\theta = 0$, and when $\theta = \pi$.
The small strip has the area $y d\theta$, *i.e.*, $\sin \theta d\theta$.

$$\therefore \quad \text{Area required} = \int_0^\pi \sin \theta d\theta = \left[-\cos \theta \right]_0^\pi = 1 + 1$$
$$= 2 \text{ square units.}$$

Notice $\cos \pi = -1$ and $-(-1) = +1$.

Example 3

Evaluate $\int_{-2\cdot9}^{2\cdot9} (1\cdot7x^3 - 4\cdot3x + 5)dx$ *and* $\int_1^2 3(x-1)^3 dx$.

(U.L.C.I.)

(i)

$$I = \int_{-2\cdot9}^{2\cdot9} (1\cdot7x^3 - 4\cdot3x + 5)dx = \left[1\cdot7\frac{x^4}{4} - 4\cdot3\frac{x^2}{2} + 5x \right]_{-2\cdot9}^{2\cdot9}$$

Observe that we do not need to substitute for the even powers of x in this case, since $(2\cdot9)^4 = (-2\cdot9)^4$ etc.

$$\therefore \quad I = 5[2\cdot9 - (-2\cdot9)]$$
$$= 5 \times 5\cdot8$$
$$= 29.$$

(ii) $I = \int_1^2 3(x-1)^3 dx = 3\left[\frac{(x-1)^4}{4} \right]_1^2 = \frac{3}{4}.$

Example 4

Evaluate $\int_1^3 (x+3)^2 dx$ *and* $\int_{\frac{a}{b}}^{\frac{b}{a}} \left(1 + \frac{1}{x^2} \right) dx$.   (N.C.)

We have $\int_1^3 (x-3)^2 dx = \left[\frac{(x-3)^3}{3} \right]_1^3$
$$= 0 - (-\tfrac{8}{3})$$
$$= \tfrac{8}{3}$$

and
$$\int_{\frac{a}{b}}^{\frac{b}{a}}\left(1+\frac{1}{x^2}\right)dx = \left[\left(x-\frac{1}{x}\right)\right]_{\frac{a}{b}}^{\frac{b}{a}}$$

$$= \left(\frac{b}{a}-\frac{a}{b}\right)-\left(\frac{a}{b}-\frac{b}{a}\right)$$

$$= 2\left(\frac{b}{a}-\frac{a}{b}\right)$$

$$= \frac{2}{ab}(b^2-a^2).$$

4. To Find a Volume of Revolution

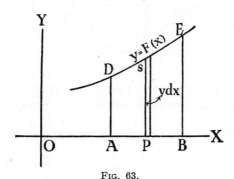

FIG. 63.

Suppose the area ABED is rotated about the x-axis. In a complete revolution the ordinate PS describes a circle whose area is πy^2.

The rectangle ydx will describe a cylinder whose volume is $\pi y^2 dx$, and the required volume, V, generated by ABED in a complete revolution will be given by:

$$\mathbf{V} = \int_a^b \pi y^2 dx$$

where OA $= a$ and OB $= b$.

We now substitute for y in terms of x.

Example 1

The part of the curve $y = x(x - 1)$ *below the x-axis is rotated about that axis. Find the volume generated in a complete rotation.*

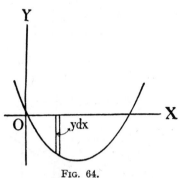

FIG. 64.

We have $y = x(x - 1)$. First find the limits of integration. The curve cuts the x-axis where $x = 0$ and $x = 1$.

Hence the volume $= \int_0^1 \pi y^2 dx$ [y is negative, but y^2 is $+$]

$$= \pi \int_0^1 (x^2 - x)^2 dx \text{ [Since } y = x^2 - x\text{].}$$

$$= \pi \int_0^1 (x^4 - 2x^3 + x^2) dx$$

$$= \pi \left[\frac{x^5}{5} - \frac{x^4}{2} + \frac{x^3}{3} \right]_0^1$$

$$= \pi \left[\frac{1}{5} - \frac{1}{2} + \frac{1}{3} \right] = \frac{\pi}{30} \text{ cubic units.}$$

Example 2

Find the volume of a sphere of radius r.

Regard the sphere as formed by rotating through four

right angles the semi-circle whose bounding diameter is along the x-axis.

Let $x^2 + y^2 = r^2$ be the equation of the boundary curve AB.

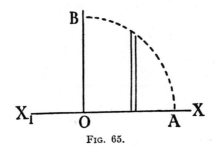

FIG. 65.

Vol. of hemi-sphere $= \displaystyle\int_0^r \pi y^2 dx.$

Now $\qquad\qquad\qquad y^2 = r^2 - x^2.$

$\therefore$ Vol. of hemi-sphere $= \displaystyle\int_0^r \pi(r^2 - x^2)dx$

$$= \pi\left[\left(r^2 x - \frac{x^3}{3}\right)\right]_0^r$$

$$= \pi\left(r^3 - \frac{r^3}{3}\right)$$

$$= \tfrac{2}{3}\pi r^3$$

$\therefore \quad \tfrac{4}{3}\pi r^3 =$ vol. of sphere.

Example 3

Find the volume of a right circular cone of height h whose base has the radius r.

Regard the volume as generated by rotating the right-angled triangle OAB through four right angles.

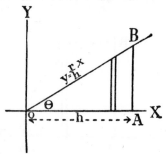

Fig. 66.

The equation of OB is $y = x \tan \theta = \dfrac{r}{h}x.$

$$\therefore \quad \text{The vol.} = \int_0^h \pi y^2 dx$$

$$= \int_0^h \pi \cdot \frac{r^2}{h^2}x^2 dx$$

$$= \frac{\pi r^2}{h^2}\left[\frac{x^3}{3}\right]_0^h$$

$$= \frac{\pi r^2}{h^2} \cdot \frac{h^3}{3} = \frac{1}{3} \cdot \pi r^2 \cdot h$$

i.e. $\frac{1}{3}$ area of base $\times$ *ht.*

EXERCISE 40

1. Evaluate the following integrals :

(a) $\displaystyle\int_1^2 (u^2 + 3u - 5)du.$ (b) $\displaystyle\int_1^2 \left(\sqrt{v} + \frac{6}{\sqrt{v}}\right)dv.$

(c) $\displaystyle\int_0^{\frac{\pi}{3}} \sin x \, dx.$ (d) $\displaystyle\int_0^{\frac{\pi}{4}} \cos 2t \, dt.$

(U.L.C.I.)

2. Evaluate :

(1) $\int_1^3 \left(u^2 - \frac{1}{u^2}\right)du.$

(2) $\int_0^2 \pi y^2 dx$, when $y = 2x^{1·5}$.

(3) $\int_2^6 p\, dv$, where $pv^{0·9} = 450$.

(4) $\int_0^{\frac{\pi}{2}} (\cos t - \sin 2t)dt.$ (U.L.C.I.)

3. The shear force in tons taken by the web of a certain girder is given by

$$0·6 \int_{-9}^9 (3·9 - 0·013y^2)dy.$$

Calculate the shear.   (U.E.I.)

4. Evaluate :

(1) $\int_{-2·9}^{2·9} (7x^3 - 3x + 5)dx$ (2) $\int_1^2 (x-1)^3 dx.$

(3) $\int_{-1}^{+3} 3(x-3)^2 dx.$

5. Evaluate :

(1) $\int_1^2 \left(x^2 - \frac{1}{x^2} + 2\right)dx$ (2) $\int_1^3 (3-x)^2 dx.$

(3) $\int_0^{\frac{\pi}{6}} (\sin 3t - \cos t)dt.$ (4) $\int_0^{\frac{\pi}{2}} \sin^2 \theta\, d\theta.$

(5) $\int_0^5 (2t^3 - 16t + 15\sqrt{t})dt.$

6. Show by integration that $\int_0^6 (x^2 - 5x + 3)dx = 0$, and given an explanation by means of a graph.   (U.L.C.I.)

7. Evaluate :

(a) $\int_0^1 (x^2 + 4)dx.$

(b) $\int_4^6 \sqrt{x}(x - 4)dx.$

(c) $\int_0^{\frac{\pi}{4}} \cos\left(2\theta + \frac{\pi}{4}\right)d\theta.$

(d) $\int_0^{\frac{\pi}{6}} \cos 3x dx.$

(U.L.C.I.)

8. Find :

(1) $\int_1^9 \left(2\sqrt{x} - \frac{5}{x^2}\right)dx.$

(2) $\int_1^{10} v^{-0.8}dv.$

(3) $\int_0^{\frac{\pi}{6}} \sin 3t dt.$

(4) $\int_0^{\frac{\pi}{4}} \cos\left(\frac{1}{2}t + 1\right)dt.$

(U.L.C.I.)

9. Evaluate :

(1) $\int_{-2}^{+1} (2x + 1)^2 dx.$

(2) $\int_{-\frac{m}{n}}^{\frac{m}{n}} \left(\frac{x^4 + 1}{x^3}\right)dx.$

(3) $\int_{-3}^{-1} \left(x - \frac{1}{2x^2}\right)dx.$

(N.C.)

10. For the curve $y = 3 + 2x + 3x^2$, find the area between the curve, the x-axis and the ordinates at $x = 1$ and $x = 4$.   (U.L.C.I.)

11. If $y = x^2$, show by a geometric illustration that $\int_a^b y dx$ will give the area between the curve the x-axis and the ordinates at $x = a$ and $x = b$.   Evaluate

$$\frac{\pi}{10}\int_1^2 (2h^{\frac{1}{2}} - h)dh.$$

(U.L.C.I.)

12. A curve whose equation is $\dfrac{y}{x^2 + 3} = m$, where m is a constant, passes through the point (2, 3·5). Find the area bounded by the curve, the x-axis and the two ordinates at $x = 2$ and $x = 6$.   (U.L.C.I.)

13. That part of the curve $y = x(x - 3)$ which lies below the x-axis revolves about that axis. Find the volume generated.

14. Find by means of the calculus the volume of part of a sphere, radius 10 ins., bounded by two parallel planes distant 3 ins. and 7 ins. from the centre of the sphere, both planes being on same side of the centre.   (U.L.C.I.)

15. In finding the B.M. at points on a beam, it was found that $y = 100x - 5x^2 + c$, where y was the B.M. at distance x from one end, and c was a constant. When $y = 520$, $x = 10$. Find c, and then find the area between

$$y = 100x - 5x^2 + c,$$

the x-axis and the ordinates at $x = 0$ and $x = 20$.

(U.L.C.I.)

16. Calculate the volume of the solid formed by rotating about the x-axis the area between the graphs of the two functions $\left(1 - \dfrac{1}{2\sqrt{x}}\right)$ and $\dfrac{1}{2\sqrt{x}}$ for the values of x from $+ 1$ to $+ 4$, the unit being 1 in. along each axis.

(N.C.)

17. The equation $y = a + bx^{\frac{3}{2}}$ is such that when $x = 1$, $y = 1·61$, and when $x = 4$, $y = 5·32$. Calculate a and b. If the curve rotates about the x-axis, find the volume enclosed by the surface of revolution between the sections at $x = 1$ and $x = 4$.   (U.E.I.)

5. Mean Values of a Function of One Variable

In Fig. 67, suppose that CD is part of the graph of $y = f(x)$.

Let   OA $= a$, and OB $= b$.

Then the area ABCD is represented by

$$\int_a^b f(x)dx \quad . \quad . \quad . \quad . \quad . \quad . \quad (1)$$

Now suppose that ABFE is a rectangle whose area equals that given by the integral (1).

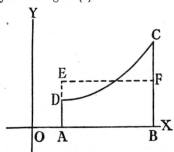

FIG. 67.

The height of this rectangle—viz., AE or BF—is called the mean value of the function $f(x)$ between $x = a$ and $x = b$.

We then have, since $AB = (b - a)$

$$(b - a) \times AE = \int_a^b f(x)dx$$

$$\therefore \quad AE = \text{mean value} = \frac{1}{b-a} \cdot \int_a^b f(x)dx \quad . \quad (2)$$

Example 1

Find the mean value of x^2 between $x = 2$ and $x = 4$.
By the formula

$$\begin{aligned}
\text{M.V.} &= \frac{1}{4-2}\int_2^4 x^2 dx \\
&= \frac{1}{2}\left[\frac{x^3}{3}\right]_2^4 \\
&= \tfrac{1}{6}(4^3 - 2^3) \\
&= \tfrac{56}{6} = 9\tfrac{1}{3}.
\end{aligned}$$

Example 2

Find the mean value of sin 2x, between x = 0 and x = $\frac{\pi}{2}$.

Here,

$$\text{M.V.} = \frac{2}{\pi}\int_0^{\frac{\pi}{2}} \sin 2x\,dx$$

$$= \frac{2}{\pi}\left[-\frac{\cos 2x}{2} \right]_0^{\frac{\pi}{2}}$$

$$= -\frac{1}{\pi}[\cos 2x]_0^{\frac{\pi}{2}}$$

$$= -\frac{1}{\pi}[(-1) - (1)]$$

$$= \frac{2}{\pi}.$$

Since $\sin 2x = \sin 2(x + \pi)$, the period is π, and we have found the M.V. of $\sin 2x$ over half a period.

Example 3

Suppose a S.H.M. is given by x = 3 cos 2t.
Find the mean value of the velocity from t = 2 to t = 5.

$$\text{velocity} = \frac{dx}{dt} = -6\sin 2t$$

$$\therefore\quad \text{M.V.} = \frac{1}{5-2}\int_2^5 (-6\sin 2t)\,dt$$

$$= -2\int_2^5 \sin 2t\,dt$$

$$= -2\left[-\frac{\cos 2t}{2} \right]_2^5$$

$$= [\cos 2t]_2^5$$

$$= \cos 10 - \cos 4$$

(the unit is a radian in this result)

$$= 0{\cdot}187 \text{ ft./sec.}$$

6. Sometimes it is necessary to find the R.M.S. (root mean square) of a given function.

First find the M.V. of the square of the function. Then find the square root of the result.

Example

Find the R.M.S. of sin pt over a period.

We have, $\sin pt = \sin (pt + 2\pi) = \sin p\left(t + \dfrac{2\pi}{p}\right)$.

Hence the period is $\dfrac{2\pi}{p}$.

$$\text{Mean Square} = \frac{p}{2\pi}\int_0^{\frac{2\pi}{p}} \sin^2 pt\,dt$$

$$= \frac{p}{2\pi}\int_0^{\frac{2\pi}{p}} \left(\frac{1 - \cos 2pt}{2}\right)dt$$

$$= \frac{p}{2\pi}\left[\frac{t}{2} - \frac{\sin 2pt}{4p}\right]_0^{\frac{2\pi}{p}}$$

$$= \frac{p}{2\pi} \times \frac{2\pi}{2p} = \frac{1}{2}$$

$$\therefore \text{ R.M.S.} = \frac{1}{\sqrt{2}} = \frac{\sqrt{2}}{2} = 0{\cdot}707.$$

EXERCISE 41

1. Find the mean values of the following functions :

    (a) $\sin x$ from $x = 0$ to $x = \pi$.

    (b) $\sin^2 x$ from $x = 0$ to $x = \pi$.

    (c) x^2 from $x = 0$ to $x = 2$.

2. If $v = u + gt$, where u is the velocity at zero time, and $g = 32$ ft./sec.², find (1) the average value of v during the first five seconds starting from rest, (2) during the first five seconds when $u = 36$ ft./sec.

3. In a S.H.M., $x = a \cos wt$. Find the mean value of the velocity over a quarter of the period.

4. A solid is generated by revolving the curve $y = \dfrac{2 \cdot 5}{x^2}$ about the x-axis. Find the volume between $x = 1$ and $x = 4$. Find the mean value of the cross section perpendicular to the x-axis between the same limits. Hence show that the M.V. of the cross section is not the same as the cross section midway between the ends.   (U.L.C.I.)

5. Tabulate the values of the function $2 \cos t - \sin 3t$ when $t = 0,\ \dfrac{\pi}{36},\ \dfrac{\pi}{18}$ to $\dfrac{\pi}{6}$ and draw the graph in this range. Find by integration the M.V. of the function from $t = 0$ to $t = \dfrac{\pi}{6}$.   (U.L.C.I.)

6. Assuming formulæ for $\cos (A + B)$ and $\cos (A - B)$, express $\cos A . \cos B$ as a sum and $\sin A . \sin B$ as a difference.

The instantaneous values e volts and i amps. of the e.m.f. and current, respectively, in an alternating circuit at time t are given by $e = E_m \sin wt$ and $i = I_m \sin (wt - \alpha)$, where E_m, I_m, w and α are constants. Show the M.V. of the product ei over the range $t = 0$ to $t = \dfrac{\pi}{w}$ is equal to $\tfrac{1}{2} E_m I_m \cos \alpha$.   (U.L.C.I.)

7. A quantity of gas expands according to the law $pv^{1 \cdot 2} = $ const. from a volume of 2 cu. ft. to a volume of 5·5 cu. ft. If $p = 140$ lb. per sq. in. when $v = 2$ cu. ft., find the average of p from $v = 2$ to $v = 5 \cdot 5$.   (U.L.C.I.)

8. Find by means of the calculus :

    (a) The area between the curve $16x^2 = y - 1$, the x-axis and the ordinates at $x = 0$ and $x = 4$.

    (b) The mean value of y between $x = 0$ and $x = 4$.
                                     (U.L.C.I.)

9. Given $x = a \cos wt$, find the mean value of the velocity over a quarter period for equal intervals of distance.

10. If $y = 2 \sin 3t$, find the M.V. of y^2, for the period $t = 0$ to $t = \dfrac{2\pi}{3}$.

11. Find the R.M.S. of

    (1) $2 \sin 3\theta$.   (2) $3 \cos 2x$.   (3) $\cos a\theta$.
    (4) $\sin (a\theta + \alpha)$, each taken over a period.

12. Given that $i = c + k \sin a\theta$, find the R.M.S. of i, where c, k, and a are constants.

13. Find the R.M.S. of $3 \sin 2t + 2 \sin 3t$.

7. Simpson's Rule

Suppose that we require the area between the curve CD, the ordinates AD and BC, and the x-axis.

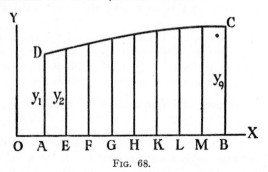

FIG. 68.

Divide the area into an even number of strips (eight in the above figure) by equidistant ordinates. Suppose

$$AE = EF = \ldots = MB = h.$$

Simpson's rule states that the approximate area is

$$\frac{h}{3}[y_1 + y_9 + 4(y_2 + y_4 + y_6 + y_8) + 2(y_3 + y_5 + y_7)]$$

i.e., $\frac{h}{3}$ [(first + last) ordinates + 4(sum of even ordinates)

+ 2 (sum of remaining odd ordinates)] .   .   (1)

8. We shall now show that Simpson's Rule is accurate when the boundary curve of the area is a parabola.

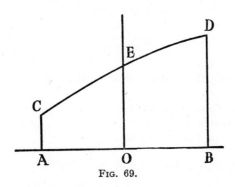

FIG. 69.

If we take the equation of CD as

$$y = a + bx + cx^2 \text{ (a parabola)} .   .   . \quad (1)$$

the form of this equation is unaltered wherever the origin O is taken.

For simplicity suppose O is the mid point of AB.

Let   OA = − h, OB = h.

Then from (1)

$$AC = y_1 = a - bh + ch^2 \text{ (putting } x = - h)$$
$$OE = y_2 = a \qquad\qquad \text{ (putting } x = 0)$$
$$BD = y_3 = a + bh + ch^2 \text{ (putting } x = h)$$

Hence AC + BD + 4 . OE = $(y_1 + y_3 + 4y_2)$
$$= 6a + 2ch^2 .   .   . \quad (2)$$

Also area ABDC $= \int_{-h}^{h} (a + bx + cx^2)dx$

$$= \left[ax + \frac{bx^2}{2} + \frac{cx^3}{3} \right]_{-h}^{h}$$

$$= 2ah + \frac{2ch^3}{3}$$

$$= \frac{6ah + 2ch^3}{3}$$

$$= \frac{h}{3}(6a + 2ch^2) \quad . \quad . \quad . \quad . \quad (3)$$

From (2), this result is exactly what we get for the area by Simpson's Rule.

In Fig. 68 we apply the result to each pair of strips, and so get the rule (1).

Thus area ABCD (Fig. 68).

$$= \frac{h}{3}[(y_1 + y_3 + 4y_2) + (y_3 + y_5 + 4y_4) + (y_5 + y_7 + 4y_6) \\ + (y_7 + y_9 + 4y_8)]$$

$$= \frac{h}{3}[y_1 + y_9 + 4(y_2 + y_4 + y_6 + y_8) + 2(y_3 + y_5 + y_7)].$$

In applying the rule to a specific area it may happen that the curve cuts the horizontal line OX.

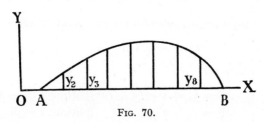

Fig. 70.

In the above case $y_1 = 0$ and $y_9 = 0$, and the area

$$= \frac{h}{3}[4(y_2 + y_4 + y_6 + y_8) + 2(y_3 + y_5 + y_7)].$$

Example

Suppose a curve passes through the points given in the table below :

x . .	1	1·5	2	2·5	3	3·5	4	4·5	5
y . .	2	2·6	2·9	3·1	3·3	3·0	2·9	2·3	2·1

Find the area between the curve, the x-axis and the ordinates at $x = 1$, $x = 5$.

In the above example, $h = 0·5$.
Area (approx.)

$$= \frac{0·5}{3}[(2 + 2·1) + 4(2·6 + 3·1 + 3 + 2·3)$$
$$+ 2(2·9 + 3·3 + 2·9)]$$
$$= \tfrac{1}{6}[66·3] = 11·05 \text{ sq. units.}$$

9. If there are only three ordinates,

$$\text{Area} = \frac{h}{3}(y_1 + y_3 + 4y_2)$$
$$= 2h\left(\frac{y_1 + 4y_2 + y_3}{6}\right).$$

Hence $\dfrac{y_1 + 4y_2 + y_3}{6}$ may be regarded as the mean ordinate, whilst $2h$ is the distance between the bounding ordinates.

10. Since Simpson's Rule is accurate when the bounding curve has an equation not higher than the second degree, it follows that we can apply it to the calculation of volumes of solids which are such that the area of any plane section is given by an expression of degree not higher than the second. This area can be treated as an ordinate.

Example 1

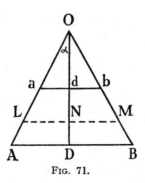

FIG. 71.

To find the volume of the frustum ABba of a cone of height L, and base-radius R.

The area of any section LM, where ON $= x$ varies as x^2,

for
$$\frac{LN}{x} = \frac{AD}{DO} = \frac{R}{h}.$$

$$\therefore \ \pi LN^2 = \text{area of section} = \frac{\pi R^2}{h^2} \cdot x^2.$$

If $ad = r$, the radius of the mid-section $= \dfrac{R + r}{2}$.

Let $\qquad Dd = H$

Here $y_1 = \pi r^2, y_2 = \pi\left(\dfrac{R + r}{2}\right)^2, y_3 = \pi R^2.$

$$\therefore \ \text{Vol. of frustum} = \frac{H}{6}\left[\pi r^2 + \frac{4\pi}{4}(R + r)^2 + \pi R^2\right]$$

$$= \frac{\pi H}{6}[2r^2 + 2R^2 + 2Rr]$$

$$= \frac{\pi H}{3}[r^2 + rR + R^2].$$

Example 2

Suppose that the areas of three cross sections of a railway cutting 20 yds. apart are 110, 140, and 172 sq. yds. respectively ; what is the volume excavated?

The average section $= \frac{1}{6}[110 + 172 + 4 \times 140]$

$\qquad\qquad\qquad = \frac{842}{6}$ sq. yds.

$\therefore \quad$ Volume $= \dfrac{40 \times 842}{6}$

$\qquad\qquad\qquad = 5613$ cu. yds.

11. Simpson's Rule Applied to a Definite Integral

Use Simpson's Rule to evaluate $\displaystyle\int_0^4 \sqrt{16 - x^2} \,.\, dx.$

The boundary curve is $y = \sqrt{16 - x^2}$.

Divide the interval $x = 0$ to $x = 4$ into eight strips each $\frac{1}{2}$ unit wide.

x . .	0	0·5	1	1·5	2	2·5	3	3·5	4
y . .	4	3·97	3·87	3·71	3·46	3·12	2·65	1·92	0

We have, $y_1 + y_9 = 4 + 0 = 4$

$4(y_2 + y_4 + y_6 + y_8) = 4[3\cdot97 + 3\cdot71 + 3\cdot12 + 1\cdot92]$

$\qquad\qquad\qquad\qquad\qquad\qquad = 50\cdot88$

$2(y_3 + y_5 + y_7) = 2[3\cdot87 + 3\cdot46 + 2\cdot65] = 19\cdot96$

$\therefore \quad \displaystyle\int_0^4 \sqrt{16 - x^2} \,.\, dx = \dfrac{0\cdot5}{3} \times 74\cdot84 = 12\cdot47.$

EXERCISE 42

1. The following are the areas of the cross-sections of a body at right angles to its axis :

Area in sq. ins.	250	292	310	273	215	180	135	120
x ins. from end	0	22	41	70	84	102	130	145

Find its volume. $\qquad\qquad\qquad\qquad\qquad\qquad$ (B.E.)

2. State Simpson's Rule. An area is divided into ten equal parts by parallel ordinates 0·2 in. apart, the first and last touching the bounding curve. The lengths of these ordinates are 0, 1·24, 2·37, 4·10, 5·28, 4·76, 4·60, 4·36, 2·45, 1·62, 0.

Find the area.   (B.E.)

3. A vessel is shaped like the frustum of a cone. Its base has a diameter 10 ins., the top a diameter 8 ins., and its vertical height is 8 ins. What is the height of the imaginary vertex of the cone? If x is the height of the surface of a liquid from the bottom plot a curve which shows for any value of x the area of the section there. Find, in cu. ins., the volume of the vessel.   (B.E.)

4. Ordinates at a common distance apart of 10 ft. are of length 5, 6·5, 9, 13, 18·5, 22, 23, 22, 18·5, and 14 ft. By any method find the area bounded by curve, the axis of x and the end ordinates. Describe a second method by which the result could be verified.   (U.L.C.I.)

5. The sections of the two ends of a barrel are 12·35 sq. ft. The mid-section is 14·16 sq. ft. The axial length is 5 ft. What is its volume?   (B.E.)

6. The ends of a prismoid have an area of 62·8 and 20·5 sq. ft., respectively. The perpendicular distance between them is 15 ft. The mid-section has an area of 36·7 sq. ft. What is the average section and what is the volume.

                                                            (B.E.)

7. To find the cross-section of a river 90 ft. in breadth the following depths, y ft., were taken across the river; x ft. is the distance from one bank.

x . . .	0	10	20	30	40	50	60	70	80	90
y . . .	3·0	4·5	5·6	6	5·7	4·8	4·7	4·5	4	3

What is the area of the cross-section? If the average velocity of the water across the section is 3·4 ft./sec., find the flow in cubic ft./sec.   (B.E.)

8. Evaluate by Simpson's rule

(1) $\int_0^2 \sqrt{8 + x^3} \cdot dx.$ (2) $\int \sqrt{1 + x^4} \cdot dx.$

9. A reservoir has sloping sides and ends. Its base is a rectangle whose sides are a and b ft. respectively. The water surface is also a rectangle of sides c and d ft. If the depth is h ft., what volume of water is there in the reservoir?

10. p is the pressure of a gas when its volume is v.

p . . .	70·2	32·5	20·3	15·4	12·5
v . . .	2	4	6	8	10

Find the work done as the gas expands from 2 to 10 units of volume. p is measured in pounds per sq. ft. and v in cu. ft.

11. Find (1) by integration, (2) by Simpson's rule the value of $\int_2^4 \frac{10}{x^2} dx.$ For (2) use six strips.

12. The area of the cross-section of a tree trunk is A sq. ins. at x ins. from one end. Plot A against x and estimate the volume of the trunk, whose total length is 140 ins.

x . . .	0	20	40	60	80	100	120	140
A . . .	108	110	114	120	118	123	135	153

(N.C.)

CHAPTER 13

PHYSICAL APPLICATIONS OF INTEGRATION

1. Centres of Gravity

Any finite body may be regarded as an aggregate of particles, whose weights form a system of parallel forces. Assuming each force to act at a point about which the mass of each particle is distributed, this system of parallel forces has a centre, called the centre of gravity of the body, at which its weight acts.

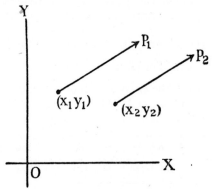

FIG. 72.

If P_1, P_2, etc., be a system of parallel forces acting at the points (x_1, y_1), (x_2, y_2), etc., and if $(\bar{x}, \bar{y})$ be the co-ordinates of their centre we know that

$$\bar{x} = \frac{P_1 x_1 + P_2 x_2 + \ldots}{P_1 + P_2 + \ldots} = \frac{\Sigma P x}{\Sigma P} \quad . \quad . \quad (1)$$

and

$$\bar{y} = \frac{P_1 y_1 + P_2 y_2 + \ldots}{P_1 + P_2 + \ldots} = \frac{\Sigma P y}{\Sigma P} \quad . \quad . \quad (2)$$

If the " points of application " of the forces are kept fixed, the co-ordinates $(\bar{x}, \bar{y})$ of their centre are independent of the particular direction in which the forces act.

Hence if the forces P_1, P_2, . . . are replaced by the weights of masses m_1, m_2, etc., at (x_1, y_1), (x_2, y_2) . . . we get, by replacing P_1 by $m_1 g$, etc. :

$$\bar{x} = \frac{\Sigma mg \, . \, x}{\Sigma mg} = \frac{\Sigma mx}{\Sigma m} \quad . \quad . \quad . \quad . \quad (3)$$

and

$$\bar{y} = \frac{\Sigma mg \, . \, y}{\Sigma mg} = \frac{\Sigma my}{\Sigma m} \quad . \quad . \quad . \quad . \quad (4)$$

It will be clear, also, from (3) and (4) that m_1, m_2, etc., need not be actual measures of the masses, but numbers proportional to such measures.

From this point of view, the centre of gravity is sometimes referred to as the centre of mass, the centre of area, the mean-centre or the centroid.

Further $\Sigma P \, . \, x$, or Σmx, and the corresponding expressions involving ordinates are often called the first moments of the system about the axes of y and of x respectively.

Hence we may write :

$$\bar{x} = \frac{\text{First moment of the system about OY}}{\text{Sum of the forces (or masses, area, etc.)}}$$

and

$$\bar{y} = \frac{\text{First moment of the system about OX}}{\text{Sum of the forces}}$$

2. To find the centre of gravity of an area bounded by a given curve, the x-axis and two ordinates, proceed as follows :

Let $y = f(x)$ be the equation of the curve DC.

Required the C.G. of the area ABCD.

Let $OA = a$ and $OB = b$.

Consider the strip PQST, where $OP = x$, ($\therefore$ PT $= y$,) and PQ $= dx$.

The area of the strip = PT . PQ(nearly) = y . dx.

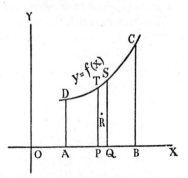

Fig. 73.

The centre of area of this strip is at R, its mid-point and we shall regard $\left(x, \dfrac{y}{2}\right)$ as the co-ordinates of R.

To apply formula (3), we regard y . dx as the " m " of that formula concentrated at R and write

$$\bar{x} = \frac{\int y dx \, . \, x}{\int y dx} \qquad \ldots \quad \ldots \quad (1)$$

replacing the sign Σ by the sign of integration, since we are summing the elements of a continuous area.

Similarly, $$\bar{y} = \frac{\int y dx \, . \, \dfrac{y}{2}}{\int y dx} \qquad \ldots \quad \ldots \quad (2)$$

Substitute $f(x)$ for y, and put in the limits of integration.

Example 1

Find the centroid of the area between the curve $y = x^3$, the x-axis and the line $x = 3$.

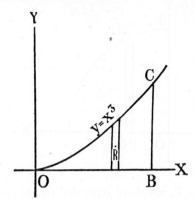

FIG. 74.

ydx is the element at R. $OB = 3$, and the line BC is $x = 3$.

$$\bar{x} = \frac{\int ydx \cdot x}{\int ydx} = \frac{\int_0^3 x^4 dx}{\int_0^3 x^3 dx} \text{ (substituting for } y)$$

Hence $\bar{x} = \dfrac{\left[\dfrac{x^5}{5}\right]_0^3}{\left[\dfrac{x^4}{4}\right]_0^3} = \dfrac{3^5}{5} \times \dfrac{4}{3^4} = \dfrac{12}{5}$ units.

Similarly

$$\bar{y} = \frac{\int ydx \cdot \frac{y}{2}}{\int ydx} = \frac{\frac{1}{2}\int_0^3 x^6 dx}{\int_0^3 x^3 dx} = \frac{1}{2} \cdot \frac{3^7}{7} \cdot \frac{4}{3^4} = \frac{54}{7} \text{ units.}$$

Example 2

Find the centre of mass of a hemi-sphere of radius **a**.

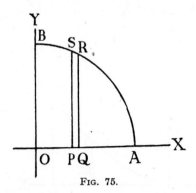

FIG. 75.

Consider the hemi-sphere generated by the revolution of the quadrant of the circle OAB about OX.

The bounding curve is $x^2 + y^2 = a^2$.

The volume of the element formed by rotating the area PQRS about OX is $\pi y^2 dx$, where OP $= x$, and PS $= y$.

The centre of mass of the element is on OX, and distant x from O.

By symmetry $\bar{y} = 0$ and

$$\bar{x} = \frac{\int_0^a \pi y^2 \,.\, dx \,.\, x}{\frac{2}{3}\pi a^3} = \frac{\int_0^a x(a^2 - x^2)dx}{\frac{2}{3}a^3}$$

The numerator

$$= \left[\frac{a^2 x^2}{2} - \frac{x^4}{4}\right]_0^a = \frac{a^4}{4} \quad \therefore \quad \bar{x} = \frac{3a}{8}$$

Example 3

The lamina ABCD *shown in the diagram is bounded by the y-axis, the line* $x = 9$ *and the two curves* $y = 2\cdot5 + 0\cdot01x^2$

and $y = -2 \cdot 5 - 0 \cdot 01x^2$ *the unit of length along each axis of reference being* 1 *in.   Find the area of the lamina and the distance of its centroid from* AB.   (U.L.C.I.)

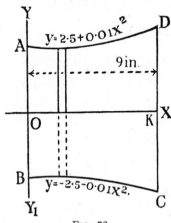

$y = 2 \cdot 5 + 0 \cdot 01x^2$

9 in.

$y = -2 \cdot 5 - 0 \cdot 01x^2$.

FIG. 76.

Notice that the area is symmetrical about OX.

The area of the vertical strip $= ydx$.

$$\therefore \quad \text{Total area} = 2 \times \text{area OKDA}$$

$$= 2 \int_0^9 y dx$$

$$= 2 \int_0^9 (2 \cdot 5 + 0 \cdot 01x^2) dx$$

$$= 2 \left[2 \cdot 5x + \frac{0 \cdot 01}{3} x^3 \right]_0^9$$

$$= 2 \times 24 \cdot 93$$

$$= 49 \cdot 86 \text{ sq. ins.}$$

The centroid lies along OX.

Let its co-ordinate be $\bar{x}$.

Then
$$\bar{x} = \frac{\int_0^9 2 \cdot y\,dx \cdot x}{\int_0^9 2y\,dx}$$

The denominator has just been found and is 49·86 sq. ins.

The numerator
$$= 2\int_0^9 (2 \cdot 5 + 0 \cdot 01x^2)x\,dx$$
$$= 2\left[\frac{2 \cdot 5x^2}{2} + \frac{0 \cdot 01x^4}{4}\right]_0^9$$
$$= 2[101 \cdot 25 + 16 \cdot 40]$$
$$= 235 \cdot 30.$$

Hence
$$\bar{x} = \frac{235 \cdot 30}{49 \cdot 86}$$
$$= 4 \cdot 72 \text{ ins.}$$

Example 4

A solid is formed by rotating about the axis of x the area under the graph of the function $\left(2 - \dfrac{3x^{\frac{1}{2}}}{4}\right)$ *between $x = 0$ and $x = 4$. Find the volume of the solid, and the distance of its centre of gravity from the origin.*   (N.C.)

The volume
$$= \int_0^4 \pi\left(2 - \frac{3x^{\frac{1}{2}}}{4}\right)^2 dx \quad . \quad . \quad . \quad (1)$$
$$= \pi\int_0^4 (4 - 3x^{\frac{1}{2}} + \tfrac{9}{16}x)\,dx$$
$$= \pi\left[4x - 2x^{\frac{3}{2}} + \frac{9}{16}\cdot\frac{x^2}{2}\right]_0^4$$
$$= \pi(16 - 16 + \tfrac{9}{2})$$
$$= \frac{9\pi}{2} \text{ cu. units.}$$

If $\bar{x}$ = distance of C.G. from the origin

$$\frac{9\pi}{2} \cdot \bar{x} = \int_0^4 \pi\left(2 - \frac{3x^{\frac{1}{2}}}{4}\right)^2 . x\,dx$$

$$= \pi\int_0^4 (4x - 3x^{\frac{3}{2}} + \tfrac{9}{16}x^2)dx$$

$$= \pi[2x^2 - \tfrac{6}{5}x^{\frac{5}{2}} + \tfrac{3}{16}x^3]_0^4$$

$$= \pi[32 - \tfrac{6}{5} . 32 + 12]$$

$$= \pi(12 - \tfrac{3\,2}{5})$$

$$= \frac{28\pi}{5}$$

$$\therefore \quad x = 1\cdot24 \text{ units.}$$

In this solution we have assumed that $x^{\frac{1}{2}} = + \sqrt{x}$, not $\pm \sqrt{x}$.

EXERCISE 43

1. Find the C.G. of the area between the curve $y^2 = 4x$ and $x = 4$.

2. Find the C.G. of that half of the above curve which lies in the first quadrant.

3. Find the C.G. of the area between $y = 4x^2$, the x-axis and $x = 4$.

4. Find the C.G. of the area between $y = x^3$, the axis of y and $y = 1$.

5. The curve $y = a + bx + cx^2$ passes through the points $(0, 2)$ $(1, 5)$ $(- 1, 3)$. Find (1) the area between the curve, the x-axis, and the ordinates at $x = 0$ and $x = 3$. Find also the co-ordinates of the centroid. (U.L.C.I.)

6. A uniform elliptical disc of metal, thickness 0·2 in., has major and minor axes of 10·6 and 7 ins. An equilateral shaped disc of the same material, and of thickness 0·3 in. has an edge of 4·5 ins. The slab is placed flat on the disc symmetrically about the major axis with a vertex at the centre of the ellipse. Find the C.G. of the combination. (U.L.C.I.)

7. A solid is formed by rotating about the x-axis the area between the graphs of $\left(1 + \dfrac{x^2}{8}\right)$ and $\dfrac{x}{4}$ for values of x

from $x = 2$ to $x = 4$. The unit is one inch along each axis.

Calculate (1) the volume of the solid, (2) the distance of its C.G. from the smaller end face.   (N.C.)

8. The distance x of the C.G. of a sector of a circle from the centre is given by

$$x = \frac{\frac{2}{3}a \int_0^B \cos A \, dA}{\int_0^B dA}.$$

Where B is the half angle of the sector in radians and a is the radius. Find x when a is 2 ins. and the angle of the sector is 120°.   (U.E.I.)

9. The dimensions of a trianglar piece PQR of metal are PQ = 8 ins., QR = 12 ins., and RP = 10 ins. M and N are mid-points of PQ and PR, and are joined by a straight line. The part PMN is cut away. Find the position of the C.G. of the remaining part.   (U.L.C.I.)

10. In order to design a tipping device of inverted cone shape to tip when loaded above a certain level, it is necessary to find the C.G. of a cone of uniform density of vertical height H and base area A. Find this by integration.

                    (U.E.I.)

11. Find the centroid of an area formed by the parabola $y^2 = 4x$ and bounded by the chord perpendicular to the axis of x where $x = 9$.   (U.E.I.)

12. A quadrant of the ellipse $\frac{x^2}{36} + \frac{y^2}{25} = 1$ rotates about the x-axis. Find the position of the C.G. of the solid generated.

13. A trapezium is formed by the axes of co-ordinates, and the straight lines $y = 2 + 3x$, $x = 3$. Find the co-ordinates of its C.G.

14. If the above trapezium is rotated about OX, find the C.G. of the frustum of the cone which it generates.

15. A spherical cap of height 4 ins. is cut from a solid sphere of radius 6 ins. Find the position of its C.G.

16. The cross-sectional area of a solid of revolution at a distance of x ins. from one end, A, of its axis is $\left(\dfrac{x}{4} + 3\sqrt{x}\right)$ sq. in. The length of the axis is 4 in. Find the volume of the solid and the distance from A of its C.G. (N.C.)

3. The Theorems of Pappus, or Guldinus

Theorem I

If a curve does not cut the x-axis, and rotates about that axis, it generates a surface whose area is length of curve × distance travelled by its C.G.

Suppose AB is the curve of length l, P is any point on it, and Q an adjacent point such that PQ $= ds$, where AP $= s$.

Let y be the ordinate of P.

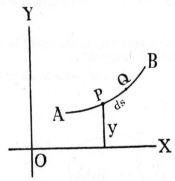

Fig. 77.

The surface generated by ds in a complete revolution about OX is $2\pi y \,.\, ds$.

∴ The total surface $= \displaystyle\int 2\pi y \, ds$

$$= 2\pi \int y \, ds \quad . \quad . \quad . \quad . \quad . \quad (1)$$

If $\bar{y}$ be the ordinate of the C.G. of the curve AB

$$\bar{y} = \frac{\int y ds}{\int ds} = \frac{\int y ds}{l}$$

i.e., $l \cdot \bar{y} = \int y ds$

∴   substituting in (1) we get

total surface $= 2\pi\bar{y} \cdot l$, which proves the proposition.

If y does not perform a complete rotation, but moves through an angle θ, the surface generated

$$= \int y\theta \cdot ds$$
$$= \theta \int y ds$$
$$= y \cdot \theta \cdot l$$

i.e., surface = distance travelled by C.G. × length of curve.

Theorem II

If an area, which does not cut the x-axis be rotated about that axis, the volume generated is

Area × distance travelled by its C.G.

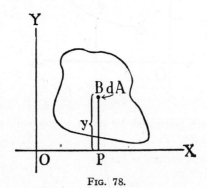

FIG. 78.

The proof is similar to that given for the first theorem.

In the above diagram suppose A to represent the area enclosed by the curve.

Let dA be an element of area, surrounding a point B, whose ordinate is y.

In turning through a complete revolution about OX the volume generated by dA is $2\pi y d$A.

∴ The total volume generated by the area is $\int 2\pi y d$A.

i.e., $2\pi \int y d$A . . . . (1)

But $\int y d$A $= \bar{y} . $A

Hence (1) becomes $2\pi \bar{y} . $A

If the area turns through an angle θ,

vol. generated $= \bar{y} . \theta . $A   . . . . (2)

Example 1

A cylindrical hole of diameter 1 *in. is drilled axially through a solid right circular cone of height* 8 *in. and base diameter* 4 *in.   By the theorems of Guldinus, or by any other method, find the volume and the outside curved surface area of the solid remaining.*   (U.L.C.I.)

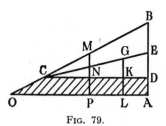

Fig. 79.

Suppose OA = 8 ins. and AB = 2 ins.   Then AD = $\frac{1}{2}$ in. By Pythagoras' theorem OB = $\sqrt{68}$ ins. = $2\sqrt{17}$ ins. The original cone was generated by rotating the area OAB about OA; what is left, can be regarded as being generated by rotating CDB about OA.

BD = $\frac{3}{2}$ in. and AB = 2 ins.

$$\therefore \quad \frac{\text{Area BCD}}{\text{Area BOA}} = \frac{9}{16}$$

i.e.,
$$\text{area BCD} = \frac{9}{16} \cdot 8 \text{ sq. ins.}$$
$$= \frac{9}{2} \text{ sq. ins.} \quad \dots \quad (1)$$

If G is the C.G. of the triangle CDB,

$$GK = \frac{2}{3} \times DE = \frac{2}{3} \times \frac{3}{4} \text{ ins.}$$
$$= \frac{1}{2} \text{ in.}$$
$$\therefore \quad GL = 1 \text{ in.} \quad \dots \quad (2)$$

Hence using Guldinus' Theorem, with (1) and (2) we get that the required volume

$$= 2\pi \times 1 \times \frac{9}{2}$$
$$= 9\pi \text{ cu. ins.}$$

For the surface, note that this is generated by CB.

Also
$$CB = \frac{3}{4} \times OB$$
$$= \frac{3}{4} \times 2\sqrt{17}$$
$$= \frac{3}{2} \times \sqrt{17}.$$

M is the mid-point of CB, *i.e.*, it is its C.G.

$$MN = \tfrac{1}{2}BD = \tfrac{3}{4} \text{ in.}$$
$$\therefore \quad MP = 1\tfrac{1}{4} \text{ ins.}$$
$$\therefore \quad \text{Required surface} \quad = 2\pi \times MP \times CB$$
$$= 2\pi \times \tfrac{5}{4} \times \tfrac{3}{2}\sqrt{17}$$
$$= \frac{15\sqrt{17} \cdot \pi}{4} \text{ sq. ins.}$$

Example 2

A length of copper has a uniform cross section which is that of a regular hexagon of 0·6 in. side. It is bent into the form of an arc of a circle whose radius to the centre line of copper is 9 ft. 3 ins. If the angle subtended by the length of bent copper

at the centre be 36°, *find the weight of the copper.   Take*
1 *cu. in. of copper to weigh* 0·32 *lb.*   (U.L.C.I.)

Clearly, the volume of copper is that generated by the
area of the hexagon turning through 36° about an axis
9 ft. 3 ins. from its C.G.

$$\text{The area} = 6 \times \frac{\sqrt{3}}{4} \times (0\!\cdot\!6)^2 \text{ sq. ins.}$$

$$= 0\!\cdot\!54 \times \sqrt{3} \text{ sq. ins.}$$

The rotation of 36° is $\frac{1}{10}$ that of a complete rotation.

$$\therefore \text{ vol. of copper} = \tfrac{1}{10} \times 2\pi \times 111 \times 0\!\cdot\!54 \times \sqrt{3} \text{ cu. ins.}$$

$$\text{and the weight} \quad = \frac{0\!\cdot\!32}{10} \times 2\pi \times 111 \times 0\!\cdot\!54 \times \sqrt{3} \text{ lb.}$$

$$= 20\!\cdot\!86 \text{ lb.}$$

EXERCISE 44

1. The section of an oil ring is shown in the sketch.   Find
the volume of the ring which is formed by rotating the area
about the horizontal line shown.

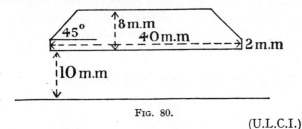

FIG. 80.
                                            (U.L.C.I.)

2. Establish the theorem of Guldinus for volumes.
   Hence determine the position of the C.G. of a semi-
circular lamina of radius 5·5 ins.   (U.E.I.)

3. An isosceles triangle has a base 4 ins. and height
6 ins.   It is placed with the base parallel to the *x*-axis, and

12 ins. away from it, its vertex being towards the axis. The triangle generates a ring by rotation about the x-axis.

Find the volume of the ring.

4. Use Guldinus' theorem to find :

      (1) The C.G. of a semi-circular arc of radius a.

      (2) The C.G. of a semi-circle of radius a.

5. A semi-circle has its bounding diameter, 8 ins. long, parallel to the x-axis (and 6 in. from it). Its circular boundary is remote from the axis. Find the volume generated in a complete rotation about the x-axis.

6. An anchor ring is generated when a circle of radius r rotates about an axis in its plane. If the axis is distant a from its centre, show that the surface area of the ring is $4\pi^2 ar$, and its volume $2a\pi^2 r^2$.

7. Find the area bounded by $y^2 = ax$, the x-axis and the straight line $x = b$. By rotating this area about the x-axis and using Guldinus' theorem find the y-coordinate of the C.G. of the area.

8. Establish the theorem of Guldinus for volumes. The head of a rivet is in the form of the frustum of a cone, base diameter 3·7 ins., diam. of smaller end 2·8 ins. and thickness 1·2 ins. If the weight of a cubic inch of the material is 0·28 lb. find the weight of 100 rivet heads. (U.E.I.)

4. Moments of Inertia or Second Moments

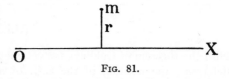

FIG. 81.

If m be an element of mass, distant r units from a fixed axis OX, mr^2 is called the moment of inertia of the mass m about the given axis.

The term second moment is used because it involves r^2. The first moment of m about OX is mr.

If we have a number of particles of masses m_1, m_2, m_3, etc., at distances r_1, r_2, r_3, etc., from OX their moment of inertia is

$$m_1{r_1}^2 + m_2{r_2}^2 + m_3{r_3}^2 + \ldots$$

i.e., writing I for the total moment of inertia, we get :

$$\text{I} = \Sigma mr^2 \quad \ldots \ldots \quad (1)$$

If M be the total mass of the particles, we put :

$$\text{I} = \Sigma mr^2 = \text{M}k^2 \quad \ldots \ldots \quad (2)$$

k is called the radius of gyration of the system of masses about the given axis.

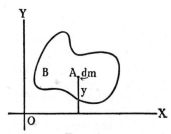

FIG. 82.

Suppose B is any continuous body.

If dm be an element of mass surrounding the point A, whose ordinate is y, its M.I. about OX is $y^2 dm$ and the M.I. of the body B about OX is $\int y^2 dm$.

The word " inertia " refers to mass, whilst the word moment is used in the sense of " important," as when we speak of a " momentous occasion " or of " things of great moment."

" Moment of inertia " (about a given axis) therefore means the " importance of the manner in which the mass is distributed with respect to the given axis," and this importance is measured by Mk^2.

When we are not dealing with mass, as for instance in problems on the bending of beams, where we deal with the areas of sections, we speak of the " second moment " of the section, usually about the neutral axis.

Example 1

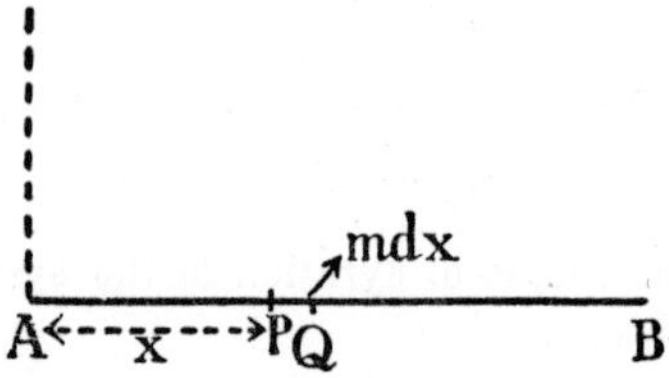

Fig. 83.

To find the second moment of the line AB about an axis through one end perpendicular to AB.

Suppose $AB = 2a$. Let m be its linear density. If $AP = x$, let $PQ = dx$.

Then $mdx \cdot x^2$ is the second moment of the element dx.

$$\therefore \quad I = \int_0^{2a} mx^2 \cdot dx \text{ is the second moment of AB}$$

$$I = \left[\frac{mx^3}{3} \right]_0^{2a} = \frac{8}{3} ma^3 \quad \cdot \quad \cdot \quad \cdot \quad \cdot \quad \cdot \quad \cdot \quad (1)$$

The total mass of $AB = m \cdot 2a$.

$$\therefore \quad 2amk^2 = \frac{8}{3} ma^3$$

i.e., $$k^2 = \frac{4a^2}{3} = \frac{(2a)^2}{3} = \frac{(\text{length})^2}{3}$$

Squares of the radii of gyration, k^2, together with the axes to which they refer, for different bodies, should be remembered.

We deduce at once the k^2 for AB when the axis is taken through its mid-point O.

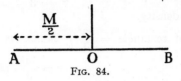

FIG. 84.

The axis is an axis through the end of half the rod. Hence

$$Mk^2 = 2 \times \frac{M}{2} \cdot \frac{a^2}{3}$$

i.e.,

$$k^2 = \frac{a^2}{3} = \frac{(\frac{1}{2} \text{ length})^2}{3}$$

Example 2

To find the M.I. of a rectangle :

(1) *About one side.*

(2) *About an axis parallel to one side through the C.G. of the rectangle.*

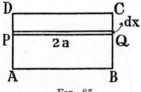

FIG. 85.

Let ABCD be the rectangle in which AB $= 2a$ and AD $= 2b$.

Find the M.I. about AD.

Since we know the area of the rectangle, all we require is the appropriate k^2.

Let AP $= x$, and suppose the breadth of the strip PQ is

dx, where PQ is perpendicular to AD.   Using the previous result, the M.I. of the strip $PQ = \dfrac{4a^2}{3} \cdot 2adx \cdot m$, where m = surface density.

$$\therefore \text{ M.I. of rectangle} = \frac{4a^2}{3} \int_0^{2b} 2a \cdot dx \cdot m$$

$$= \frac{4a^2}{3} \cdot (2a \times 2b \times m)$$

$$= \text{M} \times \frac{(2a)^2}{3}.$$

Hence k^2 (about a side) $= \dfrac{(\text{other side})^2}{3}$.

Similarly, k^2 about an axis through the C.G. parallel to AD, is given by $\dfrac{(\frac{1}{2}\text{ other side})^2}{3}$.

Example 3

The moment of inertia of a ring about an axis through its centre perpendicular to its plane is Ma^2 where M = mass of the ring and a is its radius.

We can use this result to find the M.I. of a circular disc of radius a, about its axle.

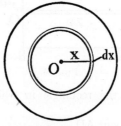

Fig. 86.

The axle is perpendicular to the plane of the paper through O. m is the surface density.

The M.I. of the ring of radius x, width dx is

$$2\pi x dx \cdot m \times x^2 = 2\pi m x^3 dx$$

$$\therefore \quad \text{M.I. of disc.} = 2\pi m \int_0^a x^3 dx$$

$$= 2\pi m \frac{a^4}{4}$$

$$= \pi a^2 m \times \frac{a^2}{2}$$

Hence $k^2 = \dfrac{a^2}{2} = \frac{1}{2}$ (radius)^2.

Example 4
To find the M.I. of a solid sphere about a diameter.

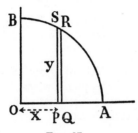

Fig. 87.

Let the sphere have a radius $= a$, and suppose it is generated by the rotation of a semi-circle about its bounding diameter.

Suppose OA is the diameter about which we require the M.I.

The M.I. of the whole = twice that of the hemi-sphere.

Let the bounding circle be

$$x^2 + y^2 = a^2 \quad \cdots \quad \cdots \quad (1)$$

The strip PQRS generates a disc whose radius is y and thickness dx.

If $m =$ the density of the sphere

M.I. of disc $= \pi y^2 dx \cdot m \times \dfrac{y^2}{2}$ (*i.e.,* mass $\times \frac{1}{2}$ radius^2)

$$= \frac{\pi m}{2} y^4 dx$$

$$= \frac{\pi m}{2} (a^2 - x^2)^2 dx \text{ from (1)}$$

$\therefore$ M.I. of sphere $= 2 \displaystyle\int_0^a \frac{\pi m}{2} \cdot (a^2 - x^2)^2 dx$

$$= \pi m \int_0^a (a^4 - 2a^2 x^2 + x^4) dx$$

$$= \pi m \left[a^4 x - \frac{2a^2 x^3}{3} + \frac{x^5}{5} \right]_0^a$$

$$= \pi m \left(a^5 - \frac{2}{3} a^5 + \frac{a^5}{5} \right)$$

$$= \pi m \cdot \tfrac{8}{15} a^5.$$

The total mass $= \frac{4}{3} \pi a^3 m$

$\therefore \quad k^2 = \frac{2}{5} a^2.$

5. If we know the M.I. of a lamina about each of two perpendicular axes in its plane, we can write down its M.I. about an axis perpendicular to its plane through the point of intersection of the other two.

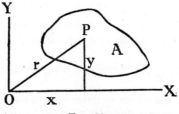

Fig. 88.

A is any area; P any point of the area whose coordinates with respect to axes OX, OY are (x, y).

Let I_x, I_y be the second moments (supposed known) of the area about OX and OY respectively.

If m be the element of area surrounding P, we have

$$I_x = \Sigma my^2$$

and $$I_y = \Sigma mx^2$$

But $$x^2 + y^2 = r^2$$

$$\therefore \quad \Sigma mx^2 + \Sigma my^2 = \Sigma mr^2$$

Now, Σmr^2 is the M.I. of A about an axis through O perpendicular to the plane of the paper; call this I_z.

Hence $$I_x + I_y = I_z$$

i.e., knowing the moments about each of two perpendicular axes in a plane, adding them gives us the moment about an axis perpendicular to the plane through the intersection of the other two.

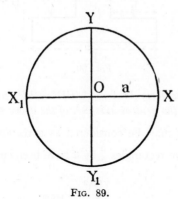

FIG. 89.

Example 1

The M.I. of a disc radius a about its axle is $\dfrac{Ma^2}{2}$.

This must be the sum of the moments about the two perpendicular diameters XOX_1, and YOY_1. But the M.I. about XOX_1, equals, by symmetry, the M.I. about YOY_1.

Hence the M.I. of a disc about a diameter $= \dfrac{Ma^2}{4}$, giving $k^2 = \dfrac{a^2}{4}$.

Similarly, it is easily seen that for a ring about a diameter

$$k^2 = \frac{a^2}{2}$$

where $a =$ its radius.

Example 2

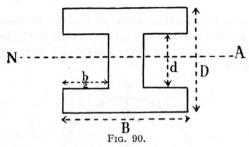

Fig. 90.

Establish the formula $I = \frac{1}{12}(BD^3 - bd^3)$ *for the second moment about the neutral axis* NA *of the above section.*

The section may be considered as a rectangle B by D from which two rectangles $\dfrac{b}{2}$ by d have been cut.

$$\text{M.I. of first} = BD \times \frac{\left(\dfrac{D}{2}\right)^2}{3} = \frac{BD^3}{12} \quad . \quad . \quad . \quad (1)$$

$$\text{M.I. of each of others} = \frac{bd}{2} \times \frac{\left(\dfrac{d}{2}\right)^2}{3} = \frac{bd^3}{24}$$

$$\therefore \ \text{M.I. of both} = \frac{bd^3}{12} \quad . \quad . \quad . \quad (2)$$

Take the difference between (1) and (2), and the result follows.

Other sections may be similarly treated.

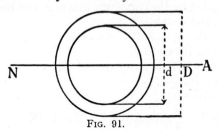

FIG. 91.

If the diagram above represents a section across a hollow shaft, its second moment about the neutral axis is the difference between the moments of the two circles whose diameters are given, *i.e.*,

$$I = \frac{\pi D^2}{4} \cdot \frac{\left(\frac{D}{2}\right)^2}{4} - \frac{\pi d^2}{4} \cdot \frac{\left(\frac{d}{2}\right)^2}{4}$$

$$= \frac{\pi}{64}(D^4 - d^4)$$

6. We now find the second moment of an area bounded by a curve whose equation is given.

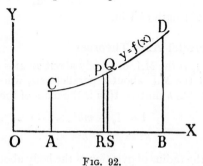

FIG. 92.

Suppose $y = f(x)$ is the equation of the curve CD.

Let OA $= a$ and OB $= b$.

Suppose we require the second moment about OX of the area bounded by the curve, the axis of x, and the ordinates at $x = a$, and $x = b$.

This is the area ABDC shown in the figure. Consider any strip on RS as base.

If OR $= x$, RP $= y = f(x)$, and RS $= dx$. Consider the strip as a rectangle.

Its area $= ydx$.

Its "k^2" $= \dfrac{y^2}{3}$, about RS, $i.e.$, about OX

$\therefore \dfrac{y^3dx}{3}$ is its second moment about OX.

$\therefore \displaystyle\int_a^b \dfrac{y^3dx}{3}$ is the second moment of the area.

Thus suppose the curve is given by $y = 2x^2$ and we require the second moment about OX of the area between the curve, the x-axis and the two ordinates at $x = 0$ and $x = 2$.

Using the above result, putting $2x^2$ for y we get

$$\text{second moment} = \int_0^2 \frac{(2x^2)^3}{3}dx = \frac{8}{3}\left[\frac{x^7}{7}\right]_0^2$$
$$= \frac{1024}{21} \text{ (ins.)}^4$$

if the unit of length $= 1$ in.

7. The Parallel Axis Theorem

Suppose I_g is the M.I. of a body about an axis through its C.G., and I the M.I. about a parallel axis, whose distance from the first is h units. If m is the mass of the body then

$$I = I_g + mh^2 \quad . \quad . \quad . \quad . \quad (1)$$
or
$$k^2 = k_g^2 + h^2 \quad . \quad . \quad . \quad . \quad (2)$$

where k is the radius of gyration of the body about any axis,

k_g the radius of gyration about a parallel axis through the C.G., and h the distance between the axes.

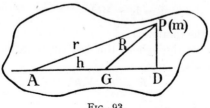

FIG. 93.

Suppose the axes are perpendicular to the paper through A and G, where G is the C.G. of the body, which for simplicity we will take as the area bounded by the wavy line in the diagram above.

P is any point of the area, and m a small element of it surrounding P.

Let PD be perpendicular to AG.

Let GD $= x$, and GA $= h$.

Using a well known geometrical theorem, we have

$$AP^2 = GP^2 + AG^2 + 2AG \cdot GD$$

i.e., $$r^2 = R^2 + h^2 + 2hx$$

$$\therefore \quad mr^2 = mR^2 + mh^2 + 2mhx$$

and $$\Sigma mr^2 = \Sigma mR^2 + \Sigma mh^2 + \Sigma 2mhx \quad . \quad . \quad (3)$$

if we sum for every element.

Notice that the last term on the right-hand side of (3)

$$= \Sigma 2mhx = 2h\Sigma mx,$$

since $2h$ is a constant and is a factor of every term of

$$\Sigma 2mhx.$$

But $\dfrac{\Sigma mx}{\Sigma m} =$ the x-coordinate of the C.G. of the area, referred to G as origin.

$$\therefore \quad \frac{\Sigma mx}{\Sigma m} = 0, \ i.e., \ \Sigma mx = 0. \quad \therefore \quad \Sigma 2mhx = 0.$$

Hence from (3)

$$\Sigma m r^2 = \Sigma m R^2 + h^2 \Sigma m$$

i.e., $$I = I_g + Mh^2$$

where M is the total area.

If we divide throughout this last equation by the total area, M, we get :

$$k^2 = k_g{}^2 + h^2.$$

Example 1

(1) *A rectangular section has sides 14 ins. by 6 ins. Find its second moment about an axis parallel to the side 6 ins., and 9 ins. from it.*

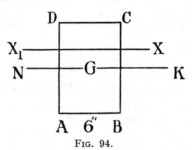

Fig. 94.

Let ABCD be the section.   AB = 6 ins., AD = 14 ins. NK is the axis through the C.G.

Let X_1X be a parallel axis, 2 ins. from NK.

For axis NK, $k_g{}^2 = \frac{49}{3}$ (ins.)².

Also $h = 2$, $\therefore$ $h^2 = 4$ (ins.)².

Hence if k be the radius of gyration about X_1X,

$$k^2 = k_g{}^2 + h^2$$
$$= (\tfrac{49}{3} + 4) \text{ (ins.}^2)$$
$$= \tfrac{61}{3} \text{ (ins.)}^2$$

$\therefore$ second moment $= 6 \times 14 \times \frac{61}{3}$ (ins.)⁴ $= 1708$ (ins.⁴).

Example 2

Find the M.I. of a circular disc of radius a and mass M about an axis through a point on its rim perpendicular to its plane.

We have $$k_g{}^2 = \frac{a^2}{2}$$

and $$h = a$$

$$\therefore \quad k^2 = \frac{a^2}{2} + a^2 = \frac{3a^2}{2}$$

Hence the required M.I. $= M \cdot \dfrac{3a^2}{2}$.

EXERCISE 45

1. Find from first principles the second moment of area (or M.I.) of a circular disc, radius r, about an axis through its centre perpendicular to its plane.

What is the value of the M.I. about an axis at right angles to its surface through a point on the circumference?
(U.L.C.I.)

2. The side of an equilateral triangular lamina ABC is 5·2 ins. Find the M.I. of the lamina (*a*) about the side AB, (*b*) about an axis through the centroid parallel to AB.
(U.L.C.I.)

3. Find the M.I. of a rectangle " b " by " d " about the side " b."

ABCD is a rectangle in which AB = 8 ins. and BC = 5 ins. AD and BC are produced to P and Q so that
$$DP = CQ = 3 \text{ ins.}$$
By applying your result to each of the rectangles ABQP, DCQP deduce the M.I. of rectangle ABCD about the line PQ.
(U.L.C.I.)

4. Find the M.I. of a cylinder, radius a, length l, (1) about its axis, (2) about a diameter of one end.
(U.L.C.I.)

5. The outside dimensions of an angle iron are 6 ins. by 6 ins. and the uniform thickness is $\frac{1}{2}$ in. Find the M.I. of the section about an axis passing through the centre of area and parallel to one of the legs.   (U.L.C.I.)

6. Find the M.I. of a square, side a, about a diagonal. Find also the M.I. about a parallel axis through one corner of the square.   (U.L.C.I.)

7. Deduce from first principles that the M.I. of a uniform right circular cone of radius r and mass M about the axis of line is given by $I = M \times \dfrac{3r^2}{10}$.   (U.L.C.I.)

8. The inside and outside diameters of a hollow cylinder are 10 ins. and 12 ins. respectively. Calculate the percentage error in taking the radius of gyration about the axis of the cylinder as the mean of the inside and outside radii. $\left(\text{Radius of gyration} = \sqrt{\dfrac{\text{M.I.}}{\text{mass}}}.\right)$

Establish any formula you use.   (U.E.I.)

9. Assuming that the moments of inertia about two perpendicular axes of an area are known, show how to find the M.I. about an axis perpendicular to the area and passing through the intersection of the former pair. Apply the result to a rectangle 10 ins. by 4 ins. when the axis passes through one corner, perpendicular to its plane.

(U.L.C.I.)

10. Prove from first principles that the M.I. of a triangle base b ins. height h ins. about the base is given by $\frac{1}{12}bh^3$ in in.⁴ units. Use the result to find the M.I. of a rectangle 8 ins. by 6 ins. about a diagonal.   (U.L.C.I.)

11. A beam section is of T shape. The flange is 6 ins. broad and 1 in. thick. The web projects 6 ins. from the flange and is 1 in. thick. Find the M.I. about an axis parallel to the flange and passing through the C.G.

12. Find the M.I. about an axis through its C.G. parallel to the side of length 5 ins., of a rectangular section with a

symmetrical rectangular cavity.   The dimensions of the outer rectangle are 8 ins. by 5 ins. and of the cavity 5 ins. by 3 ins.

13. Supposing the mass of a flywheel is concentrated in its rim, find its moment of inertia about its axle if the internal and external radii are 8 ins. and 12 ins. respectively, and its mass is 50 lb., the section of the rim being rectangular.

CHAPTER 14

THE EXPONENTIAL, HYPERBOLIC, AND LOGARITHMIC FUNCTIONS

1. The Exponential Function, e^x

Suppose that the following problem is proposed for solution :

" Find a function of x whose gradient at any point is equal to the value of the function at that point, and which is such that when $x = 0$, the function has the value unity."

If $y =$ the required function we have,

$$\frac{dy}{dx} = y \quad . \quad . \quad . \quad . \quad . \quad . \quad . \quad (1)$$

and $\qquad y = 1$ when $x = 0 \quad . \quad . \quad . \quad . \quad (2)$

Solution.

Suppose $\qquad y = 1 + a_1 x + \frac{a_2}{\lfloor 2} x^2 + \frac{a_3 x^3}{\lfloor 3} + \cdots \quad (3)$

where the series on the right-hand side of (3) proceeds indefinitely. Notice that condition (2) above is satisfied.

Differentiating both sides of (3), we get :

$$\frac{dy}{dx} = a_1 + a_2 x + \frac{a_3 x^2}{\lfloor 2} + \frac{a_4 x^3}{\lfloor 3} + \cdots \quad (4)$$

Condition (1) above makes (3) $\equiv$ (4).

i.e., $1 + a_1 x + \frac{a_2 x^2}{\lfloor 2} + \frac{a_3 x^3}{\lfloor 3} + \cdots$

$$\equiv a_1 + a_2 x + \frac{a_3 x^2}{\lfloor 2} + \frac{a_4 x^3}{\lfloor 3} + \cdots$$

266

These two series are identical.

$\therefore$ by equating coefficients of like powers of x we get :

$$1 = a_1$$
$$a_1 = a_2 = 1$$
$$\frac{a_2}{\lfloor 2} = \frac{a_3}{\lfloor 2}, \; i.e., \; a_2 = a_3 = 1$$

and so on.   Every a, no matter what its suffix may be, has the value 1.

Substituting these values in (3) we have :

$$y = 1 + x + \frac{x^2}{\lfloor 2} + \frac{x^3}{\lfloor 3} + \frac{x^4}{\lfloor 4} + \ldots \quad \cdot \quad \cdot \quad (5)$$

This is the function of x we set out to find.

Now in (5) write ax for x, and y_1 for y.

Then $y_1 = 1 + ax + \dfrac{a^2 x^2}{\lfloor 2} + \dfrac{a^3 x^3}{\lfloor 3} + \ldots \quad \cdot \quad \cdot \quad (5a)$

and $\dfrac{dy_1}{d(ax)} = y_1$, from (1)

Now $\dfrac{dy_1}{d(ax)} = y_1$, may be written $\dfrac{1}{a}\dfrac{dy_1}{dx} = y_1$

$i.e.,$ $$\frac{dy_1}{dx} = ay_1 \; . \quad \cdot \quad \cdot \quad \cdot \quad \cdot \quad \cdot \quad (6)$$

Also $$\frac{d}{dx}(y^n) = ny^{n-1}\frac{dy}{dx} = ny^n \quad \cdot \quad \cdot \quad \cdot \quad (7)$$

since $$\frac{dy}{dx} = y \; (\text{from (1)}).$$

Notice that (7) has the same form as (6) with y^n written for y_1 and n for a.

Make this substitution in (5a) :

then $\qquad y^n = 1 + nx + \dfrac{n^2x^2}{\lfloor 2} + \dfrac{n^3x^3}{\lfloor 3} + \cdots$

Now put $n = \dfrac{1}{x}$, so that

$$y^{\frac{1}{x}} = 1 + 1 + \frac{1}{\lfloor 2} + \frac{1}{\lfloor 3} + \cdots \quad . \quad . \quad (8)$$

The series on the right-hand side of (8) is denoted by e. Its value is indeterminate, but by an easy calculation is found to be 2·718 correct to three places.

From (8) then, we have :

$$y^{\frac{1}{x}} = e$$

$$\therefore \quad y = e^x = 1 + x + \frac{x^2}{\lfloor 2} + \frac{x^3}{\lfloor 3} + \cdots \quad . \quad (9)$$

This function of x is called the **Exponential function.** It may be generalised thus :

Noting that $a = e^{\log_e a}$, we get :

$$a^x = e^{\log_e a \cdot x} = 1 + x \log_e a + \frac{x^2}{\lfloor 2} (\log_e a)^2 + \cdots \quad (10)$$

The graph $y = e^{\pm x}$ is shown below.

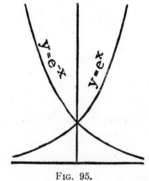

Fig. 95.

Summary

(1) $$e^x = 1 + x + \frac{x^2}{\lfloor 2} + \frac{x^3}{\lfloor 3} + \cdots$$

If $x = 1$, we get $e = 1 + 1 + \frac{1}{\lfloor 2} + \frac{1}{\lfloor 3} + \cdots = 2{\cdot}718 \ldots$

(2) if $$y = e^x$$
$$\frac{dy}{dx} = e^x$$

(3) if $$y = e^{ax}$$
$$\frac{dy}{dx} = \frac{dy}{d(ax)} \cdot \frac{d(ax)}{dx} = e^{ax} \cdot a = ae^{ax}.$$

Thus if $$y = e^{3x}$$
$$\frac{dy}{dx} = 3e^{3x}$$

Similarly if $$y = 6e^{-2x}$$
$$\frac{dy}{dx} = -12e^{-2x}$$

(4) $$a^x = e^{x \log_e a} = 1 + x \log_e a + \frac{x^2 (\log_e a)^2}{\lfloor 2} + \cdots$$

If $$y = 3^x = e^{x \log_e 3}$$
$$\frac{dy}{dx} = \log_e 3 \cdot e^{x \log_e 3} = 3^x \cdot \log_e 3.$$

Example 1

Differentiate $\qquad y = x^2 e^x.$
We have, by differentiating as a product.

$$\frac{dy}{dx} = 2x \cdot e^x + x^2 e^x$$
$$= e^x (2x + x^2).$$

Example 2

Differentiate $y = 3e^{2x} \sin x$.
We have :

$$\frac{dy}{dx} = 3(2e^{2x} \sin x + e^{2x} \cos x)$$
$$= 3e^{2x}(2 \sin x + \cos x).$$

Example 3

Find $\frac{d}{dx}(e^{-2x} \sin 3x)$.

Put $y = e^{-2x} \sin 3x$

then $\frac{dy}{dx} = -2e^{-2x} \sin 3x + 3e^{-2x} \cos 3x$
$$= e^{-2x}(3 \cos 3x - 2 \sin 3x)$$

Example 4

If $y = e^{ax}$, find y_2 and y_3 and deduce the value of y_n.

$$y = e^{ax}$$
$$y_1 = ae^{ax}$$
$$y_2 = a^2 e^{ax}$$
$$y_3 = a^3 e^{ax}$$

and $y_n = a^n e^{ax}$.

2. Integration of the Exponential Function.

We have found that if

$$y = e^x$$
$$dy = e^x dx.$$

Hence, reversing the process :

$$\int e^x dx = y = e^x + C.$$

adding the constant of integration.

The form of this result should be noted as

$$\int e^{(\ )} d(\ ) = e^{(\ )} + \text{const.}$$

Thus $\qquad \int e^{2x} dx = \frac{1}{2} \int e^{2x} d(2x) = \frac{e^{2x}}{2} + C.$

Similarly, in the general case,

$$\int e^{ax} dx = \frac{1}{a} \int e^{ax} d(ax) = \frac{e^{ax}}{a} + C$$

Thus $\qquad \int e^{-2x} dx = -\frac{e^{-2x}}{2} + C$

and $\qquad \int 3e^{-\frac{x}{2}} dx = -6e^{-\frac{x}{2}} + C.$

3. The Hyperbolic Functions cosh x and sinh x

These functions are defined below :

$$\cosh x = \frac{e^x + e^{-x}}{2} \quad \dots \quad (1)$$

and $\qquad \sinh x = \frac{e^x - e^{-x}}{2} \quad \dots \quad (2)$

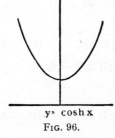

y = cosh x

FIG. 96.

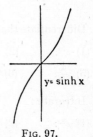

y = sinh x

FIG. 97.

By expanding e^x and e^{-x} we see that

$$\cosh x = 1 + \frac{x^2}{\underline{|2}} + \frac{x^4}{\underline{|4}} + \dots$$

and $\qquad \sinh x = x + \frac{x^3}{\underline{|3}} + \frac{x^5}{\underline{|5}} + \dots$

If $\qquad y = \cosh x, = \dfrac{e^x + e^{-x}}{2}$

$$\frac{dy}{dx} = \frac{e^x - e^{-x}}{2}$$

$$= \sinh x \quad . \quad . \quad . \quad . \quad . \quad (3)$$

and $\qquad \displaystyle\int \sinh x\,dx = \cosh x + C \quad . \quad . \quad . \quad (4)$

Similarly if $\qquad y = \sinh x = \dfrac{e^x - e^{-x}}{2}$

$$\frac{dy}{dx} = \frac{e^x + e^{-x}}{2} = \cosh x \quad . \quad . \quad (5)$$

and $\qquad \displaystyle\int \cosh x\,dx = \sinh x + C \quad . \quad . \quad . \quad (6)$

Also

$$\cosh^2 x - \sinh^2 x = \tfrac{1}{4}(e^x + e^{-x})^2 - \tfrac{1}{4}(e^x - e^{-x})^2$$
$$= \tfrac{1}{4}[(e^{2x} + 2 + e^{-2x}) - (e^{2x} - 2 + e^{-2x})]$$
$$= 1 \quad . \quad . \quad . \quad . \quad . \quad . \quad . \quad (7)$$

Notice the analogy between (7) and

$$\cos^2 x + \sin^2 x = 1.$$

EXERCISE 46

1. Differentiate the following :

   (1) e^{3x}.   (2) e^{-4x}.   (3) $3e^{\frac{x}{3}}$.   (4) $-4e^{-\frac{x}{4}}$.

   (5) $\dfrac{1}{e^{2x}}$.   (6) $\dfrac{5}{e^{4x}}$.   (7) $2e^{3x} - 4e^{-2x}$.

2. Integrate :

   (1) e^{2x}.   (2) e^{-4x}.   (3) $5e^{\frac{x}{4}}$.   (4) $-2e^{-3x}$.

3. Differentiate the following :

   (1) $x^2 e^x$.   (2) $3x^3 e^{2x}$.   (3) $x^{-2} e^{-4x}$.

   (4) $e^x \sin x$.   (5) $e^{3x} \cos 4x$.   (6) $k e^{ax} \sin bx$.

   (7) $e^{-2t} \cos 3t$.   (8) $\dfrac{e^{4x}}{x^3}$.   (9) $a e^{-kt} \sin (kt)$.

4. Differentiate :

    (1) $\cosh 3x$.   (2) $\sinh 4x$.   (3) $3 \cosh \frac{x}{3}$.

5. Differentiate :

    (1) $e^{\sin x}$.   (2) $e^{3 \sin 2x}$.   (3) $\dfrac{ax^2 + bx + c}{e^x}$.

6. Differentiate :

    (1) a^x.   (2) 3^x.   (3) 4^{2x}.   (4) 5^{-3x}.

7. (1) If $y = e^{3x}$, find y_5.   (2) If $y = e^{-2x}$, find y_6.

8. If $\dfrac{d^2y}{dx^2} - 7\dfrac{dy}{dx} + 12y = 0$, show that $y = Ae^{4x} + Be^{3x}$.

9. If $y = 2e^x + 3e^{-2x}$, find the value of $\dfrac{d^2y}{dx^2} + \dfrac{dy}{dx} - 2$.

10. The curve $y = c \cosh\dfrac{x}{c}$ is called the catenary. It is the form assumed when a uniform chain hangs between two fixed points.

Find the area between the curve, the x axis, and the ordinates $x = 0$, $x = a$.

11. A curve is represented by the equation $y = 2e^x - 3e^{-x}$. Find (1) the gradient where $x = 1$, and (2) the mean value of y over the range $x = 0$, to $x = 0.5$.   (U.L.C.I.)

12. Evaluate (1) $\displaystyle\int_0^1 e^{2x}\,dx$, (2) $\displaystyle\int_0^2 e^{-x}\,dx$.

4. The Logarithmic Function, $\log_e x$

If we put $y = \log_e x$ . . . . . (1)

we have $e^y = x$ . . . . . . (2)

Differentiating both sides of (2) with respect to y, we get

$$e^y = \frac{dx}{dy}$$

or, inverting, $\dfrac{dy}{dx} = \dfrac{1}{e^y}$

$$= \frac{1}{x} \text{ from (2)}.$$

Hence

$$\frac{d}{dx} \log_e x = \frac{1}{x} \quad . \quad . \quad . \quad . \quad . \quad . \quad (3)$$

This is an important result.

Similarly if
$$y = \log_e ax$$
$$= \log_e a + \log_e x$$

then
$$\frac{dy}{dx} = \frac{1}{x}$$

since $\log_e a$ is a constant, and its differential coefficient is zero.   The graph of $y = \log_e x$ is shown below.

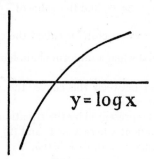

$$y = \log x$$

FIG. 98.

Example 1

$$y = \log_e 3x$$
$$\frac{dy}{dx} = \frac{1}{x}.$$

Example 2

If
$$y = \log_e (x^2 + x + 1), \text{ find } \frac{dy}{dx}.$$

Put
$$z = x^2 + x + 1$$

Then
$$y = \log_e z$$
$$\frac{dy}{dz} = \frac{1}{z}$$

But
$$\frac{dy}{dx} = \frac{dy}{dz} \cdot \frac{dz}{dx}$$

$$= \frac{1}{z} \cdot (2x + 1)$$

$$= \frac{2x + 1}{x^2 + x + 1}.$$

Example 3

Similarly if
$$y = \log_e (3 - x)$$

$$\frac{dy}{dx} = \frac{1}{3 - x} \cdot \frac{d}{dx}(3 - x)$$

$$= \frac{-1}{3 - x}.$$

Example 4

Find $\dfrac{d}{dx} \log_e \dfrac{x^2 - 4x + 3}{x^2 + 3x + 1}$.

Put
$$y = \log_e \frac{x^2 - 4x + 3}{x^2 + 3x + 1}$$

$$= \log_e (x^2 - 4x + 3) - \log_e (x^2 + 3x + 1)$$

$$\therefore \quad \frac{dy}{dx} = \frac{2x - 4}{x^2 - 4x + 3} - \frac{2x + 3}{x^2 + 3x + 1}$$

by differentiating as in Example 2.

Example 5

Find $\dfrac{d}{dx} \log_e y$.

If
$$z = \log_e y$$

$$\frac{dz}{dx} = \frac{1}{y} \cdot \frac{dy}{dx}$$

$$\therefore \quad \frac{d}{dx} \log_e y = \frac{1}{y} \frac{dy}{dx}$$

This result should be noted well.

Example 6

Differentiate $e^{2x} \log_e x$.

Put $$y = e^{2x} \log_e x \quad \text{(a product)}$$

then $$\frac{dy}{dx} = 2e^{2x} \log x + \frac{e^{2x}}{x}.$$

Example 7

Differentiate $$(5 + x)^x.$$

In this example notice that the index is a variable.

Put $$y = (5 + x)^x$$

Taking logs to base e, we get

$$\log_e y = x \log_e (5 + x) \quad . \quad . \quad . \quad . \quad . \quad (4)$$

$$\therefore \ \frac{1}{y} \cdot \frac{dy}{dx} = \log (5 + x) + \frac{x}{5 + x}.$$

$$\therefore \ \frac{dy}{dx} = (5 + x)^x \left[\log (5 + x) + \frac{x}{5 + x} \right]$$

Notice that the right-hand side of (4) is a product. The left-hand side is differentiated as in Example 5.

N.B.   If $$y = (5 + x)^n \text{ where } n \text{ is a constant,}$$
$$\frac{dy}{dx} = n(5 + x)^{n-1}.$$

Example 8

Differentiate $\log_{10} x$ with respect to x.

Put $$y = \log_{10} x = \frac{\log_e x}{\log_e 10} = 0\cdot4343 \log_e x$$

$$\therefore \ \frac{dy}{dx} = \frac{1}{x \cdot \log_e 10} = \frac{\log_{10} e}{x} = \frac{0\cdot4343}{x}.$$

5. Logarithmic Integrals

If $$y = \log_e x$$
$$dy = \frac{dx}{x}$$

Hence $$\int \frac{dx}{x} = y = \log_e x + C \quad . \quad . \quad . \quad . \quad . \quad (1)$$

The " form " of (1) should be noted thus

$$\int \frac{d(\quad)}{(\quad)} = \log_e (\quad) + C$$

or $\quad \int \frac{d(\text{denominator})}{\text{denominator}} = \log_e (\text{denominator}) + C.$

Example 1

$$\int \frac{3dx}{x + 4} = 3 \int \frac{dx}{x + 4}$$
$$= 3 \log_e (x + 4) + C$$

Since $\qquad dx = d(x + 4)$

Example 2

$$\int \frac{dx}{5 - x} = - \int \frac{d(5 - x)}{(5 - x)}$$
$$= - \log_e (5 - x) + C.$$

Example 3

$$\int \frac{xdx}{x^2 + 5} = \frac{1}{2} \int \frac{2xdx}{x^2 + 5}$$
$$= \tfrac{1}{2} \log (x^2 + 5) + C.$$

Notice the method of putting the integrand into the correct " form."

Example 4

$$\int \frac{(x + 2)dx}{x^2 + 4x + 1}$$
$$= \frac{1}{2} \int \frac{(2x + 4)dx}{x^2 + 4x + 1}$$
$$= \tfrac{1}{2} \log_e (x^2 + 4x + 1) + C.$$

Example 5

$$\int \cot \theta d\theta$$
$$= \int \frac{\cos \theta d\theta}{\sin \theta}$$
$$= \int \frac{d(\sin \theta)}{\sin \theta}$$
$$= \log_e \sin \theta + C.$$

Example 6

Similarly

$$\int \tan \theta \, d\theta$$

$$= \int \frac{\sin \theta \, d\theta}{\cos \theta}$$

$$= - \int \frac{d(\cos \theta)}{\cos \theta}$$

$$= - \log_e \cos \theta + C$$

$$= \log_e \sec \theta + C.$$

Example 7

$$\int \operatorname{cosec} \theta \, d\theta = \int \frac{d\theta}{\sin \theta}$$

$$= \int \frac{d\theta}{2 \sin \frac{\theta}{2} \cos \frac{\theta}{2}}$$

$$= \int \frac{\sec^2 \frac{\theta}{2} \cdot d\frac{\theta}{2}}{\tan \frac{\theta}{2}}$$

$$= \int \frac{d \tan \frac{\theta}{2}}{\tan \frac{\theta}{2}}$$

$$= \log_e \tan \frac{\theta}{2} + C.$$

We can readily prove that $\operatorname{cosec} \theta - \cot \theta = \tan \frac{\theta}{2}$.
Hence another form for the last result is

$$\int \operatorname{cosec} \theta \, d\theta = \log_e (\operatorname{cosec} \theta - \cot \theta) + C.$$

Example 8

Notice $\int \sec \theta \, d\theta = \int \frac{\sec \theta (\sec \theta + \tan \theta) \, d\theta}{\sec \theta + \tan \theta}$.

The numerator is seen to be the differential of the denominator.

Hence $\int \sec \theta d\theta = \log_e (\sec \theta + \tan \theta) + C.$

The last four results should be remembered.

Example 9

$$\int_0^1 \frac{dx}{4 + 3x} = \left[\tfrac{1}{3} \log (4 + 3x) \right]_0^1 = \tfrac{1}{3} \log_e \tfrac{7}{4}.$$

Example 10

$$\int_0^1 4e^x dx = \left[4e^x \right]_0^1 = 4(e - e^0) = 4(e - 1).$$

EXERCISE 47

1. Differentiate :

(1) $\log_e 3x.$ (2) $\log (5 - x).$ (3) $\log \left(\dfrac{x + 2}{x + 5} \right).$

(4) $\log (4 - 3x).$ (5) $\log \dfrac{x^2 + 3x}{x + 1}.$ (6) $\log \dfrac{5 - 4x^2}{3 + 5x^2}$

2. Differentiate :

(1) $x^2 \log x.$ (2) $3x^{-2} \log (x + 1).$

(3) $\sin x \log x.$ (4) $\dfrac{3 \log x}{x + 1}.$

(5) $e^{3x} \log x.$ (6) $3e^{-3x} \log (1 + x).$

(7) $\sin 3x \log (x^2 + x + 1).$ (8) $\tan x \log x.$

(9) $\log_{10} x.$ (10) $\log_{10} (3x^2 + x + 1).$

(11) $\log \sqrt[5]{x^2 + 1}.$ (12) $\log \dfrac{\sin x}{1 + \cos x}.$

(13) $\log \sqrt{\dfrac{1 + x}{1 - x}}.$

3. Integrate :

(1) $\dfrac{1}{x+2}$.

(2) $\dfrac{3}{2-x}$.

(3) $\dfrac{x}{x^2+1}$.

(4) $\dfrac{\cos x}{1+\sin x}$.

(5) $\dfrac{\sin x}{1+\cos x}$.

(6) $\dfrac{e^x}{3+e^x}$.

(7) $\dfrac{1}{3x+2}$.

(8) $\dfrac{5}{4-3x}$.

(9) $\dfrac{ax}{b+cx^2}$.

(10) $\dfrac{x+3}{x^2+6x+4}$.

(11) $\dfrac{x-1}{x^2-2x+4}$.

4. Explain what you understand by " a definite integral."
If $y = \dfrac{3}{x} + 7x^{\frac{1}{2}}$, find the value of $\int_a^b y\,dx$.   (U.L.C.I.)

5. Evaluate :

(1) $\displaystyle\int_0^1 \dfrac{dx}{x+3}$.

(2) $\displaystyle\int_0^2 \dfrac{3\,dx}{5-2x}$.

(3) $\displaystyle\int_{-1}^2 \dfrac{dx}{4+x}$.

(4) $\displaystyle\int_0^{\frac{\pi}{2}} \dfrac{\cos x\,dx}{1+\sin x}$.

(5) $\displaystyle\int_0^1 \dfrac{(x+3)\,dx}{x^2+6x+4}$.

CHAPTER 15

SOME STANDARD METHODS OF INTEGRATION

1. Success in evaluating a given integral depends largely on the student's knowledge of the standard integrals, and any unfamiliar integral must be reduced to one of the standard forms.

In this chapter we describe some of the methods used to reduce the unfamiliar integrals to those of a more familiar form.

2. Integration by Substitution

In using this method we introduce a new variable, and the procedure adopted will be clear from the examples which follow :

Example 1

Evaluate,
$$I = \int \frac{x\,dx}{\sqrt{x+5}}.$$

Put
$$\sqrt{x+5} = y$$

i.e.,
$$x + 5 = y^2$$
$$\therefore \quad x = y^2 - 5$$

and
$$dx = 2y\,dy.$$

Hence
$$I = \int \frac{(y^2 - 5)2y\,dy}{y}$$
$$= \int (y^2 - 5)2\,dy$$
$$= \frac{2y^3}{3} - 10y + C$$
$$= \tfrac{2}{3}(x+5)^{\frac{3}{2}} - 10(x+5)^{\frac{1}{2}} + C.$$

Example 2

$$I = \int \frac{x^2 dx}{6 + x^3}.$$

Notice that the numerator is $\frac{1}{3}d(6 + x^3)$, or formally, put

$$6 + x^3 = z$$
$$\therefore \quad 3x^2 dx = dz$$
$$x^2 dx = \tfrac{1}{3}dz$$
$$\therefore \quad I = \frac{1}{3} \int \frac{dz}{z} = \frac{1}{3} \log z = \frac{1}{3} \log (6 + x^3) + C.$$

Example 3

$$I = \int sin^3 \theta \cos \theta d\theta.$$

Notice that $\quad \cos \theta d\theta = d(\sin \theta)$

If $\quad\quad\quad \sin \theta = x$

$$\cos \theta d\theta = dx$$
$$\therefore \quad\quad I = \int x^3 dx = \frac{x^4}{4} + C$$
$$= \frac{\sin^4 \theta}{4} + C.$$

Example 4

$$I = \int \frac{dx}{\sqrt{a^2 - x^2}}$$

Put $\quad\quad x = a \sin \theta$
$$dx = a \cos \theta d\theta$$
$$I = \int \frac{a \cos \theta d\theta}{\sqrt{a^2 - a^2 \sin^2 \theta}}$$
$$= \int \frac{a \cos \theta d\theta}{a \cos \theta} = \int d\theta = \theta + C.$$
$$\therefore \quad I = \sin^{-1} \frac{x}{a} + C$$

i.e., $\quad\quad \int \frac{dx}{\sqrt{a^2 - x^2}} = \sin^{-1} \frac{x}{a} + C$

This result should be memorised as it is standard. It should be observed that in order to obtain it, we made use of a substitution which rationalised the denominator of the integrand.

Many integrals can be reduced to the above form.

Example 5

$$I = \int \frac{dx}{\sqrt{3 - 2x - x^2}}$$

" Completing the square," we get :

$$I = \int \frac{d(x + 1)}{\sqrt{4 - (x + 1)^2}}$$

$$= sin^{-1} \frac{x + 1}{2} + C.$$

Example 6

$$I = \int \frac{dx}{a^2 + x^2}$$

Let $\qquad x = a \tan \theta \qquad . \quad . \quad . \quad . \quad . \quad \langle 1 \rangle$

$$\therefore \quad dx = a \sec^2 \theta d\theta.$$

Denominator $= a^2(1 + \tan^2 \theta) = a^2 \sec^2 \theta.$

$$\therefore \quad I = \int \frac{a \sec^2 \theta d\theta}{a^2 \sec^2 \theta} = \int \frac{d\theta}{a}$$

$$= \frac{\theta}{a} + C.$$

But from (1) $\qquad \theta = \tan^{-1} \frac{x}{a}$

$$\therefore \quad \int \frac{dx}{a^2 + x^2} = \frac{1}{a} \tan^{-1} \frac{x}{a} + C$$

This is another standard form to which many integrals can be reduced

Example 7

$$I = \int \frac{dx}{2 + 2x + x^2}$$

$$= \int \frac{dx}{1 + (x + 1)^2}$$

$$= \tan^{-1} (x + 1) + C.$$

Example 8

$$I = \int \frac{dx}{2x^2 + 4x + \frac{9}{2}}$$

$$= \frac{1}{2} \int \frac{dx}{x^2 + 2x + \frac{9}{4}}$$

$$= \frac{1}{2} \int \frac{dx}{(x + 1)^2 + \frac{5}{4}}$$

$$\left(\text{Here,} \qquad a = \frac{\sqrt{5}}{2}\right)$$

$$\therefore \quad I = \frac{1}{\sqrt{5}} \tan^{-1} \frac{2(x + 1)}{\sqrt{5}} + C.$$

3. The Intergration of Products Involving Multiples of θ

Products such as $\sin 2\theta \cos 3\theta$, $\sin 3\theta \sin 4\theta$, or $\cos 5\theta \cos \theta$ are simply integrated by employing the trigonometrical transformations proved on p. 169.

Example 1

Thus $\qquad 2 \cos 3\theta \sin 2\theta = \sin 5\theta - \sin \theta$

Hence $\qquad \int \cos 3\theta \sin 2\theta \, d\theta = \frac{1}{2} \int (\sin 5\theta - \sin \theta) d\theta$

$$= -\frac{1}{2}\left[\frac{\cos 5\theta}{5} - \cos \theta\right] + C.$$

Example 2

Evaluate $\qquad \int \sin 4\theta \sin 3\theta \, d\theta.$

We have

$$2 \sin 4\theta \sin 3\theta = \cos \theta - \cos 7\theta$$

$$\therefore \quad \int \sin 4\theta \sin 3\theta \, d\theta = \frac{1}{2} \int (\cos \theta - \cos 7\theta) d\theta$$

$$= \frac{1}{2}\left(\sin \theta - \frac{\sin 7\theta}{7}\right) + C.$$

EXERCISE 48

1. Integrate the following :

(1) $\dfrac{1}{\sqrt{x+3}}.$ (2) $\dfrac{1}{\sqrt{5-x}}.$ (3) $\dfrac{a}{\sqrt{b+cx}}.$

2. First reduce the following expressions by division and then integrate each :

(1) $\dfrac{x}{x+4}.$ (2) $\dfrac{x^2}{x-4}.$ (3) $\dfrac{2x}{x+3}.$ (4) $\dfrac{x}{2x+3}.$

3. Integrate :

(1) $\dfrac{1}{\sqrt{4-x^2}}.$ (2) $\dfrac{1}{\sqrt{2-x^2}}.$ (3) $\dfrac{1}{\sqrt{8-2x^2}}.$

(4) $\dfrac{1}{\sqrt{8-2x-x^2}}.$ (5) $\dfrac{1}{\sqrt{12-4x-x^2}}.$ (6) $\dfrac{1}{\sqrt{8-4x-2x^2}}.$

4. Integrate :

(1) $\dfrac{1}{1+x^2}.$ (2) $\dfrac{3}{4+x^2}.$ (3) $\dfrac{1}{8+2x^2}.$

(4) $\dfrac{1}{x^2+2x+5}.$ (5) $\dfrac{1}{x^2-4x+8}.$

(6) $\dfrac{1}{2x^2+6x+20}.$ (7) $\dfrac{1}{3x^2+9x+9}.$

5. Integrate :

(1) $\sin 2\theta \cos 4\theta.$ (2) $\cos 5x \sin 3x.$ (3) $2 \sin 4t \cos 2t.$
(4) $2 \sin 5t \sin 3t.$ (5) $\cos 6x \cos 2x.$ (6) $2 \sin \tfrac{1}{2}t \cos t.$

6. Integrate :

(1) $\sin^3 \theta \cos \theta.$ (2) $\dfrac{\sin \theta}{\cos^3 \theta}.$ (3) $\cos^4 x \sin x.$

(4) $\tan^3 \theta \sec^2 \theta.$ (5) $\sin \theta (\cos^3 \theta + 1).$

4. The Use of Partial Fractions in Integration

The addition of a given number of fractions can be readily performed. Thus :

$$\frac{2}{x} + \frac{3}{x+5} = \frac{5x+10}{x(x+5)}.$$

The problem of partial fractions is to start with an expression like $\frac{5x+10}{x(x+5)}$ and to find its constituent fractions. These are called partial fractions.

Thus $\frac{2}{x}$ and $\frac{3}{x+5}$ are the partial fractions of $\frac{5x+10}{x(x+5)}$. We deal below with one case which is useful to the student at this stage of his work.

Case I. When the denominator of the given fraction contains factors of the first degree only.

Example 1

Put $\frac{3x+1}{(x+4)(x+5)}$ *into partial fractions.*

Observe that the numerator of the given fraction is of lower degree than the denominator.

Let
$$\frac{3x+1}{(x+4)(x+5)} \equiv \frac{A}{x+4} + \frac{B}{x+5}$$
$$\equiv \frac{A(x+5) + B(x+4)}{(x+4)(x+5)}.$$

The numerators on both sides must be identical, since the denominators are the same

$$\therefore \quad 3x + 1 \equiv A(x+5) + B(x+4) \quad . \quad . \quad (1)$$

There are two ways of finding A and B from (1).

First Method.

Since (1) is an identity, it is true for all values of *x*.

Put $\qquad\qquad x = -4$

Then $\qquad -12 + 1 = A(-4 + 5) + 0$

giving $\qquad\qquad A = -11$

Then put $\qquad\quad x = -5$

Then $\qquad\qquad -14 = -B$

$$\therefore \quad B = 14.$$

Second Method.

(1) may be written

$$3x + 1 \equiv x(A + B) + 5A + 4B$$

$$\therefore \quad \left.\begin{array}{l} A + B = 3 \\ 5A + 4B = 1 \end{array}\right\}$$

Solving these we get $A = -11, B = 14$ as before.

Example 2

Put $\dfrac{1}{x(x - 2)}$ *into partial fractions.*

$$\frac{1}{x(x - 2)} \equiv \frac{A}{x} + \frac{B}{x - 2}.$$

Equating numerators we get :

$$1 \equiv A(x - 2) + Bx$$

Put $x = 0$, and get $A = -\frac{1}{2}$.

Put $x = 2$, and get $B = \frac{1}{2}$.

Hence $\qquad \dfrac{1}{x(x - 2)} = -\dfrac{1}{2} \cdot \dfrac{1}{x} + \dfrac{1}{2} \cdot \dfrac{1}{x - 2}.$

Example 3

Evaluate $\qquad I = \displaystyle\int \frac{(3x + 1)dx}{(x + 4)(x + 5)}.$

Put $\dfrac{3x + 1}{(x + 4)(x + 5)}$ into partial fractions; this has been done in Example 1.

$$\frac{3x+1}{(x+4)(x+5)} = \frac{-11}{x+4} + \frac{14}{x+5}$$

$$\therefore \quad I = -11\int \frac{dx}{x+4} + 14\int \frac{dx}{x+5}$$

$$= -11\log(x+4) + 14\log(x+5) + C.$$

Example 4

Find $\qquad I = \int \frac{dx}{x(x-2)}.$

Using the result of Example 2 above,

$$I = -\frac{1}{2}\int \frac{dx}{x} + \frac{1}{2}\int \frac{dx}{x-2}$$

$$= -\tfrac{1}{2}\log x + \tfrac{1}{2}\log(x-2) + C.$$

$$= \log \sqrt{\frac{x-2}{x}} + C.$$

Example 5

Find $\qquad \int \frac{dx}{x^2 - a^2}.$

We have

$$\frac{1}{x^2 - a^2} = \frac{1}{2a}\left[\frac{1}{x-a} - \frac{1}{x+a}\right]$$

$$\therefore \quad \int \frac{dx}{x^2 - a^2} = \frac{1}{2a}\int \left(\frac{1}{x-a} - \frac{1}{x+a}\right)dx$$

$$= \frac{1}{2a}\log \frac{x-a}{x+a} + C.$$

This is a standard form, and should be remembered.
Many examples can be reduced to the above form, *e.g.*

Example 6

Find $\qquad \int \frac{dx}{x^2 + 2x - 3}$

$$I = \int \frac{dx}{(x+1)^2 - 4} = \frac{1}{4}\log \frac{x-1}{x+3} + C.$$

Example 7

$$I = \int \frac{dx}{x^2 + x - 4}$$

$$= \int \frac{dx}{(x + \frac{1}{2})^2 - \frac{17}{4}}$$

$$= \frac{1}{\sqrt{17}} \log \frac{x + \frac{1}{2} - \frac{\sqrt{17}}{2}}{x + \frac{1}{2} + \frac{\sqrt{17}}{2}} + C.$$

The logs in these examples are to base e.

EXERCISE 49

1. Put the following into partial fractions, and then find the integrals :

(1) $\dfrac{2x}{x^2 - 1}$.   (2) $\dfrac{2x - 3}{x^2 - 5x + 6}$.   (3) $\dfrac{2x + 3}{x^2 + x - 30}$.

(4) $\dfrac{x}{x^2 - 9}$.   (5) $\dfrac{x + 1}{3x^2 - x - 2}$.   (6) $\dfrac{2x + 1}{x^2 - 5x + 4}$.

(7) $\dfrac{4}{x(x + 2)}$.   (8) $\dfrac{1}{3x(x + 2)}$.   (9) $\dfrac{3x + 1}{(x+6)(x+1)}$.

2. Find the integrals of the following functions :

(1) $\dfrac{1}{x^2 + x - \frac{1}{2}}$.   (2) $\dfrac{1}{x^2 + 2x - 8}$.   (3) $\dfrac{1}{x^2 + 3x + 1}$.

(4) $\dfrac{1}{x^2 + 4x + 1}$.   (5) $\dfrac{1}{2t^2 + 4t + 1}$.

5. Integration by Parts

This is a method of integration which readily evaluates certain types of integrals.

Suppose u and v are two functions of x.

Then $\dfrac{d}{dx}(uv) = u\dfrac{dv}{dx} + v\dfrac{du}{dx}$

T

or using differentials

$$d(uv) = udv + vdu$$
$$\therefore \quad udv = d(uv) - vdu \quad . \quad . \quad . \quad . \quad (1)$$

Integrating (1), we have :

$$\int udv = uv - \int vdu \quad . \quad . \quad . \quad . \quad (2)$$

The form (2) should be remembered in words, after first noting that the left-hand side $\int udv$ is the integral of the product if two functions of x ;

For $\int udv = \int u \cdot \dfrac{dv}{dx} \cdot dx$; both u and $\dfrac{dv}{dx}$ are functions of x.

Hence, in words (2) becomes :

" The integral of a product = first function $\times$ the integral of the second—the integral of (D.C. first $\times$ integral of second)."

It might appear from formula (2) that the integral on the right-hand side is just as difficult to evaluate as the one on the left. In many cases, by a careful choice of our first function, this is found not to be the case.

Example 1

Evaluate $\qquad\qquad \int xe^x dx.$

Take x as the " first " function, and e^x as second

$$\int xe^x dx = xe^x - \int e^x dx$$
$$= xe^x - e^x + \mathrm{C}$$
$$= e^x(x - 1) + \mathrm{C}.$$

Example 2

Find $\qquad\qquad \int x^2 e^{2x} dx$

$$\int x^2 e^{2x} dx = x^2 \cdot \frac{e^{2x}}{2} - \int 2x \cdot \frac{e^{2x}}{2} dx$$

$$= x^2 \frac{e^{2x}}{2} - \int x e^{2x} dx$$

$$= x^2 \frac{e^{2x}}{2} - \left[x \cdot \frac{e^{2x}}{2} - \int \frac{e^{2x}}{2} dx \right]$$

(Notice a second application of the formula.)

$$= x^2 \frac{e^{2x}}{2} - x \frac{e^{2x}}{2} + \frac{e^{2x}}{4} + C$$

$$= \frac{e^{2x}}{4} (2x^2 - 2x + 1) + C.$$

Example 3

Find $\quad \int x^3 \log_e x dx.$

Take $\log_e x$ as the " first " function

$$\int \log_e x \cdot x^3 \, dx = \log_e x \cdot \frac{x^4}{4} - \int \frac{1}{x} \cdot \frac{x^4}{4} dx$$

$$= \log_e x \cdot \frac{x^4}{4} - \frac{1}{4} \int x^3 dx$$

$$= \log_e x \cdot \frac{x^4}{4} - \frac{x^4}{16} + C$$

$$= \frac{x^4}{16} (4 \log_e x - 1) + C$$

Example 4

Evaluate $\quad \int x^2 \sin 2x dx.$

Take x^2 as the " first " function and apply the formula twice.

$$\int x^2 \sin 2x dx = x^2 \frac{(- \cos 2x)}{2} - \int \frac{2x \cdot (- \cos 2x)}{2} dx$$

$$= -\frac{x^2}{2} \cos 2x + \int x \cos 2x dx$$

$$= -\frac{x^2}{2} \cos 2x + \left[x \frac{\sin 2x}{2} - \int \frac{\sin 2x}{2} dx \right]$$

$$= -\frac{x^2}{2} \cos 2x + x \frac{\sin 2x}{2} + \frac{\cos 2x}{4} + C.$$

Example 5

Find $\qquad\qquad \int e^x \cos x\, dx.$

In this type of example neither function can be simplified either by differentiation or integration. The formula must be applied twice, and either function may be taken as the " first "; but, when the choice has been made, it must be retained in both applications of the formula. Notice that we return to the original integral.

Put $\qquad I = \int e^x \cos x\, dx.$

Then, taking e^x as " first " function

$$I = e^x \sin x - \int e^x \sin x\, dx$$

$$= e^x \sin x - \left[e^x(- \cos x) - \int e^x(- \cos x)dx \right]$$

$$= e^x \sin x + [e^x \cos x - I]$$

$$= e^x \sin x + e^x \cos x - I$$

Now bring I over to the left-hand side, we get :

$$2I = e^x \sin x + e^x \cos x$$

$$\therefore \quad I = \frac{e^x}{2} (\sin x + \cos x) + C.$$

Example 6

$$I = \int e^{-2x} \sin 3x\, dx.$$

Take e^{-2x} as the " first " function.

$$I = e^{-2x} \cdot \frac{(- \cos 3x)}{3} - \int (- 2e^{-2x}) \frac{(- \cos 3x)}{3} dx$$

$$= -\frac{e^{-2x}}{3} \cos 3x - \frac{2}{3} \int e^{-2x} \cos 3x\, dx$$

$$= -\frac{e^{-2x}}{3} \cos 3x - \frac{2}{3} \left[e^{-2x} \frac{\sin 3x}{3} - \int - 2e^{-2x} \frac{\sin 3x}{3} dx \right]$$

$$= -\frac{e^{-2x} \cos 3x}{3} - \frac{2}{9} e^{-2x} \sin 3x - \frac{4}{9} I$$

Hence $\dfrac{13}{9} I = - \dfrac{e^{-2x}}{9} [3 \cos 3x + 2 \sin 3x]$

∴ $I = - \dfrac{e^{-2x}}{13} (3 \cos 3x + 2 \sin 3x) + C.$

EXERCISE 50

1. Integrate the following by " parts " :

(1) xe^x.   (2) $x^2 e^x$.   (3) $x^2 e^{2x}$.

(4) xe^{-2x}.   (5) $x^2 e^{-3x}$.

2. Integrate :

(1) $x \sin x$.   (2) $x \cos x$.   (3) $x^2 \sin x$.

(4) $x^3 \sin 2x$.   (5) $x \cos \frac{1}{2}x$.   (6) $x^2 \cos x$.

3. Integrate the following (take $\log x$ as " first ") :

(1) $x^2 \log x$.   (2) $x^{-3} \log x$.   (3) $\dfrac{\log x}{x}$.

4. Integrate :

(1) $e^x \sin x$.   (2) $e^x \cos x$.   (3) $e^{2x} \sin x$.

(4) $e^{-2x} \sin x$.   (5) $e^{3x} \sin 2x$.   (6) $e^{4x} \cos 2x$.

(7) $e^{-x} \cos 3x$.   (8) $e^{-2x} \sin 3x$.

5. Integrate :

(1) $e^{ax} \cos bx$.   (2) $e^{ax} \sin bx$.

Observe that all the examples in 4 above are included in these two types.

CHAPTER 16

GRAPHS OF TRIGONOMETRICAL FUNCTIONS, AND THE GRAPHIC SOLUTION OF TRIGONOMETRICAL EQUATIONS

1. The Graphical Solution of Equations Involving Trigonometrical Functions

Example 1

Solve $\quad cos\,(x + 30) = \frac{1}{2}\,sin\,x.$

where angles are measured in degrees.

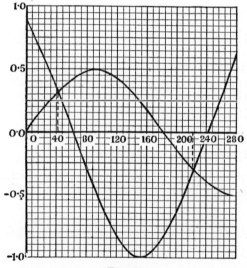

Fig. 99.

$x = 41°$ and $221°$ (nearly).

Construct the table below.

x	0	20	40	60	80	100	120	140	160	180
$\cos(x + 30)$	0·87	0·64	0·34	0	−0·34	−0·64	−0·87	−0·98	−0·98	−0·87
$\frac{1}{2}\sin x$	0	0·17	0·32	0·43	0·49	0·49	0·43	0·32	0·17	0

In making the table, observe that the values of $\cos(x + 30)$ repeat themselves in reverse order starting from $x = 160°$ to $x = 360°$.

Similarly, when we have found $\frac{1}{2}\sin x$ from $x = 0°$ to $x = 80°$, the values are reversed to $x = 180°$. From $180°$ to $360°$, the values of $\frac{1}{2}\sin x$ are negative, but the same numerically as from $0°$ to $180°$.

Take 5 squares along OX to represent $40°$.
      10   ,,   ,,   OY ,,   ,,   0·5.

Now plot $y = \cos(x + 30)$ ⎱
and $y = \frac{1}{2}\sin x$. ⎰ Fig. 99.
The abscissæ of the intersections give the roots.

Example 2

Tabulate values of $2\cos x° + 3\sin x°$ at intervals of $10°$; then solve graphically $2\cos x° + 3\sin x° = 3·5$.

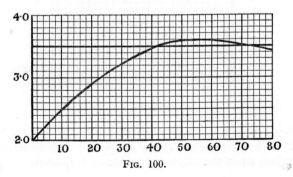

Fig. 100.

x	0°	10°	20°	30°	40°	50°	60°	70°	80°
$2 \cos x$	2	1·969	1·879	1·732	1·532	1·286	1·0	0·684	0·347
$3 \sin x$	0	0·521	1·026	1·5	1·928	2·298	2·598	2·819	2·954
$2 \cos x + 3 \sin x$	2	2·490	2·905	3·232	3·460	3·584	3·598	3·503	3·301

To solve the equation plot

$$y = 2 \cos x + 3 \sin x \quad . \quad . \quad . \quad (1)$$
and
$$y = 3 \cdot 5 \quad . \quad . \quad . \quad . \quad . \quad (2)$$

It will be seen that (1) cuts (2) very close to the values $x = 42°$ and $x = 70°$. To get a more accurate value for the root near 42°, make the following table.

x	41°	43°
$2 \cos x$	1·5094	1·4628
$3 \sin x$	1·9683	2·0460
$2 \cos x + 3 \sin x$	3·4777	3·5088

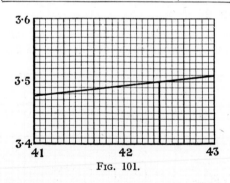

Fig. 101.

From the graph, a more accurate solution is $x = 42° \, 24'$.

2. It is often necessary to graph the trigonometrical functions when the angles are measured in radians.

It is, of course, always possible to change from degrees to radians or from radians to degrees.

Example 1

Plot $y = \sin \theta$ (θ in radians).

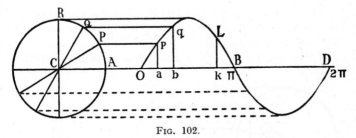

Fig. 102.

Draw a circle, any size, and call its radius one unit of length. C is its centre. Divide the four right angles round C into any number of equal parts—12 in the figure. Each angle is thus $\frac{\pi}{6}$.

Produce the diameter CA indefinitely. Take any point O as origin, and take any convenient length, OB to represent π radians (*i.e.*, two right angles).

Notice, that we may be using different horizontal and vertical scales.

Divide OB into six equal parts. One of these Oa is shown, and Oa represents $\frac{\pi}{6}$. Erect the perpendicular ap, where Pp has been drawn parallel to the diameter CA.

It is clear that $pa = \text{CP} \sin \text{ACP}$

$$= \sin \frac{\pi}{6}, \text{ since CP} = \text{unity.}$$

Similarly $qb = \sin 2\frac{\pi}{6}$,

where $Ob = \frac{1}{3}OB$.

Proceeding in this way all round the circle we get the curve in Fig. 102.

The part from B to D repeats that from O to B on the other side of the axis OBD.

The wave form clearly repeats itself to the right of D, and to the left of O.

The greatest height above OB is called the amplitude of the wave, whilst the horizontal length OD, of the *complete* wave is called the period.

3. The general form $y = a \sin (n\theta + \alpha)$ is now readily plotted.

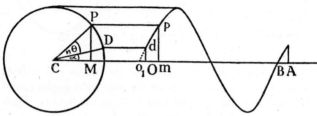

Fig. 103.

The amplitude $= a =$ radius of the circle.

The period $= \dfrac{2\pi}{n} = $ OA, measured on any convenient scale, using O as origin.

Corresponding to any angle DOP $= n\theta$ measure O$m = \theta$ (to scale).

Then PM $= pm = a \sin (n\theta + \alpha)$.

The whole curve may now be plotted by taking any number of convenient points round the circle.

Since $a \sin (n\theta + \alpha) = a \sin n\left(\theta + \dfrac{\alpha}{n}\right) = \alpha \sin nx$

where $$x = \theta + \dfrac{\alpha}{n},$$

if O_1 be taken to the left of O so that $OO_1 = \dfrac{\alpha}{n}$ (to scale), we get the same curve by plotting $y = a \sin nx$, using O_1 as origin; or what is the same thing, plot $y = a \sin z$, where abscissæ are measured from O_1, and corresponding to $z = \widehat{MCP}$, take $O_1 m = \dfrac{z}{n}$ to scale. The plotting is thus reduced to that of the preceding paragraph.

4. Since $$\cos \theta = \sin\left(\theta + \frac{\pi}{2}\right)$$

then, $$a \cos(n\theta + \alpha) = a \sin\left(n\theta + \frac{\pi}{2} + \alpha\right).$$

We thus take an origin O_1, $\dfrac{1}{n}\left(\alpha + \dfrac{\pi}{2}\right)$ units to the left of O and plot $y = \sin z$, where the abscissa corresponding to any angle z is $\dfrac{z}{n}$.

Example 1

Plot $$y = 3 \cdot 5 \cos\left(\frac{5\pi}{6} - 4\theta\right)$$
$$= 3 \cdot 5 \sin\left(4\theta - \frac{\pi}{3}\right)$$

using the complement of $\dfrac{5\pi}{6} - 4\theta$.

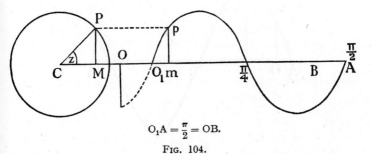

$$O_1 A = \frac{\pi}{2} = OB.$$

FIG. 104.

We plot $y = 3{\cdot}5 \sin z$, using O_1 as origin where $OO_1 = \dfrac{\pi}{12}$, measured to the *right*.

The period $= \dfrac{\pi}{2}$. Radius of circle is $3{\cdot}5$ units.

Corresponding to the angle z, measure $O_1m = \dfrac{z}{4}$, and proceed similarly for all angles round the circle.

Example 2

Put $4 \sin \theta + 3 \cos \theta$ *in the form* $R \sin (\theta + \alpha)$ *where* R *and* α *are known. Then plot the function.*

Put $\qquad\qquad\qquad R \cos \alpha = 4$
and $\qquad\qquad\qquad R \sin \alpha = 3$
So that $\qquad\qquad\qquad R = \sqrt{4^2 + 3^2} = 5$
and $\qquad\qquad\qquad \tan \alpha = 0{\cdot}75.$

$$\alpha = 36° \, 52'$$
$$= 0{\cdot}64 \text{ radians (nearly)}.$$

Now plot

$$y = 5 \sin (\theta + 0{\cdot}64).$$

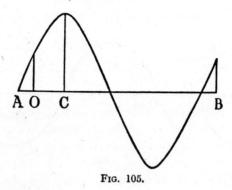

Fig. 105.

If OA = 0·64, we could get the curve by plotting
$$y = 5 \sin x,$$
using A as origin.   The amplitude is 5, and AC = $\dfrac{\pi}{2}$.

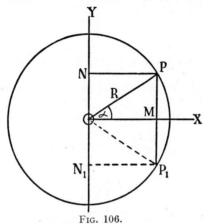

Fig. 106.

5. The method of graphing used in the preceding paragraphs is sometimes called the " crank " method, the radius of the circle becoming the " representative crank."

For such functions as $4 \sin \theta + 3 \cos \theta$ (see Example 2, par. 4) we could construct the representative crank.

On OX make OM = 4 units.

On OY make ON = 3 units, and complete the rectangle MONP.

If
$$\widehat{MOP} = \alpha$$
$$R \cos \alpha = 4$$
$$R \sin \alpha = 3$$

∴ $R^2 = 25$, and $\tan \alpha = \frac{3}{4}$, and $\alpha = 0·64$ radians.

Hence
$$4 \sin \theta + 3 \cos \theta$$
$$= R \cos \alpha \sin \theta + R \sin \alpha \cos \theta$$
$$= R \sin (\theta + \alpha)$$
$$= 5 \sin (\theta + 0·64).$$

This is simply $5 \sin x$ with the origin A, Fig. 105 taken 0·64 unit to the left of O.

To plot $4 \sin \theta - 3 \cos \theta$, measure $ON_1 = ON$ along the negative sense of OY. Then OP_1 is the initial position of the crank.

6. To graph

$$y = 3 \sin (\theta + \alpha) + 2 \cos (\theta + \beta) \quad . \quad . \quad (1)$$

We employ a method similar to that employed in the last paragraph.

Expanding $\sin (\theta + \alpha)$ and $\cos (\theta + \beta)$, (1) may be written :

$$y = \sin \theta (3 \cos \alpha - 2 \sin \beta)$$
$$+ \cos \theta (3 \sin \alpha + 2 \cos \beta) \quad . \quad . \quad (2)$$

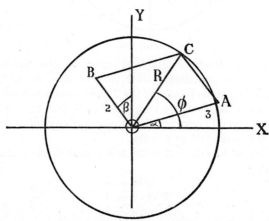

Fig. 107.

Take $OA = 3$ units, making α with OX, and $OB = 2$ units making β with OY. Complete the parallelogram AOBC.

If OC = R, and XOC = ϕ,

R cos ϕ = sum of projections of OA and AC on the x-axis.

      = ,,   ,,   ,, OA ,, OB ,,   ,,

      = 3 cos α − 2 sin β.

Similarly, projecting OC on the y-axis

$$R \sin \phi = 3 \sin \alpha + 2 \cos \beta.$$

Hence (2) becomes

$$\begin{aligned} y &= R \cos \phi \sin \theta + R \sin \phi \cos \theta \\ &= R \sin (\theta + \phi) \end{aligned} \quad . \quad . \quad . \quad . \quad (3)$$

Read R and ϕ from the diagram, and plot, using the circle shown.

If we had to plot

$$y = 3 \sin (\theta + \alpha) - 2 \cos (\theta - \beta)$$

measure OA and α, as before; then measure OB 2 units down and rotate OB clockwise through an angle β. Complete the parallelogram OACB as before and OC is the initial position of the crank.   Fig. 108.

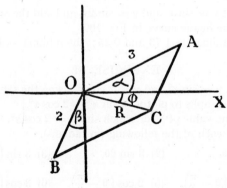

FIG. 108.

Now plot $y = \text{R} \sin (\theta + \phi)$, where $\text{R} = \text{OC}$, and $\widehat{\text{XOC}} = \phi$.

7. The method of plotting used in the following example is sometimes useful.

Example

Find, by plotting, the maximum and minimum values of $\sin x + \sin 2x$.

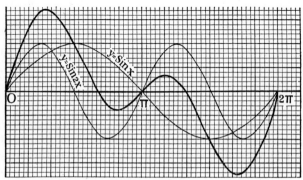

Fig. 109.

We plot $y = \sin x$, and $y = \sin 2x$, and add the ordinates, getting the heavy curve in Fig. 109.

The maxima are $1\cdot73$ and $0\cdot35$; the minima $-1\cdot73$ and $-0\cdot35$.

EXERCISE 51

1. Plot $y = \sin x°$ and $y = 2 \cos x°$ using the same axes. Use the graphs to plot $y = \sin x° \pm 2 \cos x°$.

Find one value of x for which $\sin x° = 2 \cos x°$.

2. Plot each of the following (in radians).

(1) $3 \sin \theta$.   (2) $3 \sin 2\theta$.   (3) $3 \sin \left(\theta + \dfrac{\pi}{4}\right)$.

(4) $3 \sin \left(\theta - \dfrac{\pi}{4}\right)$.   (5) $2 \cos \left(\theta - \dfrac{\pi}{3}\right)$.   (6) $3 \cos \left(\theta + \dfrac{\pi}{5}\right)$.

3. Plot the following where the angles are given in radians

(1) $4 \sin \left(3\theta + \dfrac{\pi}{4}\right).$ (2) $4 \sin \left(3\theta - \dfrac{\pi}{4}\right).$

(3) $3 \cos \left(4\theta - \dfrac{\pi}{6}\right).$ (4) $2 \cos \left(3\theta + \dfrac{\pi}{2}\right).$

4. Express the following functions in the form

$$R \sin (\theta \pm \alpha);$$

state the values of R and α.

(1) $2 \sin \theta + 4 \cos \theta.$ (2) $3 \sin \theta - 2 \cos \theta.$
(3) $1 \cdot 5 \sin \theta + \cos \theta.$

5. On the usual axes, show the initial position of the representative crank for the functions :

(1) $y = 3 \sin \left(\theta + \dfrac{\pi}{6}\right) + 2 \cos \left(\theta + \dfrac{\pi}{3}\right).$

(2) $y = 3 \sin \left(\theta - \dfrac{\pi}{6}\right) + 2 \cos \left(\theta - \dfrac{\pi}{3}\right).$

(3) $y = 3 \sin \left(\theta + \dfrac{\pi}{6}\right) - 2 \cos \left(\theta - \dfrac{\pi}{3}\right).$

6. Find correct to three decimal places a value of x in radians satisfying $4 \sin x = 2 + 0 \cdot 82x.$

7. Solve, for one value of θ correct to three decimal places

$$5 \cos \theta = 4 + 0 \cdot 92\theta \quad (\theta \text{ is in radians}).$$

8. The end P of a crank OP, 6 ins. long, describes a circle centre O, with an angular velocity 0·5 radians per sec. If p is the projection of P at any time, t, on a vertical diameter, plot a curve showing the motion of p during one revolution of the crank.

9. A crank OP 6 ins. long makes 20 revs./min. It starts from rest when OP makes 60° with the horizontal and moves counter clockwise. p is the projection of P on a vertical diameter.

VOL. III.   U

Write down the equation of the curve giving the motion of p.

10. Find, by calculation, the maxima and minima of $2 \sin x + \sin 3x$ between 0 and π. Then plot

$$y = 2 \sin x + \sin 3x$$

by adding the ordinates of $y = 2 \sin x$ and $y = \sin 3x$.

11. Plot $y = \sin x . \sin 2x$ (1) by plotting each sine separately and then multiplying ordinates (2) by expressing $\sin x . \sin 2x$ in the form $\frac{1}{2}(\cos x - \cos 3x)$ and adding ordinates.

CHAPTER 17

THE COMPLEX NUMBER

1. The Operator j

The student is familiar with the idea of associating both magnitude and direction with a number.

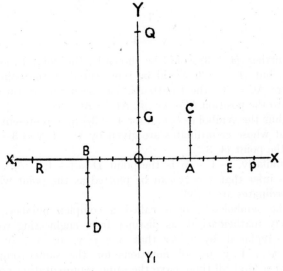

FIG. 110.

Thus he would indicate $+ 4$ either by the point A (Fig. 110), or by the length $\overline{OA}$.   Similarly $- 4$ would be shown by the point B, or by the length $\overline{OB}$.   The unit of length chosen is arbitrary.

Now (Fig. 110) let $\overline{OP} = + x$; and let "j" be defined as an operator, which, when operating on a length such as $\overline{OP}$, rotates that length through 90° in the positive (anticlockwise) sense.

Now make OP = OQ = OR.

Then $j\overline{OP} = \overline{OQ}$; and operating with j a second time, we get :

$$j(j\overline{OP}) = j\overline{OQ} = \overline{OR} \quad . \quad . \quad . \quad (1)$$

Writing jj as j^2, (1) gives (since $\overline{OP} = + x$),

$$j^2 x = - x = - 1 \times x,$$

i.e., $j^2 = - 1.$

and $j = \sqrt{-1} \quad . \quad . \quad . \quad . \quad . \quad . \quad (2)$

Further, $(4 + 3)$ would be shown by the point E, or by $\overline{OE}$; but $(4 + j \cdot 3)$ would be represented by the point C, where AC = 3; the length AE has been turned through 90° to the position AC—*i.e.*, $j \cdot \overline{AE} = \overline{AC}$.

Thus the symbol $4 + j \cdot 3$ (or $4 + 3j$) may represent the point whose co-ordinates are given by $x = 4$, $y = 3$—*i.e.*, by the point $(4, 3)$.

Similarly, $- 4 - 5j$ is the point D $\equiv (- 4, - 5)$. We thus infer that $x + jy$ can be plotted as the point whose co-ordinates are (x, y).

The symbol $x + jy$ is called a complex number. In purely mathematical, as distinct from engineering work, j is replaced by i, so that $x + j \cdot y$, or $x + iy$, or $x + \sqrt{-1} \cdot y$ are all notations for the same complex number, and all three have the same representative point. The student has met these numbers in his previous work. Thus, solving the quadratic equation $x^2 - 4x + 13 = 0$ we get

$$x = \frac{4 \pm \sqrt{16 - 52}}{2} = \frac{4 \pm \sqrt{-36}}{2}.$$

Now notice that $- 36 = - 1 \cdot 36 = j^2 \cdot 36$,
and $\sqrt{- 36} = j \cdot 6.$
So that $x = 2 \pm j \cdot 3.$

Previously he called such roots imaginary.   He can now designate them as complex roots.

In $x + jy$, x is called the real part of the complex number; y, or jy, is the imaginary part; whilst X_1OX is called the real axis, and Y_1OY the imaginary axis.   A number like $3j$ represented by G, or $\overline{OG}$ (Fig. 110), is called a purely imaginary number.   All such are plotted on the y-axis, just as all real numbers like 5, $- 2 \cdot 6$, or $\sqrt{7}$ are on the x-axis.

EXERCISE 52

1. State the co-ordinates of the points represented by the following numbers.   Plot the points on the same diagram.

(a) $2 + 3j$.   (b) $- 2 + j$.   (c) 5.
(d) $- 2j$.   (e) $1 - 2j$.   (f) $3j$.

2. Express the roots of the following equations as complex numbers :

(a) $x^2 + x + 2 = 0$.   (b) $2x^2 - 3x + 4 = 0$.
(c) $x^2 - 0 \cdot 7x + 2 \cdot 1 = 0$.

2. The Argand Diagram

If P represent the complex number $x + jy$, we see from Fig. 111 an alternative representation of the same number, viz. by the vector $\overline{OP}$.   The student will recall that a vector involves both magnitude and direction, and that physical entities like velocity and force, whose specifications involve both magnitude and direction, can be represented by straight lines.   Such lines as $\overline{OP}$ are usually designated by their end letters, the order of the letters showing the sense of the vector, the *length* OP its magnitude, whilst the bar over the letters indicates that we are dealing with a vector.

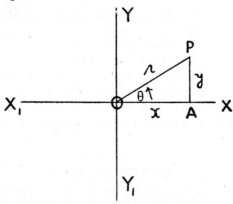

FIG. 111.—THE ARGAND DIAGRAM.

From Fig. 111 we see that $x = r \cos \theta = $ OA, $y = r \sin \theta$ = AP, and

$$x + jy = r \cos \theta + jr \sin \theta$$
$$= r (\cos \theta + j \sin \theta).$$

This way of writing a complex number is called the polar form. It is often abbreviated to $r \lfloor \theta$. We can easily change this form into the other. Thus :

$$3 \lfloor 30° = 3 (\cos 30° + j \sin 30°)$$
$$= 3 \left(\frac{\sqrt{3}}{2} + j \cdot \frac{1}{2} \right)$$
$$= \frac{3\sqrt{3}}{2} + j \cdot \frac{3}{2},$$

which is the form $x + jy$.

3. Modulus and Amplitude (or Argument)

In Fig. 111 (called an Argand diagram) the *length* OP— *i.e.*, r—is called the modulus of the complex number, whilst θ is called its amplitude or argument; abbreviations are mod., am. (sometimes amp.) or arg.

Another notation for mod. $(x + jy)$ is $|x + jy|$. Thus $r = +\sqrt{x^2 + y^2} = $ mod. $(x + jy) = |x + jy|$, and it should be observed that the modulus of any complex number is the length of the straight line joining the origin O to the point representing the number.

Also am. $(x + jy) = $ arg. $(x + jy) = \tan^{-1}\dfrac{y}{x} = \theta$.

Note that we get the same point P (Fig. 111) if its am. is increased or decreased by any integral multiple of 360°. To prevent ambiguity amplitudes will be taken to lie between 0° and $+180°$ or 0° and $-180°$, and these values will be called the principal values of the amplitudes.

Am. $(-x)$ is taken as 180° or π.

Example 1

Plot the numbers $(2 + 3j)$ and $(-3 - 2j)$. State their moduli and the principal value of their ams.   (See Fig. 112.)

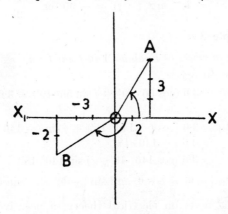

FIG. 112.

$|2 + 3j| = OA = \sqrt{4 + 9} = \sqrt{13} = 3 \cdot 6$;

am. $(2 + 3j) = \tan^{-1} \frac{3}{2} = 56° \ 19'$;

and mod. $(-3 - 2j) = OB = \sqrt{13} = 3 \cdot 6$.

Am. $(-3 - 2j) =$ the negative angle XOB $= -(180° -$ X₁OB$) = -(180° - \tan^{-1} \frac{2}{3}) = -(180° - 33° \ 42') = -146° \ 18'$.

Example 2

State the mod. and arg. of each of the following numbers :
$-5, \ 3j, \ 2, \ -j.$

If the student will plot the above numbers (or imagine them on an Argand diagram) the results below will be apparent.

$|-5| \quad = 5, \quad$ arg. $(-5) = 180°$ or π.

Mod. $(3j) = 3, \quad$ arg. $(3j) \quad = 90°$ or $\frac{\pi}{2}$.

Mod. $2 \quad = 2, \quad$ arg. $2 \quad = 0°$.

$|-j| \quad = 1, \quad$ arg. $(-j) = -90°$ or $-\frac{\pi}{2}$.

Example 3

Put the numbers in Example 1 in polar form.

We have at once :

$(2 + 3j) = 3 \cdot 6 \ (\cos 56° \ 19' + j \sin 56° \ 19') = 3 \cdot 6 \ \underline{|56° \ 19'}$

and

$(-3 - 2j) = 3 \cdot 6 \ [\cos (-146° \ 18') + j \sin (-146° \ 18')]$
$\qquad\qquad = 3 \cdot 6 \ \underline{|-146° \ 18'}$
$\qquad\qquad = 3 \cdot 6 \ (\cos 146° \ 18' - j \sin 146° \ 18')$

since $\cos (-\theta) = \cos \theta$, and $\sin (-\theta) = -\sin \theta$.

In some texts on electrical theory, a negative am. is shown $\diagdown$; thus $3 \cdot 6 \ \angle -146° \ 18' = 3 \cdot 6 \ \diagdown 146° \ 18'$.

4. Addition and Subtraction of Complex Numbers

In adding $(3 + 2j)$ and $(5 + 4j)$ we add the two real parts to get a new real part, and the two imaginary parts for a new imaginary part—*e.g.* :

$$(3 + 2j) + (5 + 4j) = (3 + 5) + j(2 + 4) = 8 + 6j.$$

Similarly with subtraction :

$$(3 + 2j) - (5 + 4j) = (3 - 5) + j(2 - 4) = -2 - 2j.$$

The rules may be proved graphically.

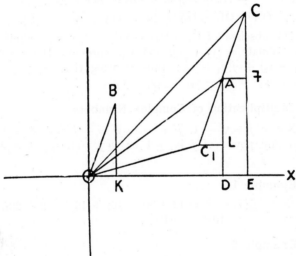

Fig. 113.

Let A (Fig. 113) represent the number $x_1 + jy_1$. Another representation is by the vector $\overline{OA}$. Similarly B represents $x_2 + jy_2 = \overline{OB}$. From A draw AC equal and parallel to OB, so that $\overline{OB}$ and $\overline{AC}$ represent the same vector.

Then, $\overline{OA} + \overline{OB} = \overline{OA} + \overline{AC} = \overline{OC}.$

Projecting OC orthogonally on the x-axis, the abscissa

of $C = OE = OD + AF$. Now observe that the projection of AC on OX = proj. of OB on $OX = x_2$. Hence the abscissa of C is $x_1 + x_2$. Similarly, by projecting OC on OY we see that its ordinate is $y_1 + y_2$.

Hence

$$C \equiv \{(x_1 + x_2),\ (y_1 + y_2)\} = (x_1 + x_2) + j(y_1 + y_2).$$

Fig. 113 shows also the subtraction

$$(x_1 + jy_1) - (x_2 + jy_2).$$

For

$$- (x_2 + jy_2) = - \overline{OB} = \overline{BO} = \overline{AC_1}.$$

$$\therefore \quad \overline{OA} - \overline{OB} = \overline{OA} + \overline{BO} = \overline{OA} + \overline{AC_1} = \overline{OC_1}.$$

The abscissa of $C_1 = OD - LC_1 = x_1 - x_2$. Similarly its ordinate $= (y_1 - y_2)$, and C_1 represents the number $(x_1 - x_2) + j(y_1 - y_2)$; thus showing that $(x_1 + jy_1) - (x_2 + jy_2) = (x_1 - x_2) + j(y_1 - y_2)$.

5. Multiplication of Complex Numbers

Notice $j = \sqrt{-1}$, $j^2 = -1$, $j^3 = -j$ and $j^4 = +1$, and any power of j is ± 1 or $\pm j$. Thus $(j)^7 = j^4 \times j^3 = -j$.

Example 1

$$(3 + 2j)(4 + 5j) = 12 + 8j + 15j + 10j^2 = 2 + 23j,$$
since $\qquad 10j^2 = -10.$

Example 2

$$(1 + j)(2 - 3j) = 2 + 2j - 3j - 3j^2 = 5 - j,$$
since $\qquad - 3j^2 = +3.$

Example 3

Evaluate $(\cos \theta_1 + j \sin \theta_1) \cdot (\cos \theta_2 + j \sin \theta_2)$.

[Notice complex numbers of the form $(\cos \alpha + j \sin \alpha)$.]

Mod. $(\cos \alpha + j \sin \alpha) = + \sqrt{\cos^2 \alpha + \sin^2 \alpha} = 1$. The am. or arg. $= \alpha$.

Hence $(\cos \alpha + j \sin \alpha) = 1 \lfloor \alpha .\rfloor$

$\therefore \ (1 \lfloor \theta_1) \times (1 \lfloor \theta_2) = (\cos \theta_1 + j \sin \theta_1)(\cos \theta_2 + j \sin \theta_2)$

$= \cos \theta_1 \cos \theta_2 + j(\sin \theta_1 \cos \theta_2 + \cos \theta_1 \sin \theta_2)$
$\qquad\qquad\qquad\qquad\qquad\qquad + j^2 \sin \theta_1 \sin \theta_2$

$= (\cos \theta_1 \cos \theta_2 - \sin \theta_1 \sin \theta_2) + j(\sin \theta_1 \cos \theta_2$
$\qquad\qquad\qquad\qquad\qquad\qquad + \cos \theta_1 \sin \theta_2)$

$= \cos (\theta_1 + \theta_2) + j \sin (\theta_1 + \theta_2) = 1 \lfloor (\theta_1 + \theta_2).$

This result we shall use later.

Example 4

$(\cos 30° + j \sin 30°) . (\cos 15° + j \sin 15°) =$
$\qquad\qquad\qquad \cos 45° + j \sin 45° = 1 \lfloor 45°.$

6. Division of Complex Numbers

Definition :—Two complex numbers, $(x + jy)$ and $(x - jy)$, which differ only in the sign of the imaginary part, are called conjugate complex numbers.

Thus $(- 3 + 4j)$ and $(- 3 - 4j)$ are conjugates.

The sum and product of two conjugates are both real.

Sum $= (x + jy) + (x - jy) = 2x.$

Product $= (x + jy)(x - jy) = x^2 - (jy)^2 = x^2 + y^2 =$ the square of the mod. of either of the two numbers.

Notice the product $(\cos \theta + j \sin \theta) . (\cos \theta - j \sin \theta) = 1.$

Example 1

Consider $\dfrac{1}{3 + 2j}$. *Multiplying numerator and denominator by the conjugate number* $3 - 2j$, *we get* :

$$\frac{1}{3 + 2j} = \frac{3 - 2j}{(3 + 2j)(3 - 2j)} = \frac{3 - 2j}{13} = \frac{3}{13} - \frac{2j}{13},$$

—*i.e.*, the form $x + jy$. $[y = -\tfrac{2}{13}.]$

Example 2

Put $\dfrac{1 - 2j}{1 + 3j}$ *in the form* $x + jy$.

$$\frac{1 - 2j}{1 + 3j} = \frac{(1 - 2j)(1 - 3j)}{(1 + 3j)(1 - 3j)} = \frac{1 - 5j + 6j^2}{10}$$

$$= \frac{-5 - 5j}{10} = -\frac{1}{2} - \frac{1}{2}j.$$

Example 3

Express in the form $x + jy$, the sum $\dfrac{2 - 3j}{1 - j} + \dfrac{3 + j}{2 + 4j}$.

$$\frac{2 - 3j}{1 - j} + \frac{3 + j}{2 + 4j} = \frac{(2 - 3j)(1 + j)}{(1 - j)(1 + j)} + \frac{(3 + j)(2 - 4j)}{(2 + 4j)(2 - 4j)}$$

$$= \frac{5 - j}{2} + \frac{10 - 10j}{20}$$

$$= \left(\frac{5}{2} - \frac{j}{2}\right) + \left(\frac{1}{2} - \frac{1}{2}j\right) = 3 - j.$$

EXERCISE 53

Put the following products in the form $x + jy$:

(1) $(3 + 5j)(2 - j)$. (2) $(0·5 + j)(0·25 + 3j)$.
(3) $(2·3 + j)(4 - 2j)$. (4) $(3 + 4j)(3 - 4j)$.
(5) $(-2 - 0·5j)(-2 + 0·5j)$. (6) $(3 - 2j)^2$.
(7) $(1 - 2j)^3$. (8) $(2 - j)^4$. (9) $(1 + 2j)^2 . (2 + j)$.
(10) $(3 - j)(3 + j)(4 - 2j)$.
(11) $(\cos 30° + j \sin 30°) . (\cos 45° + j \sin 45°)$.
(12) $(\cos 45° + j \sin 45°)(\cos 15° - j \sin 15°)$.

Evaluate the following :

(13) $\dfrac{2}{3 - 2j}$. (14) $\dfrac{2 + 3j}{4 - j}$. (15) $\dfrac{3}{4 + 6j} + \dfrac{1}{2 + 3j}$.

(16) $\dfrac{2 - j}{4 + 6j} - \dfrac{3 + j}{2 + 3j}$. (17) $\dfrac{(3 + 4j)(2 + j)}{3 - 2j}$.

(18) $\dfrac{2 + 4j}{3 + j} + \dfrac{1 - j}{1 + j}$.

7. Products in Polar Form

Let $z_1 = r \lfloor\theta_1, \quad z_2 = r_2\lfloor\theta_2,$

then $z_1 z_2 = r_1 (\cos \theta_1 + j \sin \theta_1) \cdot r_2 (\cos \theta_2 + j \sin \theta_2)$

$$= r_1 r_2 [\cos (\theta_1 + \theta_2) + j \sin (\theta_1 + \theta_2)].$$

(See Example 3, par. 5.)

We infer from this result that the mod. of a product is the product of the mods. of the factors, whilst am. product = the sum of the ams. of the factors.

Example 1

$3 \lfloor 25° \times 2 \lfloor 33° = 6 \lfloor 58° = 6 (\cos 58° + j \sin 58°).$

Example 2

$3 \lfloor 48° \times 4 \lfloor -22° = 12 \lfloor 26° = 12 (\cos 26° + j \sin 26°).$

Example 3

$(r \lfloor \alpha)^2 = r^2 \lfloor 2\alpha = r^2 (\cos 2\alpha + j \sin 2\alpha),$

i.e., $(r \lfloor \alpha)^2 = R \lfloor 2\alpha$ (where $R = r^2$)   .   .   .   (1)

This example shows us how to get the square root of a complex number when the latter is in polar form; for from (1) we see $(R \lfloor 2\alpha)^{\frac{1}{2}} = \pm r \lfloor \alpha.$ But $r = \sqrt{R},$ and $\alpha = \frac{1}{2} (2\alpha).$

Hence to get the square root of a complex number, we take the square root of the mod. of the number, halve its am., and prefix $\pm$.

Example 4

Evaluate $\sqrt{3 + 2j}.$

Mod. $(3 + 2j) = \sqrt{13} = 3.6,$ and $\sqrt{3.6} = 1.9.$

Am. $(3 + 2j) = \tan^{-1} \frac{2}{3} = 33° 42'.$ Half of this is $16° 51'.$

Hence $\sqrt{3 + 2j} = \pm 1.9 \lfloor 16° 51' = \pm 1.9 (\cos 16° 51' + j \sin 16° 51').$

8. De Moivre's Theorem

We have proved that $(\cos \theta_1 + j \sin \theta_1) \times (\cos \theta_2 + j \sin \theta_2) = [\cos (\theta_1 + \theta_2) + j \sin (\theta_1 + \theta_2)]$.

Hence, putting $\theta_1 = \theta_2 = \alpha$ we get :

$$(\cos \alpha + j \sin \alpha)^2 = (\cos 2\alpha + j \sin 2\alpha) \quad . \quad (1)$$

Multiplying both sides of (1) by $(\cos \alpha + j \sin \alpha)$ gives :

$$(\cos \alpha + j \sin \alpha)^3 = (\cos 2\alpha + j \sin 2\alpha)(\cos \alpha + j \sin \alpha)$$
$$= \cos 3\alpha + j \sin 3\alpha,$$

and continuing the process for n factors we see that :

$$(\cos \alpha + j \sin \alpha)^n = \cos n\alpha + j \sin n\alpha \quad . \quad (2)$$

(2) is De Moivre's Theorem; and it is true not only when n is a positive integer, but also when n is a negative integer or a positive or negative fraction. (See Exercise 54, nos. 29, 30.)

Example 1

$$(\cos 30° + j \sin 30°)^4 = \cos 120° + j \sin 120° = -\frac{1}{2} + \frac{j\sqrt{3}}{2}.$$

Example 2

$$(\cos 20° - j \sin 20°)^6 = [\cos (- 20°) + j \sin (- 20°)]^6$$
$$= \cos (- 120°) + j \sin (- 120°) = \cos 120° - j \sin 120°.$$

Example 3

Put $(2 + 3j)$ *in polar form, and then evaluate* $(2 + 3j)^4$.

We have :

Mod. $(2 + 3j) = \sqrt{13}$, and am. $(2 + 3j) = \tan^{-1} \frac{3}{2} = 56° \ 19'$.

$$\therefore \quad 2 + 3j = \sqrt{13} \lfloor 56° \ 19'$$
$$= \sqrt{13} (\cos 56° \ 19' + j \sin 56° \ 19').$$

Hence

$$(2 + 3j)^4 = (\sqrt{13})^4 \cdot [\cos (4 \times 56° \ 19') + j \sin (4 \times 56° \ 19')]$$
$$= 169 (\cos 225° \ 16' + j \sin 225° \ 16')$$
$$= 169 (- 0\cdot704 - 0\cdot71 \, j)$$
$$= - 119 - 120j.$$

Example 4

$(\cos 60° + j \sin 60°)^{\frac{1}{2}} = \cos \frac{1}{2} \times 60° + j \sin \frac{1}{2} \times 60°$
$= \cos 30° + j \sin 30°$ (assuming De Moivre's Th.).

Example 5

Evaluate $\sqrt{3 + 2j}$.   (See Example 4, par. 7.)

$3 + 2j = \sqrt{13} \lfloor 33° \, 42' = 3·6 (\cos 33° \, 42' + j \sin 33° \, 42')$

$\therefore \quad \sqrt{3 + 2j} = \pm \sqrt{3·6} (\cos 33° \, 42' + j \sin 33° \, 42')^{\frac{1}{2}}$
$= \pm 1·9 \lfloor 16° \, 51' $ as before.

9. Division in Polar Form

Example 1

Consider $\dfrac{1}{\cos \theta + j \sin \theta}$.

$\dfrac{1}{\cos \theta + j \sin \theta} = \dfrac{\cos \theta - j \sin \theta}{(\cos \theta + j \sin \theta)(\cos \theta - j \sin \theta)}$

$= \dfrac{\cos \theta - j \sin \theta}{\cos^2 \theta + \sin^2 \theta} = (\cos \theta - j \sin \theta)$

$= \cos (- \theta) + j \sin (- \theta)$.

Hence

$\dfrac{1}{\cos \theta + j \sin \theta} = \cos (- \theta) + j \sin (- \theta) = \cos \theta - j \sin \theta,$

i.e., $(\cos \theta + j \sin \theta)^{-1} = \cos (- 1 \times \theta) + j \sin (- 1 \times \theta),$

which proves De Moivre's Th. for $n = - 1$.

Example 2

Evaluate $\dfrac{r_1 \lfloor \theta_1}{r_2 \lfloor \theta_2}$.

We have :

$\dfrac{r_1 \lfloor \theta_1}{r_2 \lfloor \theta_2} = \dfrac{r_1}{r_2} \dfrac{(\cos \theta_1 + j \sin \theta_1)}{(\cos \theta_2 + j \sin \theta_2)}$

$= \dfrac{r_1}{r_2} \dfrac{(\cos \theta_1 + j \sin \theta_1)(\cos \theta_2 - j \sin \theta_2)}{(\cos \theta_2 + j \sin \theta_2)(\cos \theta_2 - j \sin \theta_2)}$

$= \dfrac{r_1}{r_2} \cos (\theta_1 - \theta_2)$.   [See Par. 6.]

We infer that the modulus of the quotient of two complex numbers is the quotient of their moduli; and the am. of a quotient is the difference

am. (numerator) — am. (denominator).

Example 3

$$\frac{3\ \lfloor 40°}{5\ \lfloor 70°} = \frac{3}{5}\ \lfloor -30° = \frac{3}{5}\ (\cos 30° - j \sin 30°).$$

EXERCISE 54

Plot the following numbers on an Argand diagram, and then put them in polar form.

(1) $3 + 4j$. (2) $3 - 4j$. (3) $1 \cdot 2 + 3 \cdot 5j$.
(4) $-6 - 2j$. (5) $-0 \cdot 5 - 0 \cdot 3j$. (6) $-32 + j$.
(7) $3 \cdot 1 - 0 \cdot 5j$.

Change each of the following to the form $x + jy$:

(8) $3 \lfloor 30°$. (9) $2 \cdot 3 \lfloor 42$.
(10) $5 \cdot 2 \lfloor -36°$. (11) $6 \cdot 3 \underline{\vee} 42°$.

Evaluate, in polar form, the following :

(12) $3 \lfloor 30° \times 2 \lfloor 15°$. (13) $2 \cdot 1 \lfloor 15° \times 3 \cdot 2 \lfloor 21°$.

(14) $2 \cdot 8 \lfloor 32° \times 1 \cdot 3 \lfloor -74°$. (15) $\dfrac{3 \lfloor 45}{2 \lfloor 15}$.

(16) $\dfrac{3 \lfloor 36°}{4 \lfloor 18°}$. (17) $\dfrac{3 \lfloor 72°}{2 \lfloor -18°}$. (18) $\dfrac{2 \cdot 3 \lfloor 24°}{1 \cdot 6 \lfloor -21°}$.

Evaluate :

(19) $\sqrt{2 + 5j}$. (20) $\sqrt{3 - 4j}$. (21) $\sqrt{2 \cdot 3 + 0 \cdot 5j}$.

(22) $\dfrac{1}{\sqrt{3 + 2j}}$. (23) $\sqrt{j}$. (24) $\sqrt{-9j}$.

(25) $\dfrac{\sqrt{4 + 2j}}{1 - 3j}$.

(26) Evaluate in the form $a + bj$ each of the numbers $\dfrac{6 - 5j}{3 + j}$ and $\dfrac{10}{2_{30°}}$, and represent $10_{60°} - 7$ graphically, and express it in polar form.

(27) Express $\dfrac{4 - 2j}{3 + j}$ and $\dfrac{5}{2_{60°}}$ in the form $a + bj$, and show them on an Argand diagram. Find also the modulus and the principal value of the argument (or am.) of their product.

(28) If z_1 and z_2 are complex numbers, show that $|z_1 z_2| = |z_1| \times |z_2|$ and am. $(z_1 z_2) = $ am. $z_1 + $ am. z_2. Verify these relations when $z_1 = 2 + 3j$, and $z_2 = 1 - 2j$, and mark the points or vectors representing $2 + 3j$, $1 - 2j$, and $(2 + 3j)(1 - 2j)$ on an Argand diagram.

(29) If n is a positive integer, show that $\dfrac{1}{(\cos \theta + j \sin \theta)^n}$ $= \cos n\theta - j \sin n\theta$ and hence deduce De Moivre's Th. for a negative integer.

(30) Starting with $\left(\cos \dfrac{\theta}{q} + j \sin \dfrac{\theta}{q}\right)^q = \cos \theta + j \sin \theta$;

show (1) $\cos \dfrac{\theta}{q} + j \sin \dfrac{\theta}{q} = (\cos \theta + j \sin \theta)^{\frac{1}{q}}$;

(2) $(\cos \theta + j \sin \theta)^{\frac{p}{q}} = \cos \dfrac{p\theta}{q} + j \sin \dfrac{p\theta}{q}$,

which proves De Moivre's Th. for a fraction $\dfrac{p}{q}$.

MISCELLANEOUS EXERCISES
CALCULATIONS

1. (a) An ammeter read 5·72 amps. when the true reading was 5·6 amps. Express the error as a percentage of the true reading.

(b) Evaluate $\sqrt{s(s - a)(s - b)(s - c)}$, given $a = 4·2$, $b = 5·5$, $c = 6·3$ and $s = \frac{1}{2}(a + b + c)$.

2. Given $\dfrac{R}{r} = \sqrt{\dfrac{f + p}{f - p}}$, find p when $f = 3000$, $R = 3 \cdot 5$ and $r = 2 \cdot 5$.

3. Find correct to three significant figures the value of $\left(\dfrac{a^3 - b^3}{a + b}\right)^{-0 \cdot 2}$, when $a = 3 \cdot 23$ and $b = 2 \cdot 75$.

4. If $\log_e \dfrac{1 + r}{1 - r} = 1 \cdot 2$, find the value of r.

5. Evaluate $(R^{\frac{2}{3}} + r^{\frac{2}{3}})^{\frac{3}{2}}$ when $R = 8 \cdot 12$, $r = 4 \cdot 76$.

6. Evaluate :

   (a) $\log_e \dfrac{A}{B}$ when $A = 344$ and $B = 215$.

   (b) $e^{Rt/L}$ when $R = 8 \cdot 6$, $L = 0 \cdot 4$, $t = 0 \cdot 05$.

7. Evaluate $a^{1 \cdot 2}(b^{0 \cdot 8} - c^{0 \cdot 6})$, when $a = 5 \cdot 17$, $b = 4 \cdot 05$, $c = 0 \cdot 91$.

8. Evaluate $e^{-Rt/L} \sin 100\pi t$, given that $e = 2 \cdot 718$, $R = 6$, $L = 0 \cdot 025$ and $t = 3 \cdot 5 \times 10^{-3}$.

9. If $y = \dfrac{0 \cdot 055 n^{4 \cdot 2}}{1 - 0 \cdot 00035 n^{2 \cdot 5}}$, find y when $n = 12 \cdot 4$.

10. Find the value, to three significant figures, of

    (a) $\dfrac{1}{n}(a^{-n} - b^{-n})$ when $a = 4$, $b = 10$ and $n = \dfrac{3}{2}$.

    (b) $\dfrac{1}{2a} \log_e \dfrac{a + x}{a - x}$ when $a = 1 + \sqrt{3}$ and $x = \sqrt{3}$.

EQUATIONS

11. Solve the following equations :

    (a) $x^4 - 8 \cdot 87 x^2 - 2 \cdot 28 = 0$.

    (b) $54^{3x - 2} = 2 \cdot 71$.

    (c) $8 = x + \sqrt{x^2 - 8}$.

12. Solve :

    (a) $8(5x - 3)^2 = 3(9 - 10x)$.

    (b) Two quantities V and R are connected by a law of the form $V = aR + \dfrac{b}{R}$, where a and b are constants.

It is known that when $V = 2 \cdot 2$, $R = 0 \cdot 8$, and $V = 2 \cdot 3$ when $R = 1 \cdot 2$. Find a and b.

13. A law of the form $E = a\theta^2 + b\theta + c$ connects E and θ. If $E = 576$ when $\theta = 100$, $E = 1320$ when $\theta = 200$ and $E = 2072$ when $\theta = 300$, determine the values of the constants a, b, c, and hence find E when $\theta = 250$.

14. Solve :
   (a) $5(2 - x)^2 = 7x - 8$.
   (b) $1 \cdot 39^{2x} = 6 \cdot 31$.
   (c) $\log_e (x^2 + 0 \cdot 05) = 0 \cdot 27$.

15. (a) Solve for R, $(3R - 1)^2 = (3R - 5)(3R + 5) + 2R - 6$.

   (b) Solve for a and b, (i) $a + \dfrac{b}{16} = 12$, (ii) $a + \dfrac{b}{64} = 0$.

16. Find the value of r (other than zero) which satisfies the equation :
$$1 \cdot 75r^{0 \cdot 75} - 1 \cdot 87r^{0 \cdot 87} = 0.$$

17. Solve :
   (a) $3x = 2\sqrt{x} + 17$.   (b) $3 \cdot 2^{2x} = 5 \cdot 1$.

18. Solve :
   (a) $8 \cdot 756^{4x-1} = 4 \cdot 328^{2x+3}$.
   (b) $\left. \begin{aligned} \log_5 (4x - 5) &= 2 \\ \log_8 (2x + 3y) &= \tfrac{1}{3} \end{aligned} \right\}$.

19. Find C, from the formulae $C = \dfrac{Q}{E}$, $Q = \dfrac{Ktd}{2}\left(1 + \dfrac{\lambda}{2}\right)$, given that $d = 1 \cdot 3$, $K = 2 \cdot 1 \times 10^{-7}$, $t = 5 \cdot 34$, $\lambda = 0 \cdot 425$, $E = 0 \cdot 91$.

20. (a) If $y = kx^n$, find k and n, if $x = 10$ when $y = 14 \cdot 5$, and $x = 40$ when $y = 116 \cdot 0$.

   (b) Solve, $3^x \times 5^{x-1} = 6 \cdot 76$ (to two significant figures).

TRIGONOMETRY

21. N is the foot of the perpendicular from the vertex **A** of a triangle ABC on the horizontal plane through BC to

which the plane of ABC is inclined at 40°. Calculate the angle BAC if $\angle$NBC $= 70° 30'$ and $\angle$NCB $= 56° 30'$.

22. (a) Show how to express $a \sin \theta + b \cos \theta$ in the form A $\sin (\theta + \alpha)$, giving the values of A and α in terms of a and b.

(b) The voltage in an electrical circuit after time t is given by E $= a \sin pt + b \cos pt$. If $a = 75$, $b = 75\pi$ and $p = 100\pi$ find the smallest positive value of t for E to have a maximum value.

23. Prove that in any triangle, $a^2 = b^2 + c^2 - 2bc \cos A$. In a force triangle ABC, $\overline{AB}$ and $\overline{BC}$ represent forces of 3·94 and 2·5 tons respectively. $\overline{AC}$ represents their resultant. If $\angle$ABC $= 98°$, find the magnitude and direction of this resultant.

24. (a) Simplify $\sin (A + B) - \sin (A - B)$ and deduce the formula for $\sin X - \sin Y$ as a product.

(b) Find the acute angle which satisfies the equation $\cos 2\theta = 2 \sin \theta$.

25. Express $5 \cos^2 \theta - 2 \sin^2 \theta$ in the form $a + b \cos 2\theta$, and draw the graph of the function from $\theta = 0°$ to $\theta = 180°$, and calculate the values of θ for which the function is zero.

26. Establish the formula $\tan \dfrac{B - C}{2} = \dfrac{b - c}{b + c} \cot \dfrac{A}{2}$.

From an observation post A on the shore a mine is observed at B on a bearing N. 15° E. and five minutes later it is observed at C on a bearing N. 33° E. The distances AB and AC are estimated as being 2800 ft. and 2000 ft. respectively. Find in m.p.h. the direction and speed of the current.

27. PQ is an arc of a circle of radius r, subtending an angle θ radians at the centre of the circle ($\theta < \pi$). Show that the area of the smaller segment cut off by the chord PQ is given by A $= \frac{1}{2}r^2(\theta - \sin \theta)$.

In a rectangle ABCD, AB $= 4·33$ in. and BC $= 2·5$ in. An arc of a circle joins the corners A and C, and DC is tangential to this arc. Find the area of that part of the rectangle bounded by the arc and the sides AB and BC.

28. Find $\sin 2\theta$ in terms of $\cos \theta$ and $\sin \theta$, and $\cos 2\theta$ in terms of $\cos \theta$; then solve $\cos 2\theta = 2 - \sqrt{3} \cos \theta$, giving the values of θ between $0°$ and $360°$.

29. In a triangle ABC, $a = 5$ in., $b = 7$ in., $c = 8$ in. Calculate the length of the perpendicular from A to BC.

30. Prove that $\sin (A + B) = \sin A \cos B + \cos A \sin B$, and state the corresponding formula for $\cos (A + B)$.

By expanding $\cos (\theta + 153°)$ and $\sin (\theta + 243°)$ prove that $\cos (\theta + 153°) = \sin (\theta + 243°)$ for all values of θ.

31. The angles of elevation of an airplane, at a certain instant, from two stations A and B, 1500 yds. apart and in the same vertical plane as the airplane, were $65°$ and $40°$ respectively. Calculate the height of the airplane.

32. In any triangle ABC, prove that $a^2 = b^2 + c^2 - 2bc \cos A$.

Two adjacent sides of a parallelogram are 3·3 ft. and 4·8 ft. long, and contain an angle of $65°$. Calculate the lengths of the diagonals.

33. Prove $\cos \theta = \dfrac{1 - t^2}{1 + t^2}$ and $\sin \theta = \dfrac{2t}{1 + t^2}$, where $t = \tan \dfrac{\theta}{2}$.

Use the above substitutions to solve $4 \cos \theta - \sin \theta = 1$, giving the values of θ (to the nearest degree) between $0°$ and $360°$ which satisfy the equation.

34. Prove that $\dfrac{\cos (45° + \theta)}{\cos (45° - \theta)} = \dfrac{1 - \tan \theta}{1 + \tan \theta}$. Hence solve the equation

$4 \cos (45° + \theta) = \cos (45° - \theta)$ $[0° < \theta < 360°]$.

35. ABC is a triangle in which $B = 50°$, $AB = 7$ in. and $BC = 10$ in. A point D is on the opposite side of AC from B, such that $AD = 4$ in. and $CD = 5$ in. Calculate the angle ADC.

36. The elevation of the top of a steeple from a place A due S. of it is 45°, and from B, 100 yds. due W. of A, the elevation is 15°. Find the height of the steeple.

37. The third harmonic of a voltage wave is given as $- 0.13 \sin 3\theta + 0.11 \cos 3\theta$. Put this in the form $r \sin (3\theta + \alpha)$, and find the values of r and α.

38. (i) If $\mu = \tan \beta$, show that $\dfrac{\sin \alpha - \mu \cos \alpha}{\cos \alpha + \mu \sin \alpha} = \tan (\alpha - \beta)$.

(ii) By expressing $\sin 3\theta - \sin \theta$ as a product, or otherwise, find the values of θ between 0° and 360° which satisfy the equation $\sin 3\theta - \sin \theta = 0$.

39. OA is a crank, length 6 in.; AB a connecting rod, length 27 in. Find the length of OB when angle AOB = 100°. Find also the greatest value of the angle ABO for all positions of the rotating crank OA.

40. A ship is travelling due E. at a steady speed of 15 knots. From the ship, the bearing of a lighthouse is observed to be N. 73° E.; 10 mins. later the bearing is N. 42° W. How far is the ship from the lighthouse when the second bearing was taken? Find the bearing of the lighthouse from the ship when they are 3 nautical miles apart. (1 nautical mile = 6080 ft.; 1 knot = 1 nautical mile per hour.)

41. Put $24 \sin \theta + 7 \cos \theta$ in the form $A \sin (\theta + \alpha)$ and find the values of A and α.

Hence find (a) when $24 \sin \theta + 7 \cos \theta$ is a maximum, (b) the values of θ which satisfy the equation $24 \sin \theta + 7 \cos \theta = 15$.

42. Establish the formula $\dfrac{a}{\sin A} = \dfrac{b}{\sin B} = \dfrac{c}{\sin C}$.

AB is a straight road, 920 yd. long, running due E. from A. There is a control tower at C, which bears N. 25° E. from A, and N. 16° 15′ W. from B. Find

(a) the length of a straight road from A to C, and (b) the shortest distance from C to AB.

43. A barrage balloon P is known to be vertically above a point A. Find its height above this point, given the following data:

$\angle ABC = 38°$; $\angle ACB = 69°$; $BC = 850$ ft., where A, B, C are in the horizontal plane through A and $\angle PBA = 68°$.

44. Assuming the formula for sin $(A + B)$ and cos $(A + B)$ (or otherwise), prove that $\tan (A + B) = \dfrac{\tan A + \tan B}{1 - \tan A \tan B}$.

PN is a vertical pole of height a, N being on the ground, and Q is a point on the pole, b above N. If O is a point on the ground c from N, and PQ subtends an angle θ at O, prove that $\tan \theta = \dfrac{(a - b)c}{ab + c^2}$.

45. If $w = 100\pi$, $R = 10$ and $L = 0.006$, express $R \sin wt - Lw \cos wt$ in the form $Z \sin (wt - \phi)$, and find the values of Z and $\cos \phi$.

CALCULUS

46. Find $\dfrac{dy}{dx}$ when (i) $y = 2x^3 - \dfrac{1}{x^3} + 1$, (ii) $y = e^x(2 - x)$,

(iii) $y = \dfrac{x}{3x + 2}$.

If $pv = 500$, find $\dfrac{dp}{dv}$ when $v = 5$.

47. If $y = 4.51 \sin x + 2.5 \cos x$ (x in radians), find (a) $\dfrac{dy}{dx}$, (b) the smallest positive value of x which makes $\dfrac{dy}{dx} = 0$, and (c) $\int_0^{\frac{\pi}{2}} y\,dx$.

48. In time t secs. a body is displaced s ft. in a straight path, so that $s = 25t + 16t^2$. Deduce from first principles expressions for the velocity and acceleration at time t.

(a) If $y = x^3 + \dfrac{2}{x}$, find the value of $\dfrac{d^2y}{dx^2}$ when $x = 2$.

(b) If $r = \theta \cos \theta$, find $\dfrac{dr}{d\theta}$.

49. State the conditions to be satisfied if $y = f(x)$ has a minimum value when $x = a$.

The total heat, H units generated in a circuit, is given by

$$H = 3x^2 + 4\cdot5(10 - x)^2.$$

Find the value of x for which H is least, and the value of H in this case.

50. Find $\dfrac{dy}{dx}$ when (a) $y = (3x^2 - 1)(4x + 3)$; (b) $y = \dfrac{e^x}{1 - x}$.

If $x = 10 \sin t - 3 \cos t$, show that $\dfrac{d^2x}{dt^2} = -x$, and (c) find the value of $\dfrac{d^2x}{dt^2}$ when $x = \dfrac{2\pi}{3}$.

51. A point moves in a plane so that its co-ordinates with respect to a pair of perpendicular axes through O are, at time t, given by $x = 3 \sin t$, $y = 2 \cos t$. Find its components of velocity along the axes when $t = \dfrac{\pi}{3}$. Hence find $\dfrac{dy}{dx}$ at this time.

52. If $y = x(2 + x)$, find from first principles the value of $\dfrac{dy}{dx}$.

(a) $y = \dfrac{8}{x} - \dfrac{x^2}{8}$, find x so that $\dfrac{d^2y}{dx^2} = 0$.

(b) Evaluate $\dfrac{d}{d\theta}(\theta + \sin \theta \cos \theta)$ when $\theta = \dfrac{\pi}{4}$.

53. Find $\dfrac{dy}{dx}$ when (a) $y = x \log_e x$, (b) $y = \dfrac{a - x}{a + x}$ (a is constant). Show that the points P $\equiv$ (1, 2), Q $\equiv$ (3, 4) lie on the curve $10y = 1 + 22x - 3x^2$, and find to the nearest degree the angles of the triangle formed by the straight line PQ and the tangents to the curve at P and Q.

54. The motion of a lift from $t = 0$ sec., to $t = 12$ secs., is given by the formula $s = \dfrac{1}{240}t^5 - \dfrac{1}{8}t^4 + t^3$, where s ft. is the distance moved. Show that the acceleration is $\dfrac{1}{12}t(t - 6)(t - 12)$ ft./sec.², and that the maximum velocity is 27 $f.\ s.$

55. The rate of loss of heat from a hot body is proportional to the area of the surface exposed. Prove that the most efficient cylindrical hot-water tank, of given volume, is one whose height equals its diameter.

56. The cross-section of an open gutter made of thin material is a trapezium, with its sloping sides equal and inclined at 60° to the base. If the area of the section is $108\sqrt{3}$ sq. in., find the dimensions of the section, if the gutter has a fixed length, and the amount of material used in its construction has to be a minimum.

57. The volume of a right-circular cylinder is 2 cu. ft. If r is the radius in ft., prove that the total length, L ft., of a piece of string which passes twice round the circumference, and once lengthwise round the cylinder, is given by

$$L = 4r(1 + \pi) + \frac{4}{\pi r^2}.$$

Find the value of r so that L is the shortest possible length.

58. Evaluate the following integrals :

(a) $\displaystyle\int_{\frac{1}{2}}^{\frac{3}{2}} \left(1 + \frac{3}{x^2}\right)dx.$ (b) $\displaystyle\int_{\frac{\pi}{6}}^{\frac{\pi}{2}} \cos 3\theta\, d\theta.$

(c) $\displaystyle\int_{0}^{0.01} 30 \sin 100\pi t\, dt.$

59. Evaluate (a) $\int_1^5 (2x - \sqrt{x})dx$, (b) $\int_0^{\frac{\pi}{12}} 5 \cos 6t\, dt$, and

(c) find the mean value of $5 \cos 6t$ between $t = 0$ and $t = \frac{\pi}{12}$.

60. If $\frac{d^2y}{dx^2} = 6x - 2$, express y as a function of x, given

that $\frac{dy}{dx} = 3$, $y = -9$, when $x = 2$, and find a value of x which makes y a minimum.

61. If $\frac{dt}{dQ} = -\frac{CR}{Q}$, and C = 0·006, R = 80, find t in terms of Q given that when $t = 0$, $Q = 10$.

62. Show that the mean value of $\sin x$, as x varies from 0 to π, is $\frac{2}{\pi}$. Sketch the graph of $y = 2 - \sqrt{x}$ ($\sqrt{x}$ positive only) and find the area between the graph, the x-axis, and the ordinates at $x = 0$ and $x = 4$.

63. Sketch the curve $y = 2 - \sqrt{x}$, between $x = 0$, $x = 4$, where $\sqrt{x}$ has both its positive and negative values. If the area bounded by the curve and part of the ordinate at $x = 4$ is rotated about the x-axis, find the volume of the hollow solid generated.

64. Employ Simpson's Rule to find the area enclosed by the curve $y = \frac{1}{10}(2x^2 + 5x + 8)$, the x-axis and the ordinates at $x = -1$ and $x = 3$. Compare your result with that got by integration.

65. The deflection, y in., of a beam at x ft. from one end is given by $\frac{d^2y}{dx^2} = \frac{1}{1200}(10 - x)^2$. Find y in terms of x given that both y and $\frac{dy}{dx}$ are zero when x is zero. Show that when $x = 10$, $y = 2\frac{1}{12}$.

66. (a) Evaluate $\int_0^2 \left(3\sqrt{x} - \dfrac{1}{3\sqrt{x}}\right)dx$ and $\int_0^{\frac{\pi}{4}} 5\sin 2\theta\, d\theta$,

and find the mean value of the latter integral between the given limits.

(b) That part of the curve $y = 3x - x^2$ which lies above the x-axis is rotated about that axis. Find the volume generated in a complete rotation.

67. If $\dfrac{d^2y}{dx^2} = 3\sin 3x + 2\cos 2x$, show that

$y = 1 - \frac{1}{3}\sin 3x - \frac{1}{2}\cos 2x$ given that when $x = 0$, $y = \frac{1}{2}$ and $\dfrac{dy}{dx} = -1$.

Verify that y has a minimum value when $x = \dfrac{\pi}{10}$.

68. (a) Express $2\sin 2x \cos x$ as the sum of two sines

and then find $\int_0^{\frac{\pi}{3}} 2\sin 2x \cos x\, dx$.

Evaluate (b) $\int_1^{6\cdot8} \dfrac{4}{x^{0\cdot8}}dx$, (c) $\int_0^{\frac{\pi}{2}} \sin 2\theta\, d\theta$.

(d) The weight of a tapering rod included between cross sections at distances x in. and $(x + dx)$ in. from the smaller end is $\dfrac{1}{4}\left(1 + \dfrac{x}{60}\right)^2 dx$ lb. Find by integration the total weight of the rod, if its length is 30 in.

69. Evaluate $\int x^2(3 - 5x^2)dx$ and $\int_1^8 \dfrac{4}{\sqrt[3]{x}}dx$, and find the area between the curve $y = 2\cos 3x$, the x-axis, and the ordinates at $x = 0$ and $x = \dfrac{\pi}{18}$.

70. Evaluate (a) $\int_1^9 \dfrac{\sqrt{x}}{4}dx$, (b) $\int \left(x^4 + \dfrac{1}{x^4}\right)dx$, (c) $\int_0^{\pi} \sin \frac{1}{2}\theta\, d\theta$.

A curve $y = f(x)$ passes through the point $(0, 6)$ and $\dfrac{dy}{dx} = 5e^x$. Determine the form of $f(x)$.

BINOMIAL THEOREM, MOMENTS OF INERTIA, ETC.

71. If x is small show that $(1 - x)^{\frac{1}{2}}$ and $\left(1 + \dfrac{x}{2}\right)^{-1}$ are approx. equal (use Binomial Th.).

Write down the approx. values of $\sqrt{0 \cdot 994}$ and $\dfrac{1}{1 \cdot 003}$.

72. Neglecting powers of x above the second, find x from the equation :

$$\left(1 + \frac{x}{2}\right)^5 + \left(1 - \frac{x}{2}\right)^5 = 2 \cdot 002.$$

73. Show from first principles that the moment of inertia I, of a triangle height h in., base b in., about an axis parallel to the base through the vertex is given by $I = \frac{1}{4}bh^3$ in.^{4} units.

ABCD is a trapezium, with AB, DC parallel and 3 in. and 5 in. long respectively. Their distance apart is 4 in. The sides DA and CB are produced to meet in O. Find the distance of O from AB and use the above formula to deduce the M.I. of the trapezium about an axis XX through O and parallel to AB.

74. Expand $(1 + x)^n$ as far as the term in x^3.

If $l = (3 + a)$, and powers of a above the first may be neglected, find the approx. value of $2l^4 - 3l^3 - 5l$. Use your result to find correct to three significant figures the value of l given by the equation $2l^4 - 3l^3 - 5l = 71$, the value of l being known to differ from 3 by a small amount.

75. A plane figure is bounded by the curve $y = 3\sqrt[3]{x}$, the axis of x, and the ordinates at $x = 0$ and $x = 8$. Sketch the figure, and find its moments of inertia about the axes of x and y, using 1 in. as the unit of length along each axis.

76. Find the approx. values of $(2 + h)^6$ and $(2 + h)^3$, if powers of h above the first may be neglected.

If $R = (2 + h)$ where h is small, find the value of R

given by the equation $R^6 - 7R^3 - 11R + 11 = 0$, correct to three significant figures.

77. Determine by integration the M.I. of (a) a rectangle b in. by d in., about a side of length b in., (b) a circle, diameter d in., about an axis through the centre perpendicular to its plane.

78. Find by integration the M.I. of a rod AB, about an axis through A perpendicular to the rod, given length AB $= l$ in., and m lb. is its mass per in. Find also the M.I. of the rod about a parallel axis through its mid-point.

79. The co-ordinates of a point A are $x = 5$, $y = 3$, and of a point B, $x = 8$, $y = 6$. Find the length of AB and the angle which the straight line AB makes with the positive sense of OX.

80. The height of the frustum of a cone is 6 in., and the diameter of the base and top are 12 in. and 10 in., respectively. Find the height of the cone and the volume of the frustum.

81. Plot $y = 2x^2 - 7x + 5$ for values of x between 0 and 3, and from the graph determine the roots of the equation $2x^2 - 7x + 5 = 0$. Find the roots of this equation by an alternative method.

82. AB is a diameter of a circle, and AC a chord 4 in. long making 60° with AB. CD is perpendicular to AB. Calculate (a) the radius, (b) the lengths BC and CD, and (c) the area of the triangle ABC.

83. With the usual notation, prove that the area of a triangle is given by $\sqrt{s(s - a)(s - b)(s - c)}$.

Find the volume of a steel bar of length 6 ft., whose cross section perpendicular to its length is a triangle of sides $3\frac{1}{2}$ in., $4\frac{1}{8}$ in. and $5\frac{3}{8}$ in.

84. Find the area between the parabola $y = x^2 - 3x$, the x-axis and the ordinates at $x = 1$ and $x = 3$. Find also the distance of the centroid of this area from the x-axis.

85. When x has the values $-2, 0, +1, +2$, the values of the function $ax^3 + bx^2 + cx + k$, where a, b, c, k are constants, are $-14, +4, -2$ and -2 respectively. For what other values of x is the function equal to $+4$?

86. For what value of θ, between $0°$ and $180°$, is $\tan \theta + 3 \sin \theta = 0$? By putting $\sin \theta + \cos \theta$ in the form $r \sin (\theta + \alpha)$, find its maximum value. If θ is one of the remaining angles of a right-angled triangle whose perimeter is 10 in., express the length of the hypotenuse as a function of θ, and find its minimum value.

87. (a) Expand $(2 + x)^5$ in ascending powers of x.

(b) Expand $(1 - \frac{3}{2}x)^{-\frac{1}{3}}$ to four terms, and hence find the value of $\dfrac{1}{\sqrt[3]{1 - \frac{3}{2}x}}$ correct to four decimal places when $x = 0·04$.

(c) Differentiate $x^{-\frac{1}{3}}$ from first principles.

88. Assuming the formula for the volume of a solid sphere of radius r, find by using Guldinus' Th. the position of the centroid of a semi-circular area of radius r.

A groove whose section is a semi-circle of diameter 1 in. is turned in a solid circular shaft of diameter 6 in. Find the volume of material removed.

89. Tabulate the values of the functions $\sin (2x + 10°)$ and $2 \cos (2x + 60°)$ for values of $x = 0°, 5°, 10°$ . . . up to $30°$. Using the same axes, draw the graphs of these two functions over the range $x = 0°$ to $x = 30°$, and read from your diagram a value of x (to the nearest degree) which satisfies the equation $\sin (2x + 10°) - 2 \cos (x + 60°) = 0$.

CONSTANTS

Constant.	Number.	Log.
π	3·1416	0·49715
$\dfrac{\pi}{4}$	0·7854	$\bar{1}$·89509
$\dfrac{1}{\pi}$	0·3183	$\bar{1}$·50285
π^2	9·8696	0·99430
$\sqrt{\pi}$	1·7725	0·24857
$\tfrac{4}{3}\pi$	4·1888	0·62209
$\dfrac{180}{\pi}$	57·2958	1·75812
$\dfrac{\pi}{180}$	0·01745	$\bar{2}$·24188
e	2·71828	0·43429
$\mathrm{Log}_e\,10$	2·3026	0·36222

CONVERSION FACTORS

To convert	Multiply by	Log.
Metres to inches . . .	39·37	1·59517
Inches to centimetres . .	2·5400	0·40483
Kilometres to miles . .	0·6214	$\bar{1}$·79335
Kilograms to lb. . . .	2·20462	0·34333
Lb. to kilograms . . .	0·45359	$\bar{1}$·65666
Gallons to cubic inches . .	277·45	2·44318
Radians to degrees . . .	57·2958	1·75812
Miles per hour to feet per second	1·4666	0·1663

G. (at Greenwich)   =   32·191 ft. per sec.^{2}
                        = 981·18 cm. per sec.^{2}
Weight of 1 cub. ft. of water =   62·42 lb. (at 4° C.)

LOGARITHMS.

No.	Log.	1	2	3	4	5	6	7	8	9	1	2	3	4	5	6	7	8	9
1·0	·0000	0043	0086	0128	0170	0212	0253	0294	0334	0374	4	8	12	17	21	25	29	33	37
1·1	·0414	0453	0492	0531	0569	0607	0645	0682	0719	0755	4	8	11	15	19	23	26	30	34
1·2	·0792	0828	0864	0899	0934	0969	1004	1038	1072	1106	3	7	10	14	17	21	24	28	31
1·3	·1139	1173	1206	1239	1271	1303	1335	1367	1399	1430	3	6	10	13	16	19	23	26	29
1·4	·1461	1492	1523	1553	1584	1614	1644	1673	1703	1732	3	6	9	12	15	18	21	24	27
1·5	·1761	1790	1818	1847	1875	1903	1931	1959	1987	2014	3	6	8	11	14	17	20	22	25
1·6	·2041	2068	2095	2122	2148	2175	2201	2227	2253	2279	3	5	8	11	13	16	18	21	24
1·7	·23C4	2330	2355	2380	2405	2430	2455	2480	2504	2529	2	5	7	10	12	15	17	20	22
1·8	·2553	2577	2601	2625	2648	2672	2695	2718	2742	2765	2	5	7	9	12	14	16	19	21
1·9	·2788	2810	2833	2856	2878	2900	2923	2945	2967	2989	2	4	7	9	11	13	16	18	20
2·0	·3010	3032	3054	3075	3096	3118	3139	3160	3181	3201	2	4	6	8	11	13	15	17	19
2·1	·3222	3243	3263	3284	3304	3324	3345	3365	3385	3404	2	4	6	8	10	12	14	16	18
2·2	·3424	3444	3464	3483	3502	3522	3541	3560	3579	3598	2	4	6	8	10	12	14	15	17
2·3	·3617	3636	3655	3674	3692	3711	3729	3747	3766	3784	2	4	6	7	9	11	13	15	17
2·4	·3802	3820	3838	3856	3874	3892	3909	3927	3945	3962	2	4	5	7	9	11	12	14	16
2·5	·3979	3997	4014	4031	4048	4065	4082	4099	4116	4133	2	3	5	7	9	10	12	14	15
2·6	·4150	4166	4183	4200	4216	4232	4249	4265	4281	4298	2	3	5	7	8	10	11	13	15
2·7	·4314	4330	4346	4362	4378	4393	4409	4425	4440	4456	2	3	5	6	8	9	11	13	14
2·8	·4472	4487	4502	4518	4533	4548	4564	4579	4594	4609	2	3	5	6	8	9	11	12	14
2·9	·4624	4639	4654	4669	4683	4698	4713	4728	4742	4757	1	3	4	6	7	9	10	12	13
3·0	·4771	4786	4800	4814	4829	4843	4857	4871	4886	4900	1	3	4	6	7	9	10	11	13
3·1	·4914	4928	4942	4955	4969	4983	4997	5011	5024	5038	1	3	4	6	7	8	10	11	12
3·2	·5051	5065	5079	5092	5105	5119	5132	5145	5159	5172	1	3	4	5	7	8	9	11	12
3·3	·5185	5198	5211	5224	5237	5250	5263	5276	5289	5302	1	3	4	5	6	8	9	10	12
3·4	·5315	5328	5340	5353	5366	5378	5391	5403	5416	5428	1·	3	4	5	6	8	9	10	11
3·5	·5441	5453	5465	5478	5490	5502	5514	5527	5539	5551	1	2	4	5	6	7	9	10	11
3·6	·5563	5575	5587	5599	5611	5623	5635	5647	5658	5670	1	2	4	5	6	7	8	10	11
3·7	·5682	5694	5705	5717	5729	5740	5752	5763	5775	5786	1	2	3	5	6	7	8	9	10
3·8	·5798	5809	5821	5832	5843	5855	5866	5877	5888	5899	1	2	3	5	6	7	8	9	10
3·9	·5911	5922	5933	5944	5955	5966	5977	5988	5999	6010	1	2	3	4	5	7	8	9	10
4·0	·6021	6031	6042	6053	6064	6075	6085	6096	6107	6117	1	2	3	4	5	6	8	9	10
4·1	·6128	6138	6149	6160	6170	6180	6191	6201	6212	6222	1	2	3	4	5	6	7	8	9
4·2	·6232	6243	6253	6263	6274	6284	6294	6304	6314	6325	1	2	3	4	5	6	7	8	9
4·3	·6335	6345	6355	6365	6375	6385	6395	6405	6415	6425	1	2	3	4	5	6	7	8	9
4·4	·6435	6444	6454	6464	6474	6484	6493	6503	6513	6522	1	2	3	4	5	6	7	8	9
4·5	·6532	6542	6551	6561	6571	6580	6590	6599	6609	6618	1	2	3	4	5	6	7	8	9
4·6	·6628	6637	6646	6656	6665	6675	6684	6693	6702	6712	1	2	3	4	5	6	7	7	8
4·7	·6721	6730	6739	6749	6758	6767	6776	6785	6794	6803	1	2	3	4	5	5	6	7	8
4·8	·6812	6821	6830	6839	6848	6857	6866	6875	6884	6893	1	2	3	4	4	5	6	7	8
4·9	·6902	6911	6920	6928	6937	6946	6955	6964	6972	6981	1	2	3	4	4	5	6	7	8
5·0	·6990	6998	7007	7016	7024	7033	7042	7050	7059	7067	1	2	3	3	4	5	6	7	8
5·1	·7076	7084	7093	7101	7110	7118	7126	7135	7143	7152	1	2	3	3	4	5	6	7	8
5·2	·7160	7168	7177	7185	7193	7202	7210	7218	7226	7235	1	2	2	3	4	5	6	7	7
5·3	·7243	7251	7259	7267	7275	7284	7292	7300	7308	7316	1	2	2	3	4	5	6	6	7
5·4	·7324	7332	7340	7348	7356	7364	7372	7380	7388	7396	1	2	2	3	4	5	6	6	7

LOGARITHMS.

No.	Log.	1	2	3	4	5	6	7	8	9	1	2	3	4	5	6	7	8	9
5·5	·7404	7412	7419	7427	7435	7443	7451	7459	7466	7474	1	2	2	3	4	5	5	6	7
5·6	·7482	7490	7497	7505	7513	7520	7528	7536	7543	7551	1	2	2	3	4	5	5	6	7
5·7	·7559	7566	7574	7582	7589	7597	7604	7612	7619	7627	1	2	2	3	4	5	5	6	7
5·8	·7634	7642	7649	7657	7664	7672	7679	7686	7694	7701	1	1	2	3	4	4	5	6	7
5·9	·7709	7716	7723	7731	7738	7745	7752	7760	7767	7774	1	1	2	3	4	4	5	6	7
6·0	·7782	7789	7796	7803	7810	7818	7825	7832	7839	7846	1	1	2	3	4	4	5	6	6
6·1	·7853	7860	7868	7875	7882	7889	7896	7903	7910	7917	1	1	2	3	4	4	5	6	6
6·2	·7924	7931	7938	7945	7952	7959	7966	7973	7980	7987	1	1	2	3	3	4	5	6	6
6·3	·7993	8000	8007	8014	8021	8028	8035	8041	8048	8055	1	1	2	3	3	4	5	5	6
6·4	·8062	8069	8075	8082	8089	8096	8102	8109	8116	8122	1	1	2	3	3	4	5	5	6
6·5	·8129	8136	8142	8149	8156	8162	8169	8176	8182	8189	1	1	2	3	3	4	5	5	6
6·6	·8195	8202	8209	8215	8222	8228	8235	8241	8248	8254	1	1	2	3	3	4	5	5	6
6·7	·8261	8267	8274	8280	8287	8293	8299	8306	8312	8319	1	1	2	3	3	4	5	5	6
6·8	·8325	8331	8338	8344	8351	8357	8363	8370	8376	8382	1	1	2	3	3	4	4	5	6
6·9	·8388	8395	8401	8407	8414	8420	8426	8432	8439	8445	1	1	2	2	3	4	4	5	6
7·0	·8451	8457	8463	8470	8476	8482	8488	8494	8500	8506	1	1	2	2	3	4	4	5	6
7·1	·8513	8519	8525	8531	8537	8543	8549	8555	8561	8567	1	1	2	2	3	4	4	5	5
7·2	·8573	8579	8585	8591	8597	8603	8609	8615	8621	8627	1	1	2	2	3	4	4	5	5
7·3	·8633	8639	8645	8651	8657	8663	8669	8675	8681	8686	1	1	2	2	3	4	4	5	5
7·4	·8692	8698	8704	8710	8716	8722	8727	8733	8739	8745	1	1	2	2	3	4	4	5	5
7·5	·8751	8756	8762	8768	8774	8779	8785	8791	8797	8802	1	1	2	2	3	3	4	5	5
7·6	·8808	8814	8820	8825	8831	8837	8842	8848	8854	8859	1	1	2	2	3	3	4	5	5
7·7	·8865	8871	8876	8882	8887	8893	8899	8904	8910	8915	1	1	2	2	3	3	4	4	5
7·8	·8921	8927	8932	8938	8943	8949	8954	8960	8965	8971	1	1	2	2	3	3	4	4	5
7·9	·8976	8982	8987	8993	8998	9004	9009	9015	9020	9025	1	1	2	2	3	3	4	4	5
8·0	·9031	9036	9042	9047	9053	9058	9063	9069	9074	9079	1	1	2	2	3	3	4	4	5
8·1	·9085	9090	9096	9101	9106	9112	9117	9122	9128	9133	1	1	2	2	3	3	4	4	5
8·2	·9138	9143	9149	9154	9159	9165	9170	9175	9180	9186	1	1	2	2	3	3	4	4	5
8·3	·9191	9196	9201	9206	9212	9217	9222	9227	9232	9238	1	1	2	2	3	3	4	4	5
8·4	·9243	9248	9253	9258	9263	9269	9274	9279	9284	9289	1	1	2	2	3	3	4	4	5
8·5	·9294	9299	9304	9309	9315	9320	9325	9330	9335	9340	1	1	2	2	3	3	4	4	5
8·6	·9345	9350	9355	9360	9365	9370	9375	9380	9385	9390	1	1	2	2	3	3	4	4	5
8·7	·9395	9400	9405	9410	9415	9420	9425	9430	9435	9440	0	1	1	2	2	3	3	4	4
8·8	·9445	9450	9455	9460	9465	9469	9474	9479	9484	9489	0	1	1	2	2	3	3	4	4
8·9	·9494	9499	9504	9509	9513	9518	9523	9528	9533	9538	0	1	1	2	2	3	3	4	4
9·0	·9542	9547	9552	9557	9562	9566	9571	9576	9581	9586	0	1	1	2	2	3	3	4	4
9·1	·9590	9595	9600	9605	9609	9614	9619	9624	9628	9633	0	1	1	2	2	3	3	4	4
9·2	·9638	9643	9647	9652	9657	9661	9666	9671	9675	9680	0	1	1	2	2	3	3	4	4
9·3	·9685	9689	9694	9699	9703	9708	9713	9717	9722	9727	0	1	1	2	2	3	3	4	4
9·4	·9731	9736	9741	9745	9750	9754	9759	9763	9768	9773	0	1	1	2	2	3	3	4	4
9·5	·9777	9782	9786	9791	9795	9800	9805	9809	9814	9818	0	1	1	2	2	3	3	4	4
9·6	·9823	9827	9832	9836	9841	9845	9850	9854	9859	9863	0	1	1	2	2	3	3	4	4
9·7	·9868	9872	9877	9881	9886	9890	9894	9899	9903	9908	0	1	1	2	2	3	3	4	4
9·8	·9912	9917	9921	9926	9930	9934	9939	9943	9948	9952	0	1	1	2	2	3	3	4	4
9·9	·9956	9961	9965	9969	9974	9978	9983	9987	9991	9996	0	1	1	2	2	3	3	3	4

ANTI-LOGARITHMS.

Log.	0	1	2	3	4	5	6	7	8	9	1	2	3	4	5	6	7	8	9
·00	1000	1002	1005	1007	1009	1012	1014	1016	1019	1021	0	0	1	1	1	1	2	2	2
·01	1023	1026	1028	1030	1033	1035	1038	1040	1042	1045	0	0	1	1	1	1	2	2	2
·02	1047	1050	1052	1054	1057	1059	1062	1064	1067	1069	0	0	1	1	1	1	2	2	2
·03	1072	1074	1076	1079	1081	1084	1086	1089	1091	1094	0	0	1	1	1	1	2	2	2
·04	1096	1099	1102	1104	1107	1109	1112	1114	1117	1119	0	1	1	1	1	2	2	2	2
·05	1122	1125	1127	1130	1132	1135	1138	1140	1143	1146	0	1	1	1	1	2	2	2	2
·06	1148	1151	1153	1156	1159	1161	1164	1167	1169	1172	0	1	1	1	1	2	2	2	2
·07	1175	1178	1180	1183	1186	1189	1191	1194	1197	1199	0	1	1	1	1	2	2	2	2
·08	1202	1205	1208	1211	1213	1216	1219	1222	1225	1227	0	1	1	1	1	2	2	2	3
·09	1230	1233	1236	1239	1242	1245	1247	1250	1253	1256	0	1	1	1	1	2	2	2	3
·10	1259	1262	1265	1268	1271	1274	1276	1279	1282	1285	0	1	1	1	1	2	2	2	3
·11	1288	1291	1294	1297	1300	1303	1306	1309	1312	1315	0	1	1	1	2	2	2	2	3
·12	1318	1321	1324	1327	1330	1334	1337	1340	1343	1346	0	1	1	1	2	2	2	2	3
·13	1349	1352	1355	1358	1361	1365	1368	1371	1374	1377	0	1	1	1	2	2	2	3	3
·14	1380	1384	1387	1390	1393	1396	1400	1403	1406	1409	0	1	1	1	2	2	2	3	3
·15	1413	1416	1419	1422	1426	1429	1432	1435	1439	1442	0	1	1	1	2	2	2	3	3
·16	1445	1449	1452	1455	1459	1462	1466	1469	1472	1476	0	1	1	1	2	2	3	3	3
·17	1479	1483	1486	1489	1493	1496	1500	1503	1507	1510	0	1	1	1	2	2	3	3	3
·18	1514	1517	1521	1524	1528	1531	1535	1538	1542	1545	0	1	1	1	2	2	3	3	3
·19	1549	1552	1556	1560	1563	1567	1570	1574	1578	1581	0	1	1	1	2	2	3	3	3
·20	1585	1589	1592	1596	1600	1603	1607	1611	1614	1618	0	1	1	1	2	2	3	3	3
·21	1622	1626	1629	1633	1637	1641	1644	1648	1652	1656	0	1	1	2	2	2	3	3	3
·22	1660	1663	1667	1671	1675	1679	1683	1687	1690	1694	0	1	1	2	2	2	3	3	3
·23	1698	1702	1706	1710	1714	1718	1722	1726	1730	1734	0	1	1	2	2	2	3	3	4
·24	1738	1742	1746	1750	1754	1758	1762	1766	1770	1774	0	1	1	2	2	2	3	3	4
·25	1778	1782	1786	1791	1795	1799	1803	1807	1811	1816	0	1	1	2	2	2	3	3	4
·26	1820	1824	1828	1832	1837	1841	1845	1849	1854	1858	0	1	1	2	2	3	3	3	4
·27	1862	1866	1871	1875	1879	1884	1888	1892	1897	1901	0	1	1	2	2	3	3	3	4
·28	1905	1910	1914	1919	1923	1928	1932	1936	1941	1945	0	1	1	2	2	3	3	4	4
·29	1950	1954	1959	1963	1968	1972	1977	1982	1986	1991	0	1	1	2	2	3	3	4	4
·30	1995	2000	2004	2009	2014	2018	2023	2028	2032	2037	0	1	1	2	2	3	3	4	4
·31	2042	2046	2051	2056	2061	2065	2070	2075	2080	2084	0	1	1	2	2	3	3	4	4
·32	2089	2094	2099	2104	2109	2113	2118	2123	2128	2133	0	1	1	2	2	3	3	4	4
·33	2138	2143	2148	2153	2158	2163	2168	2173	2178	2183	0	1	1	2	2	3	3	4	4
·34	2188	2193	2198	2203	2208	2213	2218	2223	2228	2234	1	1	2	2	3	3	4	4	5
·35	2239	2244	2249	2254	2259	2265	2270	2275	2280	2286	1	1	2	2	3	3	4	4	5
·36	2291	2296	2301	2307	2312	2317	2323	2328	2333	2339	1	1	2	2	3	3	4	4	5
37	2344	2350	2355	2360	2366	2371	2377	2382	2388	2393	1	1	2	2	3	3	4	4	5
·38	2399	2404	2410	2415	2421	2427	2432	2438	2443	2449	1	1	2	2	3	3	4	5	5
·39	2455	2460	2466	2472	2477	2483	2489	2495	2500	2506	1	1	2	2	3	3	4	5	5
·40	2512	2518	2523	2529	2535	2541	2547	2553	2559	2564	1	1	2	2	3	4	4	5	5
·41	2570	2576	2582	2588	2594	2600	2606	2612	2618	2624	1	1	2	2	3	4	4	5	5
·42	2630	2636	2642	2649	2655	2661	2667	2673	2679	2685	1	1	2	2	3	4	4	5	6
·43	2692	2698	2704	2710	2716	2723	2729	2735	2742	2748	1	1	2	3	3	4	4	5	6
·44	2754	2761	2767	2773	2780	2786	2793	2799	2805	2812	1	1	2	3	3	4	4	5	6
·45	2818	2825	2831	2838	2844	2851	2858	2864	2871	2877	1	1	2	3	3	4	5	5	6
·46	2884	2891	2897	2904	2911	2917	2924	2931	2938	2944	1	1	2	3	3	4	5	5	6
·47	2951	2958	2965	2972	2979	2985	2992	2999	3006	3013	1	1	2	3	3	4	5	5	6
·48	3020	3027	3034	3041	3048	3055	3062	3069	3076	3083	1	1	2	3	3	4	5	5	6
·49	3090	3097	3105	3112	3119	3126	3133	3141	3148	3155	1	1	2	3	4	4	5	6	6

ANTI-LOGARITHMS.

Log.	0	1	2	3	4	5	6	7	8	9	1	2	3	4	5	6	7	8	9
·50	3162	3170	3177	3184	3192	3199	3206	3214	3221	3228	1	1	2	3	4	4	5	6	7
·51	3236	3243	3251	3258	3266	3273	3281	3289	3296	3304	1	2	2	3	4	5	5	6	7
·52	3311	3319	3327	3334	3342	3350	3357	3365	3373	3381	1	2	2	3	4	5	5	6	7
·53	3388	3396	3404	3412	3420	3428	3436	3443	3451	3459	1	2	2	3	4	5	6	6	7
·54	3467	3475	3483	3491	3499	3508	3516	3524	3532	3540	1	2	2	3	4	5	6	6	7
·55	3548	3556	3565	3573	3581	3589	3597	3606	3614	3622	1	2	2	3	4	5	6	7	7
·56	3631	3639	3648	3656	3664	3673	3681	3690	3698	3707	1	2	3	3	4	5	6	7	8
·57	3715	3724	3733	3741	3750	3758	3767	3776	3784	3793	1	2	3	3	4	5	6	7	8
·58	3802	3811	3819	3828	3837	3846	3855	3864	3873	3882	1	2	3	4	4	5	6	7	8
·59	3890	3899	3908	3917	3926	3936	3945	3954	3963	3972	1	2	3	4	5	5	6	7	8
·60	3981	3990	3999	4009	4018	4027	4036	4046	4055	4064	1	2	3	4	5	6	6	7	8
·61	4074	4083	4093	4102	4111	4121	4130	4140	4150	4159	1	2	3	4	5	6	7	8	9
·62	4169	4178	4188	4198	4207	4217	4227	4236	4246	4256	1	2	3	4	5	6	7	8	9
·63	4266	4276	4285	4295	4305	4315	4325	4335	4345	4355	1	2	3	4	5	6	7	8	9
·64	4365	4375	4385	4395	4406	4416	4426	4436	4446	4457	1	2	3	4	5	6	7	8	9
·65	4467	4477	4487	4498	4508	4519	4529	4539	4550	4560	1	2	3	4	5	6	7	8	9
·66	4571	4581	4592	4603	4613	4624	4634	4645	4656	4667	1	2	3	4	5	6	7	9	10
·67	4677	4688	4699	4710	4721	4732	4742	4753	4764	4775	1	2	3	4	5	7	8	9	10
·68	4786	4797	4808	4819	4831	4842	4853	4864	4875	4887	1	2	3	4	6	7	8	9	10
·69	4898	4909	4920	4932	4943	4955	4966	4977	4989	5000	1	2	3	5	6	7	8	9	10
·70	5012	5023	5035	5047	5058	5070	5082	5093	5105	5117	1	2	4	5	6	7	8	9	11
·71	5129	5140	5152	5164	5176	5188	5200	5212	5224	5236	1	2	4	5	6	7	8	10	11
·72	5248	5260	5272	5284	5297	5309	5321	5333	5346	5358	1	2	4	5	6	7	9	10	11
·73	5370	5383	5395	5408	5420	5433	5445	5458	5470	5483	1	3	4	5	6	8	9	10	11
·74	5495	5508	5521	5534	5546	5559	5572	5585	5598	5610	1	3	4	5	6	8	9	10	12
·75	5623	5636	5649	5662	5675	5689	5702	5715	5728	5741	1	3	4	5	7	8	9	10	12
·76	5754	5768	5781	5794	5808	5821	5834	5848	5861	5875	1	3	4	5	7	8	9	11	12
·77	5888	5902	5916	5929	5943	5957	5970	5984	5998	6012	1	3	4	5	7	8	10	11	12
·78	6026	6039	6053	6067	6081	6095	6109	6124	6138	6152	1	3	4	6	7	8	10	11	13
·79	6166	6180	6194	6209	6223	6237	6252	6266	6281	6295	1	3	4	6	7	9	10	11	13
·80	6310	6324	6339	6353	6368	6383	6397	6412	6427	6442	1	3	4	6	7	9	10	12	13
·81	6457	6471	6486	6501	6516	6531	6546	6561	6577	6592	2	3	5	6	8	9	11	12	14
·82	6607	6622	6637	6653	6668	6683	6699	6714	6730	6745	2	3	5	6	8	9	11	12	14
·83	6761	6776	6792	6808	6823	6839	6855	6871	6887	6902	2	3	5	6	8	9	11	13	14
·84	6918	6934	6950	6966	6982	6998	7015	7031	7047	7063	2	3	5	6	8	10	11	13	15
·85	7079	7096	7112	7129	7145	7161	7178	7194	7211	7228	2	3	5	7	8	10	12	13	15
·86	7244	7261	7278	7295	7311	7328	7345	7362	7379	7396	2	3	5	7	8	10	12	13	15
·87	7413	7430	7447	7464	7482	7499	7516	7534	7551	7568	2	3	5	7	9	10	12	14	16
·88	7586	7603	7621	7638	7656	7674	7691	7709	7727	7745	2	4	5	7	9	11	12	14	16
·89	7762	7780	7798	7816	7834	7852	7870	7889	7907	7925	2	4	5	7	9	11	13	14	16
·90	7943	7962	7980	7998	8017	8035	8054	8072	8091	8110	2	4	6	7	9	11	13	15	17
·91	8128	8147	8166	8185	8204	8222	8241	8260	8279	8299	2	4	6	8	9	11	13	15	17
·92	8318	8337	8356	8375	8395	8414	8433	8453	8472	8492	2	4	6	8	10	12	14	15	17
·93	8511	8531	8551	8570	8590	8610	8630	8650	8670	8690	2	4	6	8	10	12	14	16	18
·94	8710	8730	8750	8770	8790	8810	8831	8851	8872	8892	2	4	6	8	10	12	14	16	18
·95	8913	8933	8954	8974	8995	9016	9036	9057	9078	9099	2	4	6	8	10	12	15	17	19
·96	9120	9141	9162	9183	9204	9226	9247	9268	9290	9311	2	4	6	8	11	13	15	17	19
·97	9333	9354	9376	9397	9419	9441	9462	9484	9506	9528	2	4	7	9	11	13	15	17	20
·98	9550	9572	9594	9616	9638	9661	9683	9705	9727	9750	2	4	7	9	11	13	16	18	20
·99	9772	9795	9817	9840	9863	9886	9908	9931	9954	9977	2	5	7	9	11	14	16	18	20

NATURAL SINES.

Angle.	0′	6′	12′	18′	24′	30′	36′	42′	48′	54′	1′	2′	3′	4′	5′
0°	·0000	·0017	·0035	·0052	·0070	·0087	·0105	·0122	·0140	·0157	3	6	9	12	15
1°	·0175	·0192	·0209	·0227	·0244	·0262	·0279	·0297	·0314	·0332	3	6	9	12	15
2°	·0349	·0366	·0384	·0401	·0419	·0436	·0454	·0471	·0488	·0506	3	6	9	12	15
3°	·0523	·0541	·0558	·0576	·0593	·0610	·0628	·0645	·0663	·0680	3	6	9	12	15
4°	·0698	·0715	·0732	·0750	·0767	·0785	·0802	·0819	·0837	·0854	3	6	9	12	14
5°	·0872	·0889	·0906	·0924	·0941	·0958	·0976	·0993	·1011	·1028	3	6	9	12	14
6°	·1045	·1063	·1080	·1097	·1115	·1132	·1149	·1167	·1184	·1201	3	6	9	12	14
7°	·1219	·1236	·1253	·1271	·1288	·1305	·1323	·1340	·1357	·1374	3	6	9	12	14
8°	·1392	·1409	·1426	·1444	·1461	·1478	·1495	·1513	·1530	·1547	3	6	9	12	14
9°	·1564	·1582	·1599	·1616	·1633	·1650	·1668	·1685	·1702	·1719	3	6	9	12	14
10°	·1736	·1754	·1771	·1788	·1805	·1822	·1840	·1857	·1874	·1891	3	6	9	11	14
11°	·1908	·1925	·1942	·1959	·1977	·1994	·2011	·2028	·2045	·2062	3	6	9	11	14
12°	·2079	·2096	·2113	·2130	·2147	·2164	·2181	·2198	·2215	·2233	3	6	9	11	14
13°	·2250	·2267	·2284	·2300	·2317	·2334	·2351	·2368	·2385	·2402	3	6	8	11	14
14°	·2419	·2436	·2453	·2470	·2487	·2504	·2521	·2538	·2554	·2571	3	6	8	11	14
15°	·2588	·2605	·2622	·2639	·2656	·2672	·2689	·2706	·2723	·2740	3	6	8	11	14
16°	·2756	·2773	·2790	·2807	·2823	·2840	·2857	·2874	·2890	·2907	3	6	8	11	14
17°	·2924	·2940	·2957	·2974	·2990	·3007	·3024	·3040	·3057	·3074	3	6	8	11	14
18°	·3090	·3107	·3123	·3140	·3156	·3173	·3190	·3206	·3223	·3239	3	6	8	11	14
19°	·3256	·3272	·3289	·3305	·3322	·3338	·3355	·3371	·3387	·3404	3	5	8	11	14
20°	·3420	·3437	·3453	·3469	·3486	·3502	·3518	·3535	·3551	·3567	3	5	8	11	14
21°	·3584	·3600	·3616	·3633	·3649	·3665	·3681	·3697	·3714	·3730	3	5	8	11	14
22°	·3746	·3762	·3778	·3795	·3811	·3827	·3843	·3859	·3875	·3891	3	5	8	11	14
23°	·3907	·3923	·3939	·3955	·3971	·3987	·4003	·4019	·4035	·4051	3	5	8	11	14
24°	·4067	·4083	·4099	·4115	·4131	·4147	·4163	·4179	·4195	·4210	3	5	8	11	13
25°	·4226	·4242	·4258	·4274	·4289	·4305	·4321	·4337	·4352	·4368	3	5	8	11	13
26°	·4384	·4399	·4415	·4431	·4446	·4462	·4478	·4493	·4509	·4524	3	5	8	10	13
27°	·4540	·4555	·4571	·4586	·4602	·4617	·4633	·4648	·4664	·4679	3	5	8	10	13
28°	·4695	·4710	·4726	·4741	·4756	·4772	·4787	·4802	·4818	·4833	3	5	8	10	13
29°	·4848	·4863	·4879	·4894	·4909	·4924	·4939	·4955	·4970	·4985	3	5	8	10	13
30°	·5000	·5015	·5030	·5045	·5060	·5075	·5090	·5105	·5120	·5135	3	5	8	10	13
31°	·5150	·5165	·5180	·5195	·5210	·5225	·5240	·5255	·5270	·5284	2	5	7	10	12
32°	·5299	·5314	·5329	·5344	·5358	·5373	·5388	·5402	·5417	·5432	2	5	7	10	12
33°	·5446	·5461	·5476	·5490	·5505	·5519	·5534	·5548	·5563	·5577	2	5	7	10	12
34°	·5592	·5606	·5621	·5635	·5650	·5664	·5678	·5693	·5707	·5721	2	5	7	10	12
35°	·5736	·5750	·5764	·5779	·5793	·5807	·5821	·5835	·5850	·5864	2	5	7	9	12
36°	·5878	·5892	·5906	·5920	·5934	·5948	·5962	·5976	·5990	·6004	2	5	7	9	12
37°	·6018	·6032	·6046	·6060	·6074	·6088	·6101	·6115	·6129	·6143	2	5	7	9	12
38°	·6157	·6170	·6184	·6198	·6211	·6225	·6239	·6252	·6266	·6280	2	5	7	9	11
39°	·6293	·6307	·6320	·6334	·6347	·6361	·6374	·6388	·6401	·6414	2	4	7	9	11
40°	·6428	·6441	·6455	·6468	·6481	·6494	·6508	·6521	·6534	·6547	2	4	7	9	11
41°	·6561	·6574	·6587	·6600	·6613	·6626	·6639	·6652	·6665	·6678	2	4	7	9	11
42°	·6691	·6704	·6717	·6730	·6743	·6756	·6769	·6782	·6794	·6807	2	4	6	9	11
43°	·6820	·6833	·6845	·6858	·6871	·6884	·6896	·6909	·6921	·6934	2	4	6	8	11
44°	·6947	·6959	·6972	·6984	·6997	·7009	·7022	·7034	·7046	·7059	2	4	6	8	10

NATURAL SINES.

Angle	0'	6'	12'	18'	24'	30'	36'	42'	48'	54'	1'	2'	3'	4	5'
45°	·7071	·7083	·7096	·7108	·7120	·7133	·7145	·7157	·7169	·7181	2	4	6	8	10
46°	·7193	·7206	·7218	·7230	·7242	·7254	·7266	·7278	·7290	·7302	2	4	6	8	10
47°	·7314	·7325	·7337	·7349	·7361	·7373	·7385	·7396	·7408	·7420	2	4	6	8	10
48°	·7431	·7443	·7455	·7466	·7478	·7490	·7501	·7513	·7524	·7536	2	4	6	8	10
49°	·7547	·7559	·7570	·7581	·7593	·7604	·7615	·7627	·7638	·7649	2	4	6	8	9
50°	·7660	·7672	·7683	·7694	·7705	·7716	·7727	·7738	·7749	·7760	2	4	6	7	9
51°	·7771	·7782	·7793	·7804	·7815	·7826	·7837	·7848	·7859	·7869	2	4	5	7	9
52°	·7880	·7891	·7902	·7912	·7923	·7934	·7944	·7955	·7965	·7976	2	4	5	7	9
53°	·7986	·7997	·8007	·8018	·8028	·8039	·8049	·8059	·8070	·8080	2	3	5	7	9
54°	·8090	·8100	·8111	·8121	·8131	·8141	·8151	·8161	·8171	·8181	2	3	5	7	8
55°	·8192	·8202	·8211	·8221	·8231	·8241	·8251	·8261	·8271	·8281	2	3	5	7	8
56°	·8290	·8300	·8310	·8320	·8329	·8339	·8348	·8358	·8368	·8377	2	3	5	6	8
57°	·8387	·8396	·8406	·8415	·8425	·8434	·8443	·8453	·8462	·8471	2	3	5	6	8
58°	·8480	·8490	·8499	·8508	·8517	·8526	·8536	·8545	·8554	·8563	2	3	5	6	8
59°	·8572	·8581	·8590	·8599	·8607	·8616	·8625	·8634	·8643	·8652	1	3	4	6	7
60°	·8660	·8669	·8678	·8686	·8695	·8704	·8712	·8721	·8729	·8738	1	3	4	6	7
61°	·8746	·8755	·8763	·8771	·8780	·8788	·8796	·8805	·8813	·8821	1	3	4	6	7
62°	·8829	·8838	·8846	·8854	·8862	·8870	·8878	·8886	·8894	·8902	1	3	4	5	7
63°	·8910	·8918	·8926	·8934	·8942	·8949	·8957	·8965	·8973	·8980	1	3	4	5	6
64°	·8988	·8996	·9003	·9011	·9018	·9026	·9033	·9041	·9048	·9056	1	3	4	5	6
65°	·9063	·9070	·9078	·9085	·9092	·9100	·9107	·9114	·9121	·9128	1	2	4	5	6
66°	·9135	·9143	·9150	·9157	·9164	·9171	·9178	·9184	·9191	·9198	1	2	3	5	6
67°	·9205	·9212	·9219	·9225	·9232	·9239	·9245	·9252	·9259	·9265	1	2	3	4	6
68°	·9272	·9278	·9285	·9291	·9298	·9304	·9311	·9317	·9323	·9330	1	2	3	4	5
69°	·9336	·9342	·9348	·9354	·9361	·9367	·9373	·9379	·9385	·9391	1	2	3	4	5
70°	·9397	·9403	·9409	·9415	·9421	·9426	·9432	·9438	·9444	·9449	1	2	3	4	5
71°	·9455	·9461	·9466	·9472	·9478	·9483	·9489	·9494	·9500	·9505	1	2	3	4	5
72°	·9511	·9516	·9521	·9527	·9532	·9537	·9542	·9548	·9553	·9558	1	2	3	3	4
73°	·9563	·9568	·9573	·9578	·9583	·9588	·9593	·9598	·9603	·9608	1	2	2	3	4
74°	·9613	·9617	·9622	·9627	·9632	·9636	·9641	·9646	·9650	·9655	1	2	2	3	4
75°	·9659	·9664	·9668	·9673	·9677	·9681	·9686	·9690	·9694	·9699	1	1	2	3	4
76°	·9703	·9707	·9711	·9715	·9720	·9724	·9728	·9732	·9736	·9740	1	1	2	3	3
77°	·9744	·9748	·9751	·9755	·9759	·9763	·9767	·9770	·9774	·9778	1	1	2	3	3
78°	·9781	·9785	·9789	·9792	·9796	·9799	·9803	·9806	·9810	·9813	1	1	2	2	3
79°	·9816	·9820	·9823	·9826	·9829	·9833	·9836	·9839	·9842	·9845	1	1	2	2	3
80°	·9848	·9851	·9854	·9857	·9860	·9863	·9866	·9869	·9871	·9874	0	1	1	2	2
81°	·9877	·9880	·9882	·9885	·9888	·9890	·9893	·9895	·9898	·9900	0	1	1	2	2
82°	·9903	·9905	·9907	·9910	·9912	·9914	·9917	·9919	·9921	·9923	0	1	1	2	2
83°	·9925	·9928	·9930	·9932	·9934	·9936	·9938	·9940	·9942	·9943	0	1	1	1	2
84°	·9945	·9947	·9949	·9951	·9952	·9954	·9956	·9957	·9959	·9960	0	1	1	1	1
85°	·9962	·9963	·9965	·9966	·9968	·9969	·9971	·9972	·9973	·9974	0	0	1	1	1
86°	·9976	·9977	·9978	·9979	·9980	·9981	·9982	·9983	·9984	·9985	0	0	1	1	1
87°	·9986	·9987	·9988	·9989	·9990	·9990	·9991	·9992	·9993	·9993	0	0	0	1	1
88°	·9994	·9995	·9995	·9996	·9996	·9997	·9997	·9997	·9998	·9998	0	0	0	0	0
89°	·9998	·9999	·9999	·9999	·9999	1·000	1·000	1·000	1·000	1·000	0	0	0	0	0

NATURAL COSINES.

	0′	6′	12′	18′	24′	30′	36′	42′	48′	54′	1′	2′	3′	4′
0°	1·0000	1·000	1·000	1·000	1·000	1·000	·9999	·9999	·9999	·9999	0	0	0	0
1°	·9998	·9998	·9998	·9997	·9997	·9997	·9996	·9996	·9995	·9995	0	0	0	0
2°	·9994	·9993	·9993	·9992	·9991	·9990	·9990	·9989	·9988	·9987	0	0	0	0
3°	·9986	·9985	·9984	·9983	·9982	·9981	·9980	·9979	·9978	·9977	0	0	1	1
4°	·9976	·9974	·9973	·9972	·9971	·9969	·9968	·9966	·9965	·9963	0	0	1	1
5°	·9962	·9960	·9959	·9957	·9956	·9954	·9952	·9951	·9949	·9947	0	1	1	1
6°	·9945	·9943	·9942	·9940	·9938	·9936	·9934	·9932	·9930	·9928	0	1	1	1
7°	·9925	·9923	·9921	·9919	·9917	·9914	·9912	·9910	·9907	·9905	0	1	1	2
8°	·9903	·9900	·9898	·9895	·9893	·9890	·9888	·9885	·9882	·9880	0	1	1	2
9°	·9877	·9874	·9871	·9869	·9866	·9863	·9860	·9857	·9854	·9851	0	1	1	2
10°	·9848	·9845	·9842	·9839	·9836	·9833	·9829	·9826	·9823	·9820	1	1	2	2
11°	·9816	·9813	·9810	·9806	·9803	·9799	·9796	·9792	·9789	·9785	1	1	2	2
12°	·9781	·9778	·9774	·9770	·9767	·9763	·9759	·9755	·9751	·9748	1	1	2	3
13°	·9744	·9740	·9736	·9732	·9728	·9724	·9720	·9715	·9711	·9707	1	1	2	3
14°	·9703	·9699	·9694	·9690	·9686	·9681	·9677	·9673	·9668	·9664	1	1	2	3
15°	·9659	·9655	·9650	·9646	·9641	·9636	·9632	·9627	·9622	·9617	1	2	2	3
16°	·9613	·9608	·9603	·9598	·9593	·9588	·9583	·9578	·9573	·9568	1	2	2	3
17°	·9563	·9558	·9553	·9548	·9542	·9537	·9532	·9527	·9521	·9516	1	2	3	4
18°	·9511	·9505	·9500	·9494	·9489	·9483	·9478	·9472	·9466	·9461	1	2	3	4
19°	·9455	·9449	·9444	·9438	·9432	·9426	·9421	·9415	·9409	·9403	1	2	3	4
20°	·9397	·9391	·9385	·9379	·9373	·9367	·9361	·9354	·9348	·9342	1	2	3	4
21°	·9336	·9330	·9323	·9317	·9311	·9304	·9298	·9291	·9285	·9278	1	2	3	4
22°	·9272	·9265	·9259	·9252	·9245	·9239	·9232	·9225	·9219	·9212	1	2	3	4
23°	·9205	·9198	·9191	·9184	·9178	·9171	·9164	·9157	·9150	·9143	1	2	3	5
24°	·9135	·9128	·9121	·9114	·9107	·9100	·9092	·9085	·9078	·9070	1	2	4	5
25°	·9063	·9056	·9048	·9041	·9033	·9026	·9018	·9011	·9003	·8996	1	3	4	5
26°	·8988	·8980	·8973	·8965	·8957	·8949	·8942	·8934	·8926	·8918	1	3	4	5
27°	·8910	·8902	·8894	·8886	·8878	·8870	·8862	·8854	·8846	·8838	1	3	4	5
28°	·8829	·8821	·8813	·8805	·8796	·8788	·8780	·8771	·8763	·8755	1	3	4	6
29°	·8746	·8738	·8729	·8721	·8712	·8704	·8695	·8686	·8678	·8669	1	3	4	6
30°	·8660	·8652	·8643	·8634	·8625	·8616	·8607	·8599	·8590	·8581	1	3	4	6
31°	·8572	·8563	·8554	·8545	·8536	·8526	·8517	·8508	·8499	·8490	2	3	5	6
32°	·8480	·8471	·8462	·8453	·8443	·8434	·8425	·8415	·8406	·8396	2	3	5	6
33°	·8387	·8377	·8368	·8358	·8348	·8339	·8329	·8320	·8310	·8300	2	3	5	6
34°	·8290	·8281	·8271	·8261	·8251	·8241	·8231	·8221	·8211	·8202	2	3	5	7
35°	·8192	·8181	·8171	·8161	·8151	·8141	·8131	·8121	·8111	·8100	2	3	5	7
36°	·8090	·8080	·8070	·8059	·8049	·8039	·8028	·8018	·8007	·7997	2	3	5	7
37°	·7986	·7976	·7965	·7955	·7944	·7934	·7923	·7912	·7902	·7891	2	4	5	7
38°	·7880	·7869	·7859	·7848	·7837	·7826	·7815	·7804	·7793	·7782	2	4	5	7
39°	·7771	·7760	·7749	·7738	·7727	·7716	·7705	·7694	·7683	·7672	2	4	6	7
40°	·7660	·7649	·7638	·7627	·7615	·7604	·7593	·7581	·7570	·7559	2	4	6	8
41°	·7547	·7536	·7524	·7513	·7501	·7490	·7478	·7466	·7455	·7443	2	4	6	8
42°	·7431	·7420	·7408	·7396	·7385	·7373	·7361	·7349	·7337	·7325	2	4	6	8
43°	·7314	·7302	·7290	·7278	·7266	·7254	·7242	·7230	·7218	·7206	2	4	6	8
44°	·7193	·7181	·7169	·7157	·7145	·7133	·7120	·7108	·7096	·7083	2	4	6	8

NATURAL COSINES.

	0'	6'	12'	18'	24'	30'	36'	42'	48'	54'	1'	2'	3'	4'	5
45°	·7071	·7059	·7046	·7034	·7022	·7009	·6997	·6984	·6972	·6959	2	4	6	8	10
46°	·6947	·6934	·6921	·6909	·6896	·6884	·6871	·6858	·6845	·6833	2	4	6	8	11
47°	·6820	·6807	·6794	·6782	·6769	·6756	·6743	·6730	·6717	·6704	2	4	6	9	11
48°	·6691	·6678	·6665	·6652	·6639	·6626	·6613	·6600	·6587	·6574	2	4	7	9	11
49°	·6561	·6547	·6534	·6521	·6508	·6494	·6481	·6468	·6455	·6441	2	4	7	9	11
50°	·6428	·6414	·6401	·6388	·6374	·6361	·6347	·6334	·6320	·6307	2	4	7	9	11
51°	·6293	·6280	·6266	·6252	·6239	·6225	·6211	·6198	·6184	·6170	2	5	7	9	11
52°	·6157	·6143	·6129	·6115	·6101	·6088	·6074	·6060	·6046	·6032	2	5	7	9	12
53°	·6018	·6004	·5990	·5976	·5962	·5948	·5934	·5920	·5906	·5892	2	5	7	9	12
54°	·5878	·5864	·5850	·5835	·5821	·5807	·5793	·5779	·5764	·5750	2	5	7	9	12
55°	·5736	·5721	·5707	·5693	·5678	·5664	·5650	·5635	·5621	·5606	2	5	7	10	12
56°	·5592	·5577	·5563	·5548	·5534	·5519	·5505	·5490	·5476	·5461	2	5	7	10	12
57°	·5446	·5432	·5417	·5402	·5388	·5373	·5358	·5344	·5329	·5314	2	5	7	10	12
58°	·5299	·5284	·5270	·5255	·5240	·5225	·5210	·5195	·5180	·5165	2	5	7	10	12
59°	·5150	·5135	·5120	·5105	·5090	·5075	·5060	·5045	·5030	·5015	3	5	8	10	13
60°	·5000	·4985	·4970	·4955	·4939	·4924	·4909	·4894	·4879	·4863	3	5	8	10	13
61°	·4848	·4833	·4818	·4802	·4787	·4772	·4756	·4741	·4726	·4710	3	5	8	10	13
62°	·4695	·4679	·4664	·4648	·4633	·4617	·4602	·4586	·4571	·4555	3	5	8	10	13
63°	·4540	·4524	·4509	·4493	·4478	·4462	·4446	·4431	·4415	·4399	3	5	8	10	13
64°	·4384	·4368	·4352	·4337	·4321	·4305	·4289	·4274	·4258	·4242	3	5	8	11	13
65°	·4226	·4210	·4195	·4179	·4163	·4147	·4131	·4115	·4099	·4083	3	5	8	11	13
66°	·4067	·4051	·4035	·4019	·4003	·3987	·3971	·3955	·3939	·3923	3	5	8	11	13
67°	·3907	·3891	·3875	·3859	·3843	·3827	·3811	·3795	·3778	·3762	3	5	8	11	13
68°	·3746	·3730	·3714	·3697	·3681	·3665	·3649	·3633	·3616	·3600	3	5	8	11	14
69°	·3584	·3567	·3551	·3535	·3518	·3502	·3486	·3469	·3453	·3437	3	5	8	11	14
70°	·3420	·3404	·3387	·3371	·3355	·3338	·3322	·3305	·3289	·3272	3	5	8	11	14
71°	·3256	·3239	·3223	·3206	·3190	·3173	·3156	·3140	·3123	·3107	3	6	8	11	14
72°	·3090	·3074	·3057	·3040	·3024	·3007	·2990	·2974	·2957	·2940	3	6	8	11	14
73°	·2924	·2907	·2890	·2874	·2857	·2840	·2823	·2807	·2790	·2773	3	6	8	11	14
74°	·2756	·2740	·2723	·2706	·2689	·2672	·2656	·2639	·2622	·2605	3	6	8	11	14
75°	·2588	·2571	·2554	·2538	·2521	·2504	·2487	·2470	·2453	·2436	3	6	8	11	14
76°	·2419	·2402	·2385	·2368	·2351	·2334	·2317	·2300	·2284	·2267	3	6	8	11	14
77°	·2250	·2233	·2215	·2198	·2181	·2164	·2147	·2130	·2113	·2096	3	6	9	11	14
78°	·2079	·2062	·2045	·2028	·2011	·1994	·1977	·1959	·1942	·1925	3	6	9	11	14
79°	·1908	·1891	·1874	·1857	·1840	·1822	·1805	·1788	·1771	·1754	3	6	9	11	14
80°	·1736	·1719	·1702	·1685	·1668	·1650	·1633	·1616	·1599	·1582	3	6	9	11	14
81°	·1564	·1547	·1530	·1513	·1495	·1478	·1461	·1444	·1426	·1409	3	6	9	12	14
82°	·1392	·1374	·1357	·1340	·1323	·1305	·1288	·1271	·1253	·1236	3	6	9	12	14
83°	·1219	·1201	·1184	·1167	·1149	·1132	·1115	·1097	·1080	·1063	3	6	9	12	14
84°	·1045	·1028	·1011	·0993	·0976	·0958	·0941	·0924	·0906	·0889	3	6	9	12	14
85°	·0872	·0854	·0837	·0819	·0802	·0785	·0767	·0750	·0732	·0715	3	6	9	12	14
86°	·0698	·0680	·0663	·0645	·0628	·0610	·0593	·0576	·0558	·0541	3	6	9	12	15
87°	·0523	·0506	·0488	·0471	·0454	·0436	·0419	·0401	·0384	·0366	3	6	9	12	15
88°	·0349	·0332	·0314	·0297	·0279	·0262	·0244	·0227	·0209	·0192	3	6	9	12	15
89°	·0175	·0157	·0140	·0122	·0105	·0087	·0070	·0052	·0035	·0017	3	6	9	12	15

NATURAL TANGENTS.

Angle	0′	6′	12′	18′	24′	30′	36′	42′	48′	54′	1′	2′	3′	4′	5′
0°	0·0000	·0017	·0035	·0052	·0070	·0087	·0105	·0122	·0140	·0157	3	6	9	12	15
1°	0·0175	·0192	·0209	·0227	·0244	·0262	·0279	·0297	·0314	·0332	3	6	9	12	15
2°	0·0349	·0367	·0384	·0402	·0419	·0437	·0454	·0472	·0489	·0507	3	6	9	12	15
3°	0·0524	·0542	·0559	·0577	·0594	·0612	·0629	·0647	·0664	·0682	3	6	9	12	15
4°	0·0699	·0717	·0734	·0752	·0769	·0787	·0805	·0822	·0840	·0857	3	6	9	12	15
5°	0·0875	·0892	·0910	·0928	·0945	·0963	·0981	·0998	·1016	·1033	3	6	9	12	15
6°	0·1051	·1069	·1086	·1104	·1122	·1139	·1157	·1175	·1192	·1210	3	6	9	12	15
7°	0·1228	·1246	·1263	·1281	·1299	·1317	·1334	·1352	·1370	·1388	3	6	9	12	15
8°	0·1405	·1423	·1441	·1459	·1477	·1495	·1512	·1530	·1548	·1566	3	6	9	12	15
9°	0·1584	·1602	·1620	·1638	·1655	·1673	·1691	·1709	·1727	·1745	3	6	9	12	15
10°	0·1763	·1781	·1799	·1817	·1835	·1853	·1871	·1890	·1908	·1926	3	6	9	12	15
11°	0·1944	·1962	·1980	·1998	·2016	·2035	·2053	·2071	·2089	·2107	3	6	9	12	15
12°	0·2126	·2144	·2162	·2180	·2199	·2217	·2235	·2254	·2272	·2290	3	6	9	12	15
13°	0·2309	·2327	·2345	·2364	·2382	·2401	·2419	·2438	·2456	·2475	3	6	9	12	15
14°	0·2493	·2512	·2530	·2549	·2568	·2586	·2605	·2623	·2642	·2661	3	6	9	12	16
15°	0·2679	·2698	·2717	·2736	·2754	·2773	·2792	·2811	·2830	·2849	3	6	9	13	16
16°	0·2867	·2886	·2905	·2924	·2943	·2962	·2981	·3000	·3019	·3038	3	6	9	13	16
17°	0·3057	·3076	·3096	·3115	·3134	·3153	·3172	·3191	·3211	·3230	3	6	10	13	16
18°	0·3249	·3269	·3288	·3307	·3327	·3346	·3365	·3385	·3404	·3424	3	6	10	13	16
19°	0·3443	·3463	·3482	·3502	·3522	·3541	·3561	·3581	·3600	·3620	3	7	10	13	16
20°	0·3640	·3659	·3679	·3699	·3719	·3739	·3759	·3779	·3799	·3819	3	7	10	13	17
21°	0·3839	·3859	·3879	·3899	·3919	·3939	·3959	·3979	·4000	·4020	3	7	10	13	17
22°	0·4040	·4061	·4081	·4101	·4122	·4142	·4163	·4183	·4204	·4224	3	7	10	14	17
23°	0·4245	·4265	·4286	·4307	·4327	·4348	·4369	·4390	·4411	·4431	3	7	10	14	17
24°	0·4452	·4473	·4494	·4515	·4536	·4557	·4578	·4599	·4621	·4642	4	7	11	14	18
25°	0·4663	·4684	·4706	·4727	·4748	·4770	·4791	·4813	·4834	·4856	4	7	11	14	18
26°	0·4877	·4899	·4921	·4942	·4964	·4986	·5008	·5029	·5051	·5073	4	7	11	15	18
27°	0·5095	·5117	·5139	·5161	·5184	·5206	·5228	·5250	·5272	·5295	4	7	11	15	18
28°	0·5317	·5340	·5362	·5384	·5407	·5430	·5452	·5475	·5498	·5520	4	8	11	15	19
29°	0·5543	·5566	·5589	·5612	·5635	·5658	·5681	·5704	·5727	·5750	4	8	12	15	19
30°	0·5774	·5797	·5820	·5844	·5867	·5890	·5914	·5938	·5961	·5985	4	8	12	16	20
31°	0·6009	·6032	·6056	·6080	·6104	·6128	·6152	·6176	·6200	·6224	4	8	12	16	20
32°	0·6249	·6273	·6297	·6322	·6346	·6371	·6395	·6420	·6445	·6469	4	8	12	16	20
33°	0·6494	·6519	·6544	·6569	·6594	·6619	·6644	·6669	·6694	·6720	4	8	13	17	21
34°	0·6745	·6771	·6796	·6822	·6847	·6873	·6899	·6924	·6950	·6976	4	9	13	17	21
35°	0·7002	·7028	·7054	·7080	·7107	·7133	·7159	·7186	·7212	·7239	4	9	13	18	22
36°	0·7265	·7292	·7319	·7346	·7373	·7400	·7427	·7454	·7481	·7508	5	9	14	18	23
37°	0·7536	·7563	·7590	·7618	·7646	·7673	·7701	·7729	·7757	·7785	5	9	14	18	23
38°	0·7813	·7841	·7869	·7898	·7926	·7954	·7983	·8012	·8040	·8069	5	9	14	19	24
39°	0·8098	·8127	·8156	·8185	·8214	·8243	·8273	·8302	·8332	·8361	5	10	15	20	24
40°	0·8391	·8421	·8451	·8481	·8511	·8541	·8571	·8601	·8632	·8662	5	10	15	20	25
41°	0·8693	·8724	·8754	·8785	·8816	·8847	·8878	·8910	·8941	·8972	5	10	16	21	26
42°	0·9004	·9036	·9067	·9099	·9131	·9163	·9195	·9228	·9260	·9293	5	11	16	21	27
43°	0·9325	·9358	·9391	·9424	·9457	·9490	·9523	·9556	·9590	·9623	6	11	17	22	28
44°	0·9657	·9691	·9725	·9759	·9793	·9827	·9861	·9896	·9930	·9965	6	11	17	23	29

NATURAL TANGENTS.

Angle	0'	6'	12'	18'	24'	30'	36'	42'	48'	54'	1'	2'	3'	4'	5'
45°	1·0000	1·0035	1·0070	1·0105	1·0141	1·0176	1·0212	1·0247	1·0283	1·0319	6	12	18	24	30
46°	1·0355	1·0392	1·0428	1·0464	1·0501	1·0538	1·0575	1·0612	1·0649	1·0686	6	12	18	25	31
47°	1·0724	1·0761	1·0799	1·0837	1·0875	1·0913	1·0951	1·0990	1·1028	1·1067	6	13	19	25	32
48°	1·1106	1·1145	1·1184	1·1224	1·1263	1·1303	1·1343	1·1383	1·1423	1·1463	7	13	20	26	33
49°	1·1504	1·1544	1·1585	1·1626	1·1667	1·1708	1·1750	1·1792	1·1833	1·1875	7	14	21	28	34
50°	1·1918	1·1960	1·2002	1·2045	1·2088	1·2131	1·2174	1·2218	1·2261	1·2305	7	14	22	29	36
51°	1·2349	1·2393	1·2437	1·2482	1·2527	1·2572	1·2617	1·2662	1·2708	1·2753	8	15	23	30	38
52°	1·2799	1·2846	1·2892	1·2938	1·2985	1·3032	1·3079	1·3127	1·3175	1·3222	8	16	24	31	39
53°	1·3270	1·3319	1·3367	1·3416	1·3465	1·3514	1·3564	1·3613	1·3663	1·3713	8	16	25	33	41
54°	1·3764	1·3814	1·3865	1·3916	1·3968	1·4019	1·4071	1·4124	1·4176	1·4229	9	17	26	34	43
55°	1·4281	1·4335	1·4388	1·4442	1·4496	1·4550	1·4605	1·4659	1·4715	1·4770	9	18	27	36	45
56°	1·4826	1·4882	1·4938	1·4994	1·5051	1·5108	1·5166	1·5224	1·5282	1·5340	10	19	29	38	48
57°	1·5399	1·5458	1·5517	1·5577	1·5637	1·5697	1·5757	1·5818	1·5880	1·5941	10	20	30	40	50
58°	1·6003	1·6066	1·6128	1·6191	1·6255	1·6319	1·6383	1·6447	1·6512	1·6577	11	21	32	43	53
59°	1·6643	1·6709	1·6775	1·6842	1·6909	1·6977	1·7045	1·7113	1·7182	1·7251	11	23	34	45	56
60°	1·7321	1·7391	1·7461	1·7532	1·7603	1·7675	1·7747	1·7820	1·7893	1·7966	12	24	36	48	60
61°	1·8040	1·8115	1·8190	1·8265	1·8341	1·8418	1·8495	1·8572	1·8650	1·8728	13	26	38	51	64
62°	1·8807	1·8887	1·8967	1·9047	1·9128	1·9210	1·9292	1·9375	1·9458	1·9542	14	27	41	55	68
63°	1·9626	1·9711	1·9797	1·9883	1·9970	2·0057	2·0145	2·0233	2·0323	2·0413	15	29	44	58	73
64°	2·0503	2·0594	2·0686	2·0778	2·0872	2·0965	2·1060	2·1155	2·1251	2·1348	16	31	47	63	78
65°	2·1445	2·1543	2·1642	2·1742	2·1842	2·1943	2·2045	2·2148	2·2251	2·2355	17	34	51	68	85
66°	2·2460	2·2566	2·2673	2·2781	2·2889	2·2998	2·3109	2·3220	2·3332	2·3445	18	37	55	73	92
67°	2·3559	2·3673	2·3789	2·3906	2·4023	2·4142	2·4262	2·4383	2·4504	2·4627	20	40	60	79	99
68°	2·4751	2·4876	2·5002	2·5129	2·5257	2·5386	2·5517	2·5649	2·5782	2·5916	22	43	65	87	108
69°	2·6051	2·6187	2·6325	2·6464	2·6605	2·6746	2·6889	2·7034	2·7179	2·7326	24	47	71	95	119
70°	2·7475	2·7625	2·7776	2·7929	2·8083	2·8239	2·8397	2·8556	2·8716	2·8878	26	52	78	104	130
71°	2·9042	2·9208	2·9375	2·9544	2·9714	2·9887	3·0061	3·0237	3·0415	3·0595	29	58	87	116	144
72°	3·0777	3·0961	3·1146	3·1334	3·1524	3·1716	3·1910	3·2106	3·2305	3·2506	32	64	96	129	161
73°	3·2709	3·2914	3·3122	3·3332	3·3544	3·3759	3·3977	3·4197	3·4420	3·4646	36	72	108	144	180
74°	3·4874	3·5105	3·5339	3·5576	3·5816	3·6059	3·6305	3·6554	3·6806	3·7062	41	81	122	163	204
75°	3·7321	3·7583	3·7848	3·8118	3·8391	3·8667	3·8947	3·9232	3·9520	3·9812					
76°	4·0108	4·0408	4·0713	4·1022	4·1335	4·1653	4·1976	4·2303	4·2635	4·2972					
77°	4·3315	4·3662	4·4015	4·4374	4·4737	4·5107	4·5483	4·5864	4·6252	4·6646					
78°	4·7046	4·7453	4·7867	4·8288	4·8716	4·9152	4·9594	5·0045	5·0504	5·0970					
79°	5·1446	5·1929	5·2422	5·2924	5·3435	5·3955	5·4486	5·5026	5·5578	5·6140					
80°	5·6713	5·7297	5·7894	5·8502	5·9124	5·9758	6·0405	6·1066	6·1742	6·2432					
81°	6·3138	6·3859	6·4596	6·5350	6·6122	6·6912	6·7720	6·8548	6·9395	7·0264	Mean differences				
82°	7·1154	7·2066	7·3002	7·3962	7·4947	7·5958	7·6996	7·8062	7·9158	8·0285	not				
83°	8·1443	8·2636	8·3863	8·5126	8·6427	8·7769	8·9152	9·0579	9·2052	9·3572	sufficiently				
84°	9·5144	9·6768	9·8448	10·019	10·199	10·385	10·579	10·780	10·988	11·205	accurate.				
85°	11·430	11·664	11·909	12·163	12·429	12·706	12·996	13·300	13·617	13·951					
86°	14·301	14·669	15·056	15·464	15·895	16·350	16·832	17·343	17·886	18·464					
87°	19·081	19·740	20·446	21·205	22·022	22·904	23·859	24·898	26·031	27·271					
88°	28·636	30·145	31·821	33·694	35·801	38·188	40·917	44·066	47·740	52·081					
89°	57·290	63·657	71·615	81·847	95·489	114·59	143·24	190·98	286·48	572·96					

LOGARITHMS OF SINES.

Angle	0′	6′	12′	18′	24′	30′	36′	42′	48′	54′	1′	2′	3′	4′	5′
0°	− ∞	$\bar{3}$·242	$\bar{3}$·543	$\bar{3}$·719	$\bar{3}$·844	$\bar{3}$·941	$\bar{2}$·020	$\bar{2}$·087	$\bar{2}$·145	$\bar{2}$·196	\	\	\	\	\
1°	$\bar{2}$·2419	2832	3210	3558	3880	4179	4459	4723	4971	5206	\	\	\	\	\
2°	$\bar{2}$·5428	5640	5842	6035	6220	6397	6567	6731	6889	7041	\	\	\	\	\
3°	$\bar{2}$·7188	7330	7468	7602	7731	7857	7979	8098	8213	8326	\	\	\	\	\
4°	$\bar{2}$·8436	8543	8647	8749	8849	8946	9042	9135	9226	9315	\	\	\	\	\
5°	$\bar{2}$·9403	9489	9573	9655	9736	9816	9894	9970	$\bar{1}$·0046	$\bar{1}$·0120	13	26	39	52	65
6°	$\bar{1}$·0192	0264	0334	0403	0472	0539	0605	0670	0734	0797	11	22	33	44	55
7°	$\bar{1}$·0859	0920	0981	1040	1099	1157	1214	1271	1326	1381	10	19	29	38	48
8°	$\bar{1}$·1436	1489	1542	1594	1646	1697	1747	1797	1847	1895	8	17	25	34	42
9°	$\bar{1}$·1943	1991	2038	2085	2131	2176	2221	2266	2310	2353	8	15	23	30	38
10°	$\bar{1}$·2397	2439	2482	2524	2565	2606	2647	2687	2727	2767	7	14	20	27	34
11°	$\bar{1}$·2806	2845	2883	2921	2959	2997	3034	3070	3107	3143	6	12	19	25	31
12°	$\bar{1}$·3179	3214	3250	3284	3319	3353	3387	3421	3455	3488	6	11	17	23	28
13°	$\bar{1}$·3521	3554	3586	3618	3650	3682	3713	3745	3775	3806	5	11	16	21	26
14°	$\bar{1}$·3837	3867	3897	3927	3957	3986	4015	4044	4073	4102	5	10	15	20	24
15°	$\bar{1}$·4130	4158	4186	4214	4242	4269	4296	4323	4350	4377	5	9	14	18	23
16°	$\bar{1}$·4403	4430	4456	4482	4508	4533	4559	4584	4609	4634	4	9	13	17	21
17°	$\bar{1}$·4659	4684	4709	4733	4757	4781	4805	4829	4853	4876	4	8	12	16	20
18°	$\bar{1}$·4900	4923	4946	4969	4992	5015	5037	5060	5082	5104	4	8	11	15	19
19°	$\bar{1}$·5126	5148	5170	5192	5213	5235	5256	5278	5299	5320	4	7	11	14	18
20°	$\bar{1}$·5341	5361	5382	5402	5423	5443	5463	5484	5504	5523	3	7	10	14	17
21°	$\bar{1}$·5543	5563	5583	5602	5621	5641	5660	5679	5698	5717	3	6	10	13	16
22°	$\bar{1}$·5736	5754	5773	5792	5810	5828	5847	5865	5883	5901	3	6	9	12	15
23°	$\bar{1}$·5919	5937	5954	5972	5990	6007	6024	6042	6059	6076	3	6	9	12	15
24°	$\bar{1}$·6093	6110	6127	6144	6161	6177	6194	6210	6227	6243	3	6	8	11	14
25°	$\bar{1}$·6259	6276	6292	6308	6324	6340	6356	6371	6387	6403	3	5	8	11	13
26°	$\bar{1}$·6418	6434	6449	6465	6480	6495	6510	6526	6541	6556	3	5	8	10	13
27°	$\bar{1}$·6570	6585	6600	6615	6629	6644	6659	6673	6687	6702	2	5	7	10	12
28°	$\bar{1}$·6716	6730	6744	6759	6773	6787	6801	6814	6828	6842	2	5	7	9	12
29°	$\bar{1}$·6856	6869	6883	6896	6910	6923	6937	6950	6963	6977	2	4	7	9	11
30°	$\bar{1}$·6990	7003	7016	7029	7042	7055	7068	7080	7093	7106	2	4	6	9	11
31°	$\bar{1}$·7118	7131	7144	7156	7168	7181	7193	7205	7218	7230	2	4	6	8	10
32°	$\bar{1}$·7242	7254	7266	7278	7290	7302	7314	7326	7338	7349	2	4	6	8	10
33°	$\bar{1}$·7361	7373	7384	7396	7407	7419	7430	7442	7453	7464	2	4	6	8	10
34°	$\bar{1}$·7476	7487	7498	7509	7520	7531	7542	7553	7564	7575	2	4	6	7	9
35°	$\bar{1}$·7586	7597	7607	7618	7629	7640	7650	7661	7671	7682	2	4	5	7	9
36°	$\bar{1}$·7692	7703	7713	7723	7734	7744	7754	7764	7774	7785	2	3	5	7	9
37°	$\bar{1}$·7795	7805	7815	7825	7835	7844	7854	7864	7874	7884	2	3	5	7	8
38°	$\bar{1}$·7893	7903	7913	7922	7932	7941	7951	7960	7970	7979	2	3	5	6	8
39°	$\bar{1}$·7989	7998	8007	8017	8026	8035	8044	8053	8063	8072	2	3	5	6	8
40°	$\bar{1}$·8081	8090	8099	8108	8117	8125	8134	8143	8152	8161	1	3	4	6	7
41°	$\bar{1}$·8169	8178	8187	8195	8204	8213	8221	8230	8238	8247	1	3	4	6	7
42°	$\bar{1}$·8255	8264	8272	8280	8289	8297	8305	8313	8322	8330	1	3	4	6	7
43°	$\bar{1}$·8338	8346	8354	8362	8370	8378	8386	8394	8402	8410	1	3	4	5	7
44°	$\bar{1}$·8418	8426	8433	8441	8449	8457	8464	8472	8480	8487	1	3	4	5	6

Differences not sufficiently accurate.

LOGARITHMS OF SINES.

Angle.	0′	6′	12′	18′	24′	30′	36′	42′	48′	54′	1′	2′	3′	4′	5′
45°	Ī·8495	8502	8510	8517	8525	8532	8540	8547	8555	8562	1	2	4	5	6
46°	Ī·8569	8577	8584	8591	8598	8606	8613	8620	8627	8634	1	2	4	5	6
47°	Ī·8641	8648	8655	8662	8669	8676	8683	8690	8697	8704	1	2	3	5	6
48°	Ī·8711	8718	8724	8731	8738	8745	8751	8758	8765	8771	1	2	3	4	6
49°	Ī·8778	8784	8791	8797	8804	8810	8817	8823	8830	8836	1	2	3	4	5
50°	Ī·8843	8849	8855	8862	8868	8874	8880	8887	8893	8899	1	2	3	4	5
51°	Ī·8905	8911	8917	8923	8929	8935	8941	8947	8953	8959	1	2	3	4	5
52°	Ī·8965	8971	8977	8983	8989	8995	9000	9006	9012	9018	1	2	3	4	5
53°	Ī·9023	9029	9035	9041	9046	9052	9057	9063	9069	9074	1	2	3	4	5
54°	Ī·9080	9085	9091	9096	9101	9107	9112	9118	9123	9128	1	2	3	4	5
55°	Ī·9134	9139	9144	9149	9155	9160	9165	9170	9175	9181	1	2	3	3	4
56°	Ī·9186	9191	9196	9201	9206	9211	9216	9221	9226	9231	1	2	3	3	4
57°	Ī·9236	9241	9246	9251	9255	9260	9265	9270	9275	9279	1	2	2	3	4
58°	Ī·9284	9289	9294	9298	9303	9308	9312	9317	9322	9326	1	2	2	3	4
59°	Ī·9331	9335	9340	9344	9349	9353	9358	9362	9367	9371	1	1	2	3	4
60°	Ī·9375	9380	9384	9388	9393	9397	9401	9406	9410	9414	1	1	2	3	4
61°	Ī·9418	9422	9427	9431	9435	9439	9443	9447	9451	9455	1	1	2	3	3
62°	Ī·9459	9463	9467	9471	9475	9479	9483	9487	9491	9495	1	1	2	3	3
63°	Ī·9499	9503	9507	9510	9514	9518	9522	9525	9529	9533	1	1	2	3	3
64°	Ī·9537	9540	9544	9548	9551	9555	9558	9562	9566	9569	1	1	2	2	3
65°	Ī·9573	9576	9580	9583	9587	9590	9594	9597	9601	9604	1	1	2	2	3
66°	Ī·9607	9611	9614	9617	9621	9624	9627	9631	9634	9637	1	1	2	2	3
67°	Ī·9640	9643	9647	9650	9653	9656	9659	9662	9666	9669	1	1	2	2	3
68°	Ī·9672	9675	9678	9681	9684	9687	9690	9693	9696	9699	0	1	1	2	2
69°	Ī·9702	9704	9707	9710	9713	9716	9719	9722	9724	9727	0	1	1	2	2
70°	Ī·9730	9733	9735	9738	9741	9743	9746	9749	9751	9754	0	1	1	2	2
71°	Ī·9757	9759	9762	9764	9767	9770	9772	9775	9777	9780	0	1	1	2	2
72°	Ī·9782	9785	9787	9789	9792	9794	9797	9799	9801	9804	0	1	1	2	2
73°	Ī·9806	9808	9811	9813	9815	9817	9820	9822	9824	9826	0	1	1	2	2
74°	Ī·9828	9831	9833	9835	9837	9839	9841	9843	9845	9847	0	1	1	1	2
75°	Ī·9849	9851	9853	9855	9857	9859	9861	9863	9865	9867	0	1	1	1	2
76°	Ī·9869	9871	9873	9875	9876	9878	9880	9882	9884	9885	0	1	1	1	2
77°	Ī·9887	9889	9891	9892	9894	9896	9897	9899	9901	9902	0	1	1	1	1
78°	Ī·9904	9906	9907	9909	9910	9912	9913	9915	9916	9918	0	1	1	1	1
79°	Ī·9919	9921	9922	9924	9925	9927	9928	9929	9931	9932	0	0	1	1	1
80°	Ī·9934	9935	9936	9937	9939	9940	9941	9943	9944	9945	0	0	1	1	1
81°	Ī·9946	9947	9949	9950	9951	9952	9953	9954	9955	9956	0	0	1	1	1
82°	Ī·9958	9959	9960	9961	9962	9963	9964	9965	9966	9967	0	0	1	1	1
83°	Ī·9968	9969	9969	9970	9971	9972	9973	9974	9975	9975	0	0	0	1	1
84°	Ī·9976	9977	9978	9978	9979	9980	9981	9981	9982	9983	0	0	0	0	1
85°	Ī·9983	9984	9985	9985	9986	9987	9987	9988	9988	9989	0	0	0	0	0
86°	Ī·9989	9990	9990	9991	9991	9992	9992	9993	9993	9994	0	0	0	0	0
87°	Ī·9994	9994	9995	9995	9996	9996	9996	9996	9997	9997	0	0	0	0	0
88°	Ī·9997	9998	9998	9998	9998	9999	9999	9999	9999	9999	0	0	0	0	0
89°	Ī·9999	9999	0·000	0·000	0·000	0·000	0·000	0·000	0·000	0·000	0	0	0	0	0

LOGARITHMS OF COSINES.

Angle.	0′	6′	12′	18′	24′	30′	36′	42′	48′	54′	1′	2′	3′	4′	5′
0°	0·0000	0000	0000	0000	0000	0000	0000	0000	0000	9999	0	0	0	0	0
1°	1̄·9999	9999	9999	9999	9999	9999	9998	9998	9998	9998	0	0	0	0	0
2°	1̄·9997	9997	9997	9997	9996	9996	9996	9995	9995	9994	0	0	0	0	0
3°	1̄·9994	9994	9993	9993	9992	9992	9991	9991	9990	9990	0	0	0	0	0
4°	1̄·9989	9989	9988	9988	9987	9987	9986	9985	9985	9984	0	0	0	0	0
5°	1̄·9983	9983	9982	9981	9981	9980	9979	9978	9978	9977	0	0	0	0	1
6°	1̄·9976	9975	9975	9974	9973	9972	9971	9970	9969	9968	0	0	0	1	1
7°	1̄·9968	9967	9966	9965	9964	9963	9962	9961	9960	9959	0	0	1	1	1
8°	1̄·9958	9956	9955	9954	9953	9952	9951	9950	9949	9947	0	0	1	1	1
9°	1̄·9946	9945	9944	9943	9941	9940	9939	9937	9936	9935	0	0	1	1	1
10°	1̄·9934	9932	9931	9929	9928	9927	9925	9924	9922	9921	0	0	1	1	1
11°	1̄·9919	9918	9916	9915	9913	9912	9910	9909	9907	9906	0	1	1	1	1
12°	1̄·9904	9902	9901	9899	9897	9896	9894	9892	9891	9889	0	1	1	1	1
13°	1̄·9887	9885	9884	9882	9880	9878	9876	9875	9873	9871	0	1	1	1	2
14°	1̄·9869	9867	9865	9863	9861	9859	9857	9855	9853	9851	0	1	1	1	2
15°	1̄·9849	9847	9845	9843	9841	9839	9837	9835	9833	9831	0	1	1	1	2
16°	1̄·9828	9826	9824	9822	9820	9817	9815	9813	9811	9808	0	1	1	2	2
17°	1̄·9806	9804	9801	9799	9797	9794	9792	9789	9787	9785	0	1	1	2	2
18°	1̄·9782	9780	9777	9775	9772	9770	9767	9764	9762	9759	0	1	1	2	2
19°	1̄·9757	9754	9751	9749	9746	9743	9741	9738	9735	9733	0	1	1	2	2
20°	1̄·9730	9727	9724	9722	9719	9716	9713	9710	9707	9704	0	1	1	2	2
21°	1̄·9702	9699	9696	9693	9690	9687	9684	9681	9678	9675	0	1	1	2	2
22°	1̄·9672	9669	9666	9662	9659	9656	9653	9650	9647	9643	1	1	2	2	3
23°	1̄·9640	9637	9634	9631	9627	9624	9621	9617	9614	9611	1	1	2	2	3
24°	1̄·9607	9604	9601	9597	9594	9590	9587	9583	9580	9576	1	1	2	2	3
25°	1̄·9573	9569	9566	9562	9558	9555	9551	9548	9544	9540	1	1	2	2	3
26°	1̄·9537	9533	9529	9525	9522	9518	9514	9510	9507	9503	1	1	2	3	3
27°	1̄·9499	9495	9491	9487	9483	9479	9475	9471	9467	9463	1	1	2	3	3
28°	1̄·9459	9455	9451	9447	9443	9439	9435	9431	9427	9422	1	1	2	3	3
29°	1̄·9418	9414	9410	9406	9401	9397	9393	9388	9384	9380	1	1	2	3	4
30°	1̄·9375	9371	9367	9362	9358	9353	9349	9344	9340	9335	1	1	2	3	4
31°	1̄·9331	9326	9322	9317	9312	9308	9303	9298	9294	9289	1	2	2	3	4
32°	1̄·9284	9279	9275	9270	9265	9260	9255	9251	9246	9241	1	2	2	3	4
33°	1̄·9236	9231	9226	9221	9216	9211	9206	9201	9196	9191	1	2	3	3	4
34°	1̄·9186	9181	9175	9170	9165	9160	9155	9149	9144	9139	1	2	3	3	4
35°	1̄·9134	9128	9123	9118	9112	9107	9101	9096	9091	9085	1	2	3	4	5
36°	1̄·9080	9074	9069	9063	9057	9052	9046	9041	9035	9029	1	2	3	4	5
37°	1̄·9023	9018	9012	9006	9000	8995	8989	8983	8977	8971	1	2	3	4	5
38°	1̄·8965	8959	8953	8947	8941	8935	8929	8923	8917	8911	1	2	3	4	5
39°	1̄·8905	8899	8893	8887	8880	8874	8868	8862	8855	8849	1	2	3	4	5
40°	1̄·8843	8836	8830	8823	8817	8810	8804	8797	8791	8784	1	2	3	4	5
41°	1̄·8778	8771	8765	8758	8751	8745	8738	8731	8724	8718	1	2	3	5	6
42°	1̄·8711	8704	8697	8690	8683	8676	8669	8662	8655	8648	1	2	3	5	6
43°	1̄·8641	8634	8627	8620	8613	8606	8598	8591	8584	8577	1	2	4	5	6
44°	1̄·8569	8562	8555	8547	8540	8532	8525	8517	8510	8502	1	2	4	5	6

348

LOGARITHMS OF COSINES.

Angle.	0′	6′	12′	18′	24′	30′	36′	42′	48′	54′	1′	2′	3′	4′	5′
45°	1̄·8495	8487	8480	8472	8464	8457	8449	8441	8433	8426	1	3	4	5	6
46°	1̄·8418	8410	8402	8394	8386	8378	8370	8362	8354	8346	1	3	4	5	7
47°	1̄·8338	8330	8322	8313	8305	8297	8289	8280	8272	8264	1	3	4	6	7
48°	1̄·8255	8247	8238	8230	8221	8213	8204	8195	8187	8178	1	3	4	6	7
49°	1̄·8169	8161	8152	8143	8134	8125	8117	8108	8099	8090	1	3	4	6	7
50°	1̄·8081	8072	8063	8053	8044	8035	8026	8017	8007	7998	2	3	5	6	8
51°	1̄·7989	7979	7970	7960	7951	7941	7932	7922	7913	7903	2	3	5	6	8
52°	1̄·7893	7884	7874	7864	7854	7844	7835	7825	7815	7805	2	3	5	7	8
53°	1̄·7795	7785	7774	7764	7754	7744	7734	7723	7713	7703	2	3	5	7	9
54°	1̄·7692	7682	7671	7661	7650	7640	7629	7618	7607	7597	2	4	5	7	9
55°	1̄·7586	7575	7564	7553	7542	7531	7520	7509	7498	7487	2	4	6	7	9
56°	1̄·7476	7464	7453	7442	7430	7419	7407	7396	7384	7373	2	4	6	8	10
57°	1̄·7361	7349	7338	7326	7314	7302	7290	7278	7266	7254	2	4	6	8	10
58°	1̄·7242	7230	7218	7205	7193	7181	7168	7156	7144	7131	2	4	6	8	10
59°	1̄·7118	7106	7093	7080	7068	7055	7042	7029	7016	7003	2	4	6	9	11
60°	1̄·6990	6977	6963	6950	6937	6923	6910	6896	6883	6869	2	4	7	9	11
61°	1̄·6856	6842	6828	6814	6801	6787	6773	6759	6744	6730	2	5	7	9	12
62°	1̄·6716	6702	6687	6673	6659	6644	6629	6615	6600	6585	2	5	7	10	12
63°	1̄·6570	6556	6541	6526	6510	6495	6480	6465	6449	6434	3	5	8	10	13
64°	1̄·6418	6403	6387	6371	6356	6340	6324	6308	6292	6276	3	5	8	11	13
65°	1̄·6259	6243	6227	6210	6194	6177	6161	6144	6127	6110	3	6	8	11	14
66°	1̄·6093	6076	6059	6042	6024	6007	5990	5972	5954	5937	3	6	9	12	15
67°	1̄·5919	5901	5883	5865	5847	5828	5810	5792	5773	5754	3	6	9	12	15
68°	1̄·5736	5717	5698	5679	5660	5641	5621	5602	5583	5563	3	6	10	13	16
69°	1̄·5543	5523	5504	5484	5463	5443	5423	5402	5382	5361	3	7	10	14	17
70°	1̄·5341	5320	5299	5278	5256	5235	5213	5192	5170	5148	4	7	11	14	18
71°	1̄·5126	5104	5082	5060	5037	5015	4992	4969	4946	4923	4	8	11	15	19
72°	1̄·4900	4876	4853	4829	4805	4781	4757	4733	4709	4684	4	8	12	16	20
73°	1̄·4659	4634	4609	4584	4559	4533	4508	4482	4456	4430	4	9	13	17	21
74°	1̄·4403	4377	4350	4323	4296	4269	4242	4214	4186	4158	5	9	14	18	23
75°	1̄·4130	4102	4073	4044	4015	3986	3957	3927	3897	3867	5	10	15	20	24
76°	1̄·3837	3806	3775	3745	3713	3682	3650	3618	3586	3554	5	11	16	21	26
77°	1̄·3521	3488	3455	3421	3387	3353	3319	3284	3250	3214	6	11	17	23	28
78°	1̄·3179	3143	3107	3070	3034	2997	2959	2921	2883	2845	6	12	19	25	31
79°	1̄·2806	2767	2727	2687	2647	2606	2565	2524	2482	2439	7	14	20	27	34
80°	1̄·2397	2353	2310	2266	2221	2176	2131	2085	2038	1991	8	15	23	30	38
81°	1̄·1943	1895	1847	1797	1747	1697	1646	1594	1542	1489	8	17	25	34	42
82°	1̄·1436	1381	1326	1271	1214	1157	1099	1040	0981	0920	10	19	29	38	48
83°	1̄·0859	0797	0734	0670	0605	0539	0472	0403	0334	0264	11	22	33	44	55
84°	1̄·0192	0120	0046	2̄·9970	2̄·9894	2̄·9816	2̄·9736	2̄·9655	2̄·9573	2̄·9489	13	26	39	52	66
85°	2̄·9403	9315	9226	9135	9042	8946	8849	8749	8647	8543	16	32	48	64	80
86°	2̄·8436	8326	8213	8098	7979	7857	7731	7602	7468	7330					
87°	2̄·7188	7041	6889	6731	6567	6397	6220	6035	5842	5640					
88°	2̄·5428	5206	4971	4723	4459	4179	3880	3558	3210	2832					
89°	2̄·2419	2̄·196	2̄·145	2̄·087	2̄·020	3̄·941	3̄·844	3̄·719	3̄·543	3̄·242					

LOGARITHMS OF TANGENTS.

Angle.	0'	6'	12'	18'	24'	30'	36'	42'	48'	54'	1'	2'	3'	4'	5
0°	− ∞	3̄·242	3̄·543	3̄·719	3̄·844	3̄·941	2̄·020	2̄·087	2̄·145	2̄·196					
1°	2̄·2419	2833	3211	3559	3881	4181	4461	4725	4973	5208					
2°	2̄·5431	5643	5845	6038	6223	6401	6571	6736	6894	7046					
3°	2̄·7194	7337	7475	7609	7739	7865	7988	8107	8223	8336					
4°	2̄·8446	8554	8659	8762	8862	8960	9056	9150	9241	9331	16	32	48	64	8
5°	2̄·9420	9506	9591	9674	9756	9836	9915	9992	1̄·0068	1̄·0143	13	26	40	53	6
6°	1̄·0216	0289	0360	0430	0499	0567	0633	0699	0764	0828	11	22	34	45	5
7°	1̄·0891	0954	1015	1076	1135	1194	1252	131C	1367	1423	10	20	29	39	4
8°	1̄·1478	1533	1587	1640	1693	1745	1797	1848	1898	1948	9	17	26	35	4
9°	1̄·1997	2046	2094	2142	2189	2236	2282	2328	2374	2419	8	16	23	31	3
10°	1̄·2463	2507	2551	2594	2637	2680	2722	2764	2805	2846	7	14	21	28	3
11°	1̄·2887	2927	2967	3006	3046	3085	3123	3162	3200	3237	6	13	19	26	3
12°	1̄·3275	3312	3349	3385	3422	3458	3493	3529	3564	3599	6	12	18	24	3
13°	1̄·3634	3668	3702	3736	3770	3804	3837	3870	3903	3935	6	11	17	22	2
14°	1̄·3968	4000	4032	4064	4095	4127	4158	4189	4220	4250	5	10	16	21	2
15°	1̄·4281	4311	4341	4371	4400	4430	4459	4488	4517	4546	5	10	15	20	2
16°	1̄·4575	4603	4632	4660	4688	4716	4744	4771	4799	4826	5	9	14	19	2
17°	1̄·4853	4880	4907	4934	4961	4987	5014	504C	5066	5092	4	9	13	18	2
18°	1̄·5118	5143	5169	5195	5220	5245	5270	5295	5320	5345	4	8	13	17	2
19°	1̄·5370	5394	5419	5443	5467	5491	5516	5539	5563	5587	4	8	12	16	2
20°	1̄·5611	5634	5658	5681	5704	5727	5750	5773	5796	5819	4	8	12	15	1
21°	1̄·5842	5864	5887	5909	5932	5954	5976	5998	6020	6042	4	7	11	15	1
22°	1̄·6064	6086	6108	6129	6151	6172	6194	6215	6236	6257	4	7	11	14	1
23°	1̄·6279	6300	6321	6341	6362	6383	6404	6424	6445	6465	3	7	10	14	1
24°	1̄·6486	6506	6527	6547	6567	6587	6607	6627	6647	6667	3	7	10	13	1
25°	1̄·6687	6706	6726	6746	6765	6785	6804	6824	6843	6863	3	7	10	13	1
26°	1̄·6882	6901	6920	6939	6958	6977	6996	7015	7034	7053	3	6	9	13	1
27°	1̄·7072	7090	7109	7128	7146	7165	7183	7202	7220	7238	3	6	9	12	1
28°	1̄·7257	7275	7293	7311	7330	7348	7366	7384	7402	7420	3	6	9	12	1
29°	1̄·7438	7455	7473	7491	7509	7526	7544	7562	7579	7597	3	6	9	12	1
30°	1̄·7614	7632	7649	7667	7684	7701	7719	7736	7753	7771	3	6	9	12	1
31°	1̄·7788	7805	7822	7839	7856	7873	7890	7907	7924	7941	3	6	9	11	1
32°	1̄·7958	7975	7992	8008	8025	8042	8059	8075	8092	8109	3	6	8	11	1
33°	1̄·8125	8142	8158	8175	8191	8208	8224	8241	8257	8274	3	5	8	11	1
34°	1̄·8290	8306	8323	8339	8355	8371	8388	8404	8420	8436	3	5	8	11	1
35°	1̄·8452	8468	8484	8501	8517	8533	8549	8565	8581	8597	3	5	8	11	1
36°	1̄·8613	8629	8644	8660	8676	8692	8708	8724	8740	8755	3	5	8	11	1
37°	1̄·8771	8787	8803	8818	8834	8850	8865	8881	8897	8912	3	5	8	10	1
38°	1̄·8928	8944	8959	8975	8990	9006	9022	9037	9053	9068	3	5	8	10	1
39°	1̄·9084	9099	9115	9130	9146	9161	9176	9192	9207	9223	3	5	8	10	1
40°	1̄·9238	9254	9269	9284	9300	9315	9330	9346	9361	9376	3	5	8	10	1
41°	1̄·9392	9407	9422	9438	9453	9468	9483	9499	9514	9529	3	5	8	10	1
42°	1̄·9544	9560	9575	9590	9605	9621	9636	9651	9666	9681	3	5	8	10	1
43°	1̄·9697	9712	9727	9742	9757	9773	9788	9803	9818	9833	3	5	8	10	1
44°	1̄·9848	9864	9879	9894	9909	9924	9939	9955	9970	9985	3	5	8	10	1

LOGARITHMS OF TANGENTS.

Angle.	0'	6'	12'	18'	24'	30'	36'	42'	48'	54'	1'	2'	3'	4'	5'
45°	0'0000	0015	0030	0045	0061	0076	0091	0106	0121	0136	3	5	8	10	13
46°	0'0152	0167	0182	0197	0212	0228	0243	0258	0273	0288	3	5	8	10	13
47°	0'0303	0319	0334	0349	0364	0379	0395	0410	0425	0440	3	5	8	10	13
48°	0'0456	0471	0486	0501	0517	0532	0547	0562	0578	0593	3	5	8	10	13
49°	0'0608	0624	0639	0654	0670	0685	0700	0716	0731	0746	3	5	8	10	13
50°	0'0762	0777	0793	0808	0824	0839	0854	0870	0885	0901	3	5	8	10	13
51°	0'0916	0932	0947	0963	0978	0994	1010	1025	1041	1056	3	5	8	10	13
52°	0'1072	1088	1103	1119	1135	1150	1166	1182	1197	1213	3	5	8	10	13
53°	0'1229	1245	1260	1276	1292	1308	1324	1340	1356	1371	3	5	8	11	13
54°	0'1387	1403	1419	1435	1451	1467	1483	1499	1516	1532	3	5	8	11	13
55°	0'1548	1564	1580	1596	1612	1629	1645	1661	1677	1694	3	5	8	11	14
56°	0'1710	1726	1743	1759	1776	1792	1809	1825	1842	1858	3	5	8	11	14
57°	0'1875	1891	1908	1925	1941	1958	1975	1992	2008	2025	3	6	8	11	14
58°	0'2042	2059	2076	2093	2110	2127	2144	2161	2178	2195	3	6	9	11	14
59°	0'2212	2229	2247	2264	2281	2299	2316	2333	2351	2368	3	6	9	12	14
60°	0'2386	2403	2421	2438	2456	2474	2491	2509	2527	2545	3	6	9	12	15
61°	0'2562	2580	2598	2616	2634	2652	2670	2689	2707	2725	3	6	9	12	15
62°	0'2743	2762	2780	2798	2817	2835	2854	2872	2891	2910	3	6	9	12	15
63°	0'2928	2947	2966	2985	3004	3023	3042	3061	3080	3099	3	6	9	13	16
64°	0'3118	3137	3157	3176	3196	3215	3235	3254	3274	3294	3	7	10	13	16
65°	0'3313	3333	3353	3373	3393	3413	3433	3453	3473	3494	3	7	10	13	17
66°	0'3514	3535	3555	3576	3596	3617	3638	3659	3679	3700	3	7	10	14	17
67°	0'3721	3743	3764	3785	3806	3828	3849	3871	3892	3914	4	7	11	14	18
68°	0'3936	3958	3980	4002	4024	4046	4068	4091	4113	4136	4	7	11	15	19
69°	0'4158	4181	4204	4227	4250	4273	4296	4319	4342	4366	4	8	12	15	19
70°	0'4389	4413	4437	4461	4484	4509	4533	4557	4581	4606	4	8	12	16	20
71°	0'4630	4655	4680	4705	4730	4755	4780	4805	4831	4857	4	8	13	17	21
72°	0'4882	4908	4934	4960	4986	5013	5039	5066	5093	5120	4	9	13	18	22
73°	0'5147	5174	5201	5229	5256	5284	5312	5340	5368	5397	5	9	14	19	23
74°	0'5425	5454	5483	5512	5541	5570	5600	5629	5659	5689	5	10	15	20	25
75°	0'5719	5750	5780	5811	5842	5873	5905	5936	5968	6000	5	10	16	21	26
76°	0'6032	6065	6097	6130	6163	6196	6230	6264	6298	6332	6	11	17	22	28
77°	0'6366	6401	6436	6471	6507	6542	6578	6615	6651	6688	6	12	18	24	30
78°	0'6725	6763	6800	6838	6877	6915	6954	6994	7033	7073	6	13	19	26	32
79°	0'7113	7154	7195	7236	7278	7320	7363	7406	7449	7493	7	14	21	28	35
80°	0'7537	7581	7626	7672	7718	7764	7811	7858	7906	7954	8	16	23	31	39
81°	0'8003	8052	8102	8152	8203	8255	8307	8360	8413	8467	9	17	26	35	43
82°	0'8522	8577	8633	8690	8748	8806	8865	8924	8985	9046	10	20	29	39	49
83°	0'9109	9172	9236	9301	9367	9433	9501	9570	9640	9711	11	22	34	45	56
84°	0'9784	9857	9932	1'0008	1'0085	1'0164	1'0244	1'0326	1'0409	1'0494	13	26	40	53	66
85°	1'0580	0669	0759	0850	0944	1040	1138	1238	1341	1446	16	32	48	65	81
86°	1'1554	1664	1777	1893	2012	2135	2261	2391	2525	2663					
87°	1'2806	2954	3106	3264	3429	3599	3777	3962	4155	4357					
88°	1'4569	4792	5027	5275	5539	5819	6119	6441	6789	7167					
89°	1'7581	1'804	1'855	1'913	1'980	2'059	2'156	2'281	2'457	2'758					

ANSWERS

EXERCISE 1

p. 12.

1. $x = \frac{3}{4}$ or $\frac{1}{3}$.
2. (a) $(x - 5)(x + 4)$;   (b) $\pi(R - 2r)(R + 2r)$;
   (c) $R(R + 4r)(R + 2r)$; (b) $= 94\cdot2$, (c) $= 877\cdot5$.
3. $\pm 5\cdot6$.   **4.** $x = 168$ or 132.   **5.** 4 ins. and $1\cdot6$ ins.
6. (1) $+ 2b^2$, (2) $(a + 2b)$ and $(a + 2b)$, (3) $(3a - b)$; $60\cdot3$.
7. (a) real; (b) complex; (c) equal; (d) real.
8. $x\left(\dfrac{P}{2} - x\right) = A$; sides $7\cdot37$ and $1\cdot63$.
9. $x = 2\cdot13$ or $-5\cdot63$.   **10.** 87 secs.

EXERCISE 2

p. 16.

1. $x = \pm \sqrt{3}$ or $\pm \sqrt{2}$.
2. $\dfrac{1}{y^2} = -3$ or 2.   The real value of y is $\pm \dfrac{\sqrt{2}}{2}$.
3. $x = \frac{1}{81}$.   **4.** $x = 1 \pm \sqrt{2}$ or $1 \pm \sqrt{17}$.
5. $z = 28$.   **6.** $\sin \theta = \frac{3}{4}$ or $\frac{1}{3}$.   **7.** $\tan \theta = \frac{1}{4}$ or -5.
8. $\sin \theta = \frac{2}{3}$ or $\frac{1}{2}$.   **9.** $\tan \theta = 4$ or -5.   **10.** $x = 2$ or 1.
11. $x = \pm 2$.   **12.** $\cos \theta = 0\cdot1287$.
13. (i) $x = 0$ or $0\cdot1761$; (ii) $\sin x = \pm \dfrac{1}{\sqrt{2}}$, *i.e.*, $x = \pm 45°$.

EXERCISE 3

p. 18.

1. $x = \frac{29}{3}$.   **2.** $x = 22$.   **3.** $x = \pm 5$.   **4.** $x = \frac{9}{4}$.
5. $x = -0\cdot29$.   **6.** $y = 4$ or $4\frac{84}{169}$.   **7.** $z = 3$.
8. $x = 1$.   **9.** $x = 11$ or 4.   **10.** $p = 2\frac{8}{11}$.

EXERCISE 4

p. 24.

1. $x = -1, y = 0$.   2. $x = 7, y = 4$.
3. $x = 3$ or $2, y = 2$ or 3.   4. $z = 8, w = 2$.
5. $x = \pm 1, y = \pm 2$.   6. $x = 1$ or $\frac{1}{5}, y = 2$ or $\frac{22}{5}$.
7. $x = 7\sqrt{2}, y = \sqrt{2}$; $x = -\sqrt{2}, y = -7\sqrt{2}$;
   $x = \sqrt{2}, y = 7\sqrt{2}$; $x = -7\sqrt{2}, y = -\sqrt{2}$.
8. $\frac{1}{x} = 4, \frac{1}{y} = 3$.   9. $x = y = \pm 1$.
10. $x = \frac{52}{25}, y = \frac{13}{25}$.   11. $x = 100, y = 173 \cdot 2$.
12. $a = 1 \cdot 6, b = 0 \cdot 4, c = -1 \cdot 5$; S $= 102 \cdot 8$.
13. A $= 2$, B $= \frac{1}{2}$, C $= \frac{1}{4}$.
14. $a = y_2$, $b = \dfrac{y_3 - y_1}{2h}$, $c = \dfrac{y_1 - 2y_2 + y_3}{2h^2}$.

EXERCISE 5

p. 26.

1. $a = 1 \cdot 37, b = 1 \cdot 86, n = 1 \cdot 46$.   2. $p = 24 \cdot 23$; T $= 328 \cdot 3$.
3. N $= 3595$ 4. $a = 1 \cdot 24, b = 0 \cdot 61, n = 2 \cdot 34$.
5. R $= 148 \cdot 10^6$.   6. $x = 1 \cdot 52$.   7. $x = 3$ or -1.
8. $x = -\frac{5}{3}, y = \frac{7}{3}$.   9. $x = 5$ or -1.
10. $x = -\frac{28}{3}, y = -4$.
11. $a = 2 \cdot 36, b = 0 \cdot 73, c = 1 \cdot 46$; (2) $y = 44 \cdot 2$.

EXERCISE 6

p. 40.

1. (a) $y - 3 = \dfrac{1}{\sqrt{3}}(x - 2)$.   (b) $y + \sqrt{3}x + \sqrt{3} - 1 = 0$.
   (c) $y + 2 = 0 \cdot 7536(x + 3)$.   (d) $3x - 7y + 27 = 0$.
   (e) $x + 6y + 2 = 0$.
2. $0 \cdot 6$ too small.   3. $a = 684$; $b = 39 \cdot 5$.
4. $n = 5 \cdot 7$; $m = 20 \cdot 1$.   5. $a = 0 \cdot 17$; $b = 9 \cdot 81$.
6. $a = 5 \cdot 5$; $b = 0 \cdot 25$.   7. $a = 6 \cdot 3$; $b = 215$.
8. $k = 0 \cdot 625$; $n = 3 \cdot 25$.

EXERCISE 8

p. 52.

1. $x = 3 \cdot 2$ or 2.   2. $x = 4 \cdot 1$ or $2 \cdot 3$.
3. $x = 1 \cdot 78$ or $-0 \cdot 28$.   4. $x = 2 \cdot 77$.
5. $x = 1 \cdot 27$ and $3 \cdot 82$.   Turning points at $(3, 5 \cdot 4)$ and $(2, 1)$.
6. (i) $5 \cdot 19, 2 \cdot 49, -1 \cdot 68$; (ii) $5 \cdot 51, 1 \cdot 92, -1 \cdot 43$.
7. $1 \cdot 11, 2 \cdot 56, -0 \cdot 67$.   8. $2 \cdot 718$.   9. $2 \cdot 15$.
   $1 \cdot 17, 2 \cdot 69, -0 \cdot 87$.

EXERCISE 9

p. 57.

1. (a) 210; (b) 1,680; (c) 720.　　2. (a) $\dfrac{\lfloor 6}{\lfloor 4}$; (b) $\lfloor 5$; (c) $\dfrac{\lfloor 8}{\lfloor 6}$.

4. 504.　　　5. 36.　　　6. 30.　　　7. 60; 125.

8. $2 \times \lfloor 7 = 10,080$.

EXERCISE 10

p. 60.

1. (a) 35; (b) 28; (c) 10; (d) 1.

2. (a) $\dfrac{\lfloor 7}{\lfloor 4 \lfloor 3}$; (b) $\dfrac{\lfloor 8}{\lfloor 2 \lfloor 6}$; (c) $\dfrac{\lfloor 10}{\lfloor 9}$; (d) $\dfrac{\lfloor 5}{\lfloor 5}$.

4. 560.　　　　　　5. (a) 28; (b) 56.　　6. $^8C_3 \times {}^6C_4 = 840$.

7. $^{17}C_7$ or $^{17}C_{10}$.　　8. $r = 5$.

EXERCISE 11

p. 67.

1. (a) $1 + \dfrac{z}{2} - \dfrac{z^2}{8} + \dfrac{z^3}{16}$;　　　(b) $1 + h + h^2 + h^3$;

(c) $1 + \dfrac{3y}{2} + \dfrac{3y^2}{8} - \dfrac{y^3}{16}$;　　(d) $1 + \dfrac{5x}{4} + \dfrac{45x^2}{32} + \dfrac{195x^3}{128}$;

(e) $1 - x + x^2 - x^3$;　　　(f) $1 + \dfrac{x}{2} + \dfrac{3x^2}{8} + \dfrac{5x^3}{16}$;

(g) $1 - \dfrac{x}{4} + \dfrac{5x^2}{32} - \dfrac{15x^3}{128}$;　　(h) $1 - 3x + 6x^2 - 10x^3$;

(k) $\dfrac{1}{a^2} - \dfrac{2x}{a^3} + \dfrac{3x^2}{a^4} - \dfrac{4x^3}{a^5}$;　　(l) $a^{\frac{1}{2}}\left(1 + \dfrac{h}{a} - \dfrac{h^2}{2a^2} + \dfrac{h^3}{2a^3}\right)$;

(m) $\dfrac{1}{2^4}\left(1 + 6x + \dfrac{45x^2}{2} + \dfrac{135x^3}{2}\right)$.

2. (a) 1·104;　　　(b) 0·988;　　　(c) 1·003;
　(d) 1·004;　　　(e) 0·332;　　　(f) 1·007.

3. $8x^7$; $\dfrac{1}{2\sqrt{x}}$.　　　　　4. $1 + x - \dfrac{x^2}{2} + \dfrac{x^3}{2} - \dfrac{5x^4}{8}$.

6. $1 - \dfrac{5x}{6} + \dfrac{19x^2}{72}$.　　　　7. $\dfrac{160}{243 \times 343}$.

8. $1 - 27x + 324x^2 - 2268x^3 + 10,206x^4$;
　4th = 0·489888;　　　5th = 0·13226976.

9. $^{12}C_6 \cdot a^{12}$.

10. $x^{\frac{1}{2}}\left(1 - \dfrac{y}{2x} - \dfrac{y^2}{8x^2} - \dfrac{y^3}{16x^3}\right)$; $1 \cdot 732$, $0 \cdot 028\,85$, $- 0 \cdot 000\,2406$.

11. (i) $0 \cdot 995$; (ii) $7 \cdot 9$.   **12.** 4th term, $- \,^{14}C_3 \cdot \left(\dfrac{3}{4}\right)^3 \left(\dfrac{x^2}{2}\right)^{11}$.

13. $\dfrac{4lm}{d^3}$.

EXERCISE 12
p. 72.

1. (a) 4; (b) 2; (c) 44; (d) $\frac{1}{4}$. **2.** (a) 4; (b) $5 \cdot 3636$; (c) $\dfrac{7\sqrt{3}}{2}$.

3. (a) 53; (b) 70. **4.** (a) $8x + 6$; (b) $2h^2 + h(4x - 1)$.

5. $6t + 11$.

EXERCISE 13
p. 75.

1. 5.   **2.** 5.   **3.** 7.   **4.** 3.   **5.** $1\frac{1}{8}$.   **6.** $\frac{3}{5}$.   **7.** $\frac{17}{11}$.

EXERCISE 14
p. 80.

1. 9 **2.** (a) 7; (b) 1; (c) $h + 2$.

3. 2; $2x - y - 1 = 0$. **4.** $16x - y - 16 = 0$.

5 $9x - y - 7 = 0$.

EXERCISE 15
p. 83.

1. (a) $2x$; (b) $6x + 1$; (c) $3x^2$.   **2.** $8t$; $4z$.

3. $6x + 2$; $8x - y + 1 = 0$.   **4.** 3.

EXERCISE 16
p. 87.

1. (i) $7x^6$; (ii) $- 8x^{-5}$; (iii) $- 6x^{-3}$; (iv) $- 15x^{-4}$.

2. $- \dfrac{10}{t^6}$; $- \frac{5}{2} \cdot y^{-\frac{3}{2}}$; $- 2z^{-\frac{3}{2}}$.

3. (a) $- \dfrac{4}{x^2}$; (b) $- \frac{50}{3}x^{-\frac{13}{3}}$; (c) $\frac{6 \cdot 6}{5}x^{\frac{6}{5}}$.

4. (i) $- \frac{3}{2}x^{-\frac{7}{4}}$; (ii) $\frac{1 \cdot 5}{4}\theta^{-\frac{1}{4}}$; (iii) $- 8z^{-5}$; (iv) $\frac{5 \cdot 5}{4} \cdot t^{\frac{7}{4}}$.

5. (i) $6 \cdot 4x^{2 \cdot 2}$;   (ii) $0 \cdot 13x^{-0 \cdot 87}$;   (iii) $- 10 \cdot 7x^{-3 \cdot 14}$;

(iv) $- \dfrac{1 \cdot 5}{\sqrt[3]{2}} \cdot x^{-1 \cdot 5}$; (v) $- 2 \cdot 5x^{-1 \cdot 5}$.

EXERCISE 17

p. 88.

1. $6x^2 - 6x + 4$; $\quad 2 \cdot 6t^{0 \cdot 3} + 8t^{-3} - \dfrac{3}{t^2}$.

2. (i) $-\dfrac{1}{x^2} + \dfrac{4}{x^3} - \dfrac{12}{x^5}$; $\qquad$ (ii) $4 \cdot 8t^{0 \cdot 6} + 2 \cdot 8t^{-1 \cdot 7} - 2t^{-2}$;

   (iii) $2x - 1$; $\qquad\qquad$ (iv) $6(3x + 1)$.

3. (a) $72x^8$; (b) $\frac{2}{3} \cdot x^{-3}$; (c) $\frac{1}{2} \cdot x^{-\frac{1}{2}} + 24x^{-\frac{5}{3}}$; (d) $\frac{3}{2}x^2 + \dfrac{1}{2x^2}$;

   (e) $2(2x^2 - x^3)(4x - 3x^2) = 2x^3(2 - x)(4 - 3x)$.

4. (i) $-\dfrac{2 \cdot 4^6}{x^3}$; $\qquad$ (ii) $8x^3 - 2 \cdot 8^4 \cdot x$; (iii) $\frac{3}{5}x^{-\frac{1}{2}}$;

   (iv) $0 \cdot 4 \cdot 2^7 x^{-0 \cdot 6}$; (v) $6x^5 + 3x^{-4}$.

   Required values (i) $-\frac{1}{4}$, (ii) 0, (iii) $\frac{3}{20}$, (iv) $\frac{32}{5}$.

5. $2x^{-\frac{1}{3}} - 3x^{-2 \cdot 5} + 15x^{-4}$.

6. (a) $3x^2 + 4x$; (b) $19 \cdot 2x^{2 \cdot 2} + \dfrac{2}{x^2}$; (c) $4x^3 - 12x^2 + 6x - 12$.

7. (a) $6x + 2$; (b) $-\frac{25}{27}$.

8. (a) (i) $8x + 1$, (ii) $3 - \dfrac{12}{x^2}$.

   (b) (i) where $x = \pm \dfrac{\sqrt{38}}{3}$; (ii) where $x = \pm 2$.

9. $2x + 2$; (i) $20 \cdot 3x^{-0 \cdot 3}$; (ii) $-\dfrac{3}{x^2} + \dfrac{6}{x^4}$.

10. $K = \frac{3}{2}$; gradient $= \frac{1}{8}$.

11. $x^2 - 6x + 5$; (i) $(3, 1)$ and $(2, \frac{14}{3})$,

    (ii) where $x = -3 + \sqrt{5}$.

12. $a = 36$; $b = \frac{1}{2}$. $\qquad$ 13. $6x$; (a) $1 - \dfrac{1}{x^2}$, (b) $-2Ax$.

EXERCISE 18

p. 91.

1. $y_1 = 12x^3 - 12x + 2$; $y_2 = 36x^2 - 12$. $\qquad$ 2. $6 - \dfrac{6}{t^3}$.

3. 6. $\qquad$ 4. (a) 5th; (b) 4th. $\qquad$ 5. where $x = \frac{1}{9}$.

EXERCISE 19

p. 94.

1. $3(x^2 + x)^2(2x + 1)$.

2. $4(3x^2 - 5x + 6)^3(6x - 5)$.

3. $10x(x^2 + 3)^4$.

4. $\dfrac{-(2x + 3)}{(x^2 + 3x + 4)^2}$.

5. $-\dfrac{1}{(x + 3)^2}$.

6. $-\dfrac{4x}{(x^2 + 3)^3}$.

7. $-\dfrac{16(3x^2 - 3)}{(x^3 - 3x + 1)^5}$.

8. $3(x^2 - 1{\cdot}3x + 4)^2(2x - 1{\cdot}3)$.

9. $-x/(x^2 + 3)^{\frac{3}{2}}$.

10. $-\frac{1}{3}(2x^2 + x + 1)^{-\frac{4}{3}} \cdot (4x + 1)$.

EXERCISE 20

p. 96.

1. $2x(x^2 + 3x + 6) + x^2(2x + 3)$.

2. $\frac{3}{2}x^{\frac{1}{2}}(x^2 + 5x - 2) + x^{\frac{3}{2}}(2x + 5)$.

3. (i) $2x(x^2 + 3x + 6)^2 + 2x^2(x^2 + 3x + 6)(2x + 3)$;
   (ii) $5x^4(x - 1)^4 + 4x^5(x - 1)^3$.

4. (i) $-9x^{-4}(x^2 + 2)^4 + 12x^{-3}(x^2 + 2)^3 \cdot 2x$;
   (ii) $-\frac{1}{2}t^{-\frac{3}{2}}(t + 3)^3 + 3t^{-\frac{1}{2}}(t + 3)^2$.

5. (i) $4x^3(x^2 + 3)^{-2} - 2x^4(x^2 + 3)^{-3} \cdot 2x$;
   (ii) $4x(1 - x^2)^{-2} + 8x^3(1 - x^2)^{-3}$;
   (iii) $3(2 - x)^{-4} + 12x(2 - x)^{-5}$.

6. (i) $(x + 2)^{-2} - 2x(x + 2)^{-3}$;
   (ii) $6x(1 - x)^{-1} + 3x^2(1 - x)^{-2}$;
   (iii) $-2x^{-3}(x + 3)^{-1} - x^{-2}(x + 3)^{-2}$;
   (iv) $(2x + 1)(x + 1)^{-2} - 2(x^2 + x + 2)(x + 1)^{-3}$;
   (v) $2t(1 + t + t^2)^{-2} - 2(t^2 + 3)(1 + t + t^2)^{-3} \cdot (1 + 2t)$.

EXERCISE 21

p. 98.

1. $\dfrac{a}{(x + a)^2}$.

2. $\dfrac{4a^2x}{(x^2 + a^2)^2}$.

3. $1 - \dfrac{1}{(x + 1)^2}$.

4. $\dfrac{(x + 2) \cdot \frac{1}{2}x^{-\frac{1}{2}} - \sqrt{x}}{(x + 2)^2} = \dfrac{(2 - x)}{2\sqrt{x}(x + 2)^2}$.

5. $3 - \dfrac{12}{(x + 2)^2}$.

6. $\dfrac{10x(x^2 + 1)^2 - 20x^3(x^2 + 1)}{(x^2 + 1)^4}$.

7. $\dfrac{(1 - x)^{\frac{1}{2}} \cdot \frac{1}{2}(1 + x)^{-\frac{1}{2}} + \frac{1}{2}(1 + x)^{\frac{1}{2}}(1 - x)^{-\frac{1}{2}}}{(1 - x)}$

$$= \dfrac{1}{(1 - x)^{\frac{3}{2}} \cdot (1 + x)^{\frac{1}{2}}}.$$

8. $\dfrac{5x^2 + 20x - 3}{3(x + 2)^{\frac{2}{3}} \cdot (5x^2 + 3)^{\frac{2}{3}}}$.

EXERCISE 22

p. 100.

1. $3 \cdot 6x^{0 \cdot 2} - 2x^{-\frac{1}{2}} - 9x^{-4}$.
2. $6(2x - 3)^2$.

3. $\frac{1}{2}(x - 4)^{-\frac{1}{2}}$.
4. $- 2(x + a)^{-3}$.

5. $- 10(4x - 2)^{-\frac{3}{2}}$. **6.** $- 3(5 - 6x)^{-\frac{1}{2}}$. **7.** $- 8x(3 - x^2)^3$.

8. $4(3x^2 - 2x + 2)^3(6x - 2)$. **9.** $\sqrt{x + a} + \frac{x}{2}(x + a)^{-\frac{1}{2}}$.

10. $3x^2(x + a)^3 + 3x^3(x + a)^2$.
11. $10x^4(x^2 + 2x + 3)^2 + 4x^5(x^2 + 2x + 3)(2x + 2)$.

12. $\frac{3x}{2}(x^2 - a^2)^{-\frac{1}{2}}$.
13. $- \frac{1}{3}(x^2 + x + 1)^{-\frac{4}{3}}(2x + 1)$.

14. $\dfrac{(x + 2)(6x + 2) - (3x^2 + 2x + 1)}{(x + 2)^2} = \dfrac{3x^2 + 12x + 3}{(x + 2)^2}$.

15. $\dfrac{3\sqrt{x + 1} \cdot x^2 - x^3 \cdot \frac{1}{2}(x + 1)^{-\frac{1}{2}}}{(x + 1)} = \dfrac{5x^3 + 6x^2}{2(x + 1)^{\frac{3}{2}}}$.

16. $\dfrac{14x}{(x^2 + 3)^2}$.
17. $- \dfrac{5}{2}\sqrt{\dfrac{2 + x}{3 - x}} \cdot \dfrac{1}{(2 + x)^2}$.

18. 5 and 11. **19.** $\frac{8}{5}$ and $\frac{3}{4}$. **20.** $- \dfrac{x}{y}$.

21. $- \dfrac{1}{3x}(2x + 3y)$.
22. $- \dfrac{2x + 3}{2y + 4}$.

EXERCISE 23

p. 107.

The constant has been omitted in the answers.

1. $\dfrac{x^5}{5} + C$. **2.** $\frac{2}{3}x^{\frac{3}{2}}$. **3.** $- 2x^{-\frac{1}{2}}$. **4.** $- \dfrac{1}{4x^4}$.

5. $\dfrac{x^6}{2}$. **6.** $\frac{8}{7}x^{\frac{7}{4}}$. **7.** $\frac{20}{3}x^{\frac{3}{4}}$. **8.** $- \dfrac{4}{3} \cdot \dfrac{1}{x^3}$.

9. $\dfrac{2}{1 \cdot 6} \cdot x^{1 \cdot 6}$. **10.** $\dfrac{3 \cdot 2}{2 \cdot 3}x^{2 \cdot 3}$. **11.** $\dfrac{2 \cdot 1}{4}x^4$.

12. $- \dfrac{0 \cdot 1}{0 \cdot 1} \cdot \dfrac{1}{x^{0 \cdot 1}} = - \dfrac{1}{x^{0 \cdot 1}}$. **13.** $\dfrac{x^3}{3} + \dfrac{3x^2}{2}$.

14. $\dfrac{x^{2 \cdot 3}}{2 \cdot 3} - \dfrac{x^{1 \cdot 4}}{1 \cdot 4} - \dfrac{1}{2x}$. **15.** $x^3 - \dfrac{1}{x^2} - \dfrac{1}{3x^3}$.

16. $\dfrac{3x^{1 \cdot 2}}{1 \cdot 2} - \dfrac{2 \cdot 1x^{2 \cdot 3}}{2 \cdot 3}$. **17.** $y = \dfrac{3x^5}{5} + \dfrac{17}{5}$.

18. $s = t^3 - 4$. **19.** $s = \dfrac{2t^3}{3} + 5t - 31$.

20. (a) $- \dfrac{1}{4x^2}$; (b) $\sqrt{2} \cdot x - \dfrac{4}{1 \cdot 25}x^{1 \cdot 25}$; (c) $\dfrac{x^3}{3} + \dfrac{2}{x} - \dfrac{1}{5x^5}$.

21. (a) $2\frac{1}{7}x^{\frac{1}{7}}$;   (b) $3x - \frac{5}{2}x^{0\cdot8}$;   (c) $\dfrac{x^7}{7} - \dfrac{x^6}{3} + \dfrac{x^5}{5}$;

     (d) $\dfrac{x^3}{3} + \dfrac{1}{x}$.   **22.** (a) $-\dfrac{1}{\sqrt{2x}}$;   (b) $\pi x - 10\sqrt{x}$;

       (c) $x - \dfrac{x^3}{9} - \sqrt{x}$;   (d) $3x^{\frac{1}{3}} + 8x^2 + 6x^{\frac{1}{2}}$.

23. (a) $\dfrac{t^2}{2}$;   (b) $12\sqrt{x} + 2x$.

EXERCISE 24
p. 110.

1. $\dfrac{(x+3)^2}{2} + C.$ 2. $\dfrac{(x+4)^3}{3}.$ 3. $-\dfrac{(5+x)^{-3}}{3}.$

4. $-\dfrac{1}{(x+3)}.$ 5. $\dfrac{(x^2+3)^2}{2}.$ 6. $\dfrac{(x^2+3)^2}{4}.$

7. $\dfrac{(x^2-1)^4}{8}.$ 8. $\dfrac{(x^3-1)^2}{6}.$ 9. $\dfrac{(x^3+3)^4}{12}.$

10. $-\dfrac{1}{2} \cdot \dfrac{1}{(x^2+5)^2}.$ 11. $-\dfrac{1}{6}\dfrac{1}{(x^2+5)^3}.$ 12. $-\dfrac{1}{(x^3-2)}.$

13. $2\sqrt{x^2+3}.$ 14. $\frac{3}{4}(x^2+a^2)^{\frac{2}{3}}.$ 15. $-\dfrac{1}{(x^2+x+3)}.$

16. $-\dfrac{1}{2} \cdot \dfrac{1}{(x^3+x^2+1)^2}.$

EXERCISE 25
p. 114.

1. (1) 2 ft.;   (2) 35 ft./sec.;   (3) after $\frac{1}{6}$ sec.;   (4) 6 ft./sec.²;
     (5) 23 ft./sec.   2. 73; $\frac{28}{15}$.
3. (a) $108 - 3t^2$;   (b) $- 6t$;   (c) after 6 secs.
4. Calculated value 19 ft./sec.²   6. At 1 and 3·1 miles.
7. Vels. are 168, 136, 104, 72, 40 ft./sec.

EXERCISE 26
p. 126.

1. (1) $5\frac{1}{6}$, $\frac{2}{3}$;   (2) 12, $-$ 20;   (3) 5, $3\frac{22}{27}$.
2. $\dfrac{4\sqrt{3}\pi}{9}$ cu. ft.   3. 206·4 cu. ins.

4. 117220 units; $V = 30.96$.

5. 2.52 is side of sq.; $ht = 1.26$ ft.

6. 5.65 in from one end.   **7.** From $-$ to $+$.

8. $\frac{3}{4}$, where $x = \frac{5}{2}$.   **9.** $a = 36$; $b = \frac{1}{2}$; 16.35.

10. Side of triangle $= 5.88$ in.; length $= 3.40$ ins.

11. 0, $\frac{8}{5}$ min.; $\frac{1}{2}$ max.   **12.** $a = \frac{3}{16}$; $b = \frac{43}{16}$.

13. $x = 0$ or -1.   **14.** 8.94 ins. by 4.47 ins.

15. (a) a min. where $x = \frac{3}{2}$; (b) $4\frac{1}{2}$.

16. $r = h = \dfrac{100}{\pi^{\frac{1}{3}}} = 68.3$ ft.

EXERCISE 27

p. 131.

1. ± 0.173 sq. in.   **2.** ± 0.4 sq. in.   **3.** $\pm \dfrac{8\pi}{100}$ sq. in.

4. $\frac{3}{20}$ in.   **5.** (1) $19\frac{4}{7}$; (2) $20\frac{1}{35}$; (3) 13.86.

6. 1% increase.   **7.** $\frac{1}{50}$.   **9.** 0.028 in.

EXERCISE 28

p. 134.

1. 14.4π cu. ins./sec.   **2.** 22.   **3.** $\dfrac{24\pi}{5}$ cu. ins./sec.

5. 0.087 ft./sec. towards O.

6. $\dfrac{2}{h \tan 20°}$, $h = ht$ at time t.

7. 6 ft./sec.   **8.** 0.744 cu. ft./sec.

EXERCISE 29

p. 146.

1. (i) 0.829; (ii) -0.6428; (iii) 0.8391; (iv) -4.8097; (v) 2.9238; (vi) 0.866; (vii) 0.9749; (viii) -0.4142.

2. $\dfrac{2\sqrt{5}}{5}$, $\dfrac{\sqrt{5}}{3}$.   **3.** $\sin A = \dfrac{3\sqrt{10}}{10}$. $\cos A = \dfrac{\sqrt{10}}{10}$.

4. $\sin \theta = \dfrac{2\sqrt{2}}{3}$. $\tan \theta = 2\sqrt{2}$.   **6.** $\dfrac{\pi}{6}$, $\dfrac{\pi}{4}$, $\dfrac{\pi}{3}$, $\dfrac{2\pi}{3}$, $\dfrac{57\pi}{45}$.

7. $36°$, $67° 30'$, $25\frac{5}{7}°$, $\dfrac{600}{\pi}$, $\dfrac{120}{\pi}$.   **10.** 5860.

EXERCISE 30

p. 151.

1. 2π, 2π, π.   2. π.

3. (i) $\dfrac{2\pi}{3}$; (ii) $\dfrac{\pi}{2}$; (iii) $\dfrac{\pi}{3}$; (iv) $\dfrac{2\pi}{5}$; (v) $\dfrac{2\pi}{a}$; (vi) 2π; (vii) 2π.

4. $\sin(90 + A) = \cos A$; $\cos(90 + A) = -\sin A$;
   $\tan(90 + A) = -\cot A$.

5. (i) $15°$ and $75°$; (ii) $10°$ and $110°$; (iii) $22\frac{1}{2}°$, $112\frac{1}{2}°$;
   (iv) $4° 15'$ and $31° 45'$; (v) $21° 9'$ and $81° 9'$; (vi) $x = 20$
   or 100.

6. $48° 12'$, $311° 48'$ ($0°$ and $360°$).

7. $120°$, $240°$ $70° 32'$, $289° 28'$.

8. $14° 29'$, $165° 31'$, $41° 48'$, $138° 12'$.

9. (i) $\dfrac{2\pi}{3}$; (ii) $\dfrac{2\pi}{5}$; (iii) π; (iv) $\dfrac{\pi}{4}$; (v) $\dfrac{2\pi}{a}$.

10. $-\sin 20°$, $\cos 60°$, $-\tan 42°$, $+\sec 130°$.

EXERCISE 31

p. 161.

1. $7 \cdot 93$ and $3 \cdot 17$ miles.   2. (i) $3 \cdot 60$; (ii) $5 \cdot 4$. $AC = 6 \cdot 49$ ins

3. (i) $r = \sqrt{5}$. $\alpha = 26° 34'$; (ii) $r = \sqrt{34}$. $\alpha = 30° 58'$.
      $\sqrt{5} \sin(x + 26° 34')$. $\sqrt{34} \cos(x + 30° 58')$.

4. $10° 24'$ or $17° 8'$.   8. $3 \cdot 61$.

9. $3 \cos 4t - 2 \cos\left(4t + \dfrac{\pi}{6}\right)$. $1 \cdot 62$ ft. $t = \frac{5}{31}$ secs.

11. $36 \cdot 8°$. $56 \cdot 3°$.

12. $A = 45 \cdot 6$. $\alpha = 64°$ $\theta_{max.} = 26°$. $\theta_{min.} = 206°$.
    zero when $\theta = -64°$; (4) $\theta = 8° 12'$ or $43° 48'$.

13. $A = \sqrt{5}$; $\alpha = 26° 34'$.

EXERCISE 32

p. 170.

1. $\tan \theta = 0 \cdot 618$ or $-1 \cdot 618$.   2. $b = \frac{1}{3}$ or $-\frac{5}{4}$. $A = 34°$.

3. $\theta = 60°$, $300°$, $36° 45'$ or $323° 15'$.

4. $4 \sin A(1 - \sin A)(1 + \sin A)$. $1 \cdot 225$.   5. $B = 11° 54'$.

6. (1) $\frac{1}{2}(\sin 50° + \sin 14°)$.   (2) $\frac{1}{2}(\sin 90° - \sin 16°)$.
   (3) $\cos 82° + \cos 6°$.   (4) $\cos 4° - \cos 80°$.
   (5) $\cos 2\alpha - \cos 4\theta$.

7. (1) $2 \sin \dfrac{5x}{2} \cos \dfrac{x}{2}$.   (2) $2 \sin 42° \cos 6°$.

    (3) $2 \cos 40° . \cos 11°$.   (4) $- 2 \sin \left(x + \dfrac{h}{2}\right) \sin \dfrac{h}{2}$.

9. $\cos^3 \theta = \tfrac{1}{4}(\cos 3\theta + 3 \cos \theta)$. $\sin^3 \theta = \tfrac{1}{4}(3 \sin \theta - \sin 3\theta)$.

10. $\theta = 77°$ or $283°$.

EXERCISE 33

p. 182.

1. $49° 28'$ and $58° 45'$.   **2.** 500 ft.   **3.** 1·995 ins.

4. 6·14 ft. $57° 54'$ and $122° 6'$.   **5.** $36° 52'$, $81° 18'$, and $61° 50'$.

6. $58°$.   **7.** 19 ft., 21·5 ft., $56° 29$.   **8.** 48 yds.

9. $70°$; 2·1 ins.   **10.** 29·8 ins.   **11.** 655 ft.

12. 446 ft.   **13.** 2576 ft.   **14.** 115·4 ft.

15. 114 ft.   **16.** 5·38 ft.

17. (1) 24 ins.; (2) $19\tfrac{1}{5}$ ins.   **18.** $77° 10'$ and $102° 50'$.

EXERCISE 34

p. 190.

1. $B = 65° 15'$; $C = 56° 21'$.   **2.** 1515 sq. ft.

3. 30·43 ft.; $92° 51'$ and $49° 5'$.   **4.** $90°$ (nearly).

5. $72° 24'$; $107° 36'$; 36·46 sq. ins.

EXERCISE 35

p. 196.

1. $\cos t$.   **2.** $4 \cos 4t$.   **3.** $\dfrac{1}{3} \cos \dfrac{t}{3}$.

4. $\pi \cos \pi t$.   **5.** $n \cos nt$.   **6.** $6 \cos 2t$.

7. $\dfrac{1}{6} \cos \dfrac{t}{3}$.   **8.** $2 \cos \pi t$.   **9.** $ab \cos bt$.

10. $5 \cos (\theta + \alpha)$.   **11.** $3 \cos (\theta + \pi)$.   **12.** $a \cos \left(\theta - \dfrac{\pi}{3}\right)$.

13. $15 \cos \left(3\theta - \dfrac{\pi}{5}\right)$.   **14.** $\dfrac{1}{4} \cos \left(\dfrac{1}{2}\theta + \dfrac{\pi}{3}\right)$.

15. $2af \cos (2ft + n\pi)$.   **16.** $- 3 \sin 3x$.

17. $- \dfrac{1}{5} \sin \dfrac{x}{5}$.   **18.** $- \pi \sin \pi x$.   **19.** $- 15 \sin 3\theta$.

20. $- 15 \sin (5\theta + \alpha)$.   **21.** $- 12 \sin \left(3\theta + \dfrac{\pi}{4}\right)$.

22. $- \dfrac{k}{2} \sin (k\theta + \alpha)$.   **23.** $- 2na \sin (2nx + k\pi)$.

EXERCISE 36

p. 198.

1. $\sec^2 \theta$.   **2.** $\sec x \tan x$.   **3.** $- \operatorname{cosec} z \cot z$.

4. $- \operatorname{cosec}^2 y$.   **5.** $3 \sec^2 3\theta$.   **6.** $\dfrac{1}{2} \sec \dfrac{\theta}{2} \tan \dfrac{\theta}{2}$.

7. $- 3 \operatorname{cosec} 3x \cot 3x$.   **8.** $- 12 \operatorname{cosec}^2 4\theta$.

9. $10 \sec \left(2\theta + \dfrac{\pi}{2} \right) \tan \left(2\theta + \dfrac{\pi}{2} \right) = 10 \operatorname{cosec} 2\theta \cdot \cot 2\theta$.

10. $3 \sec^2 \theta$.   **11.** $\dfrac{\pi}{60} \cdot \cos 3x°$.   **12.** $- \dfrac{\pi}{120} \sin \dfrac{1}{2}x°$.

13. $\dfrac{\pi}{90} \sec^2 x°$.

EXERCISE 37

p. 200.

1. $2x \sin x + x^2 \cos x$.   **2.** $6x^2 \sin x + 2x^3 \cos x$.
3. $4x^3 \sin 2x + 2x^4 \cos 2x$.   **4.** $12x^5 \cos 3x - 6x^6 \sin 3x$.
5. $\dfrac{2x^2 \cos 2x - 2x \sin 2x}{x^4} = 2x^{-3}(x \cos 2x - \sin 2x)$.

6. $- 12x^{-5} \cos 4x - 12x^{-4} \sin 4x$.
7. $\cos \theta \cdot \cos 2\theta - 2 \sin \theta \sin 2\theta$.
8. $6 \cos 2\theta \cos 4\theta - 12 \sin 2\theta \cdot \sin 4\theta$.
9. $\dfrac{\cos 2\theta \cdot \cos \theta + 2 \sin 2\theta \cdot \sin \theta}{\cos^2 2\theta}$.

10. $12 \cos 3\theta \cdot \cos 4\theta - 16 \sin 3\theta \sin 4\theta$.
11. $2\pi \cos 2\pi t \cdot \cos \pi t - \pi \sin 2\pi t \cdot \sin \pi t$.
12. $\sin 2x$.   **13.** $9 \sin^2 x \cos x$.   **14.** $- 3 \cos^2 \theta \cdot \sin \theta$.
15. $- 30 \cos 3\theta \cdot \sin 3\theta = - 15 \sin 6\theta$.
16. $24 \sin^2 4x \cos 4x$.
17. $\dfrac{- \sin x (2 \cos x \cdot \sin x) - \cos^3 x}{\sin^2 x} = - 2 \cos x - \dfrac{\cos^3 x}{\sin^2 x}$.
18. $- 6 \cos^2 x \sin x - 12 \sin 2x \cos 2x$.

EXERCISE 38

p. 207.

1. (a) $0 \cdot 49975$; (b) $1 \cdot 0006$; (c) $0 \cdot 49975$.
2. $\cdot 088$ ft.   **3.** $k \sec^2 \theta \cdot d\theta$. $1 \cdot 75\%$.   **4.** $0 \cdot 72$ ft.

5. (1) where $\theta = \dfrac{\pi}{4}, \dfrac{5\pi}{4}$, etc.   Max. at $\dfrac{\pi}{4}, \dfrac{9\pi}{4}$, etc.; $y = \sqrt{2}$.

(2) Max. at $(0 \cdot 64, 1 \cdot 76)$.

(3) Where $\sin x = \frac{1}{4}$ or $\cos x = 0$—i.e., at $\sin^{-1} \frac{1}{4}$ or $(n + \frac{1}{2})\pi$; max. value of $y = \frac{9}{8}$.

(4) Max. at $\left(\dfrac{\pi}{2}, 1 \right)$.

6. At 55°. **7.** 3·8 lb. **8.** 0·35 sec.
9. 2450 lb.; 1733 lb. **10.** Just more than 115.
11. Vel. = 0·185 ft./sec.; Accel. = − 0·347 ft./sec.²; max. displacement = 4·717 ins.

EXERCISE 39
p. 210.

1. $\sin\theta + c$. **2.** $-\cos\theta$. **3.** $-\frac{1}{3}\cos 3\theta$.
4. $-\frac{3}{2}\cos 2\theta$. **5.** $\frac{1}{2}\sin 4\theta$. **6.** $2\sin\frac{1}{2}\theta$.
7. $-\frac{9}{8}\cos\frac{2\theta}{3}$. **8.** $-\frac{3}{2}\cos 2\theta - \frac{4}{5}\sin 5\theta$.
9. $-\cos(\theta + \alpha)$. **10.** $\frac{1}{3}\sin\left(3\theta + \frac{\pi}{7}\right)$.
11. $2\cos\left(\frac{\pi}{5} - \theta\right)$. **12.** $-6\sin\left(\alpha - \frac{\theta}{2}\right)$.

EXERCISE 40
p. 220.

1. (a) $\frac{11}{8}$; (b) 6·19; (c) $\frac{1}{2}$; (d) $\frac{1}{2}$.
2. (1) 8; (2) 16π; (3) 54·8; (4) 0. **3.** 38·33.
4. (1) 29; (2) $\frac{1}{4}$; (3) 64.
5. (1) $\frac{23}{6}$; (2) $\frac{8}{3}$; (3) $-\frac{1}{6}$; (4) $\frac{\pi}{4}$; (5) $224\frac{1}{2}$.
7. (a) $\frac{13}{3}$; (b) 4·61; (c) 0; (d) $\frac{1}{3}$.
8. (1) $30\frac{2}{3}$; (2) 2·925; (3) $\frac{1}{3}$; (4) $2\sin\left(\frac{\pi}{8} + 1\right) - 2\sin 1$.
9. (1) 9; (2) 0; (3) $-4\frac{1}{3}$. **10.** 87.
11. 0·295. **12.** $m = \frac{1}{2}$; $40\frac{2}{3}$. **13.** 8·1.
14. $294\frac{2}{3}\pi$. **15.** $c = 20$; $7066\frac{2}{3}$. **16.** π cu. ins.
17. $a = 1·08$; $b = 0·53$. 35·6.

EXERCISE 41
p. 226.

1. (a) $\frac{2}{\pi}$; (b) $\frac{1}{2}$; (c) $\frac{1}{3}$. **2.** 80. 116.
3. $\frac{2wa}{\pi}$. **4.** 6·442. M.V. = 2·147.
5. $\frac{4}{\pi}$. **7.** 63·76. **8.** $345\frac{1}{3}$. $84\frac{1}{3}$.
9. $\frac{a^2w^2}{2}$. **10.** 2.

11. (1) 1·41; (2) $\dfrac{3\sqrt{2}}{2}$; (3) 0·707; (4) 0·707.

12. $\sqrt{c^2 + \dfrac{k^2}{2}}$. **13.** 2·55.

EXERCISE 42
p. 233.

1. 33,600 cu. ins. **2.** 6·25 sq. ins.
3. 16 ins. 367 cu. ins. **4.** 1425·8. **5.** 67·78 cu. ft.
6. 38·35; 575·25. **7.** 430 sq. ft.; 1462 cu. ft./sec.
8. (1) 6·28; (2) 1·1. **9.** $\dfrac{h}{6}[ab + cd + (a + c)(b + d)]$.
10. 210 ft./lb. **11.** 2·5 and 2·502 **12.** 17,000 cu. ins.

EXERCISE 43
p. 243.

1. $x = \dfrac{12}{5}$. **2.** $\left(\dfrac{12}{5}, \dfrac{3}{2}\right)$. **3.** $(3, \tfrac{9}{5})$. **4.** $(\tfrac{2}{5}, \tfrac{4}{7})$.
5. (1) $28\frac{1}{2}$; (2) $(2·05, 6·78)$. **6.** 0·48 in. from centre.
7. (1) $\dfrac{43\pi}{5}$ cu. ins.; (2) $\tfrac{39}{172}$ in. from face. **8.** $\dfrac{2\sqrt{3}}{\pi}$.
9. $\tfrac{7}{9}$ of median from P. **10.** $\dfrac{3\mathrm{H}}{4}$. **11.** $x = \tfrac{27}{5}$.
12. $2\frac{1}{4}$ from centre. **13.** $(2\tfrac{4}{13}, 4\tfrac{8}{13})$. **14.** $x = 2·1$ (nearly).
15. $3\frac{3}{7}$ ins. from centre. **16.** 18 cu. ins.; $x = \tfrac{328}{135}$.

EXERCISE 44
p. 249.

1. 24·54 cu. cms. **2.** $2\frac{1}{3}$ ins. from centre.
3. (1) 240π cu. ins. **4.** (1) $\dfrac{2a}{\pi}$; (2) $\dfrac{4a}{3\pi}$ from centre.
5. 1215·3 cu. ins. **7.** $\tfrac{3}{8}\sqrt{ab}$. **8.** 281 lb.

EXERCISE 45
p. 263.

1. $\mathrm{M}\dfrac{r^2}{2}$; $\dfrac{3\mathrm{M}\cdot r^2}{2}$. **2.** 39·6 ins.⁴; 22 ins.⁴.
3. $\dfrac{bd^3}{3}$; 1293 ins.⁴. **4.** (1) $\mathrm{M}\cdot\dfrac{a^2}{2}$; (2) $\dfrac{\mathrm{M}}{12}(3a^2 + 4l^2)$.
5. 19·9 ins.⁴. **6.** $\dfrac{a^4}{12}$; $\dfrac{7a^4}{12}$. **8.** 0·4%.

19. $1546\frac{2}{3}$ ins.^{4}.   **10.** $184 \cdot 32$ ins.^{4}.   **11.** 55 ins.^{4}.
2. 182 ins.^{4}.   **13.** 5200.

EXERCISE 46
p. 272.

1. (1) $3e^{3x}$;   (2) $-4e^{-4x}$;   (3) $e^{\frac{x}{3}}$;   (4) $e^{-\frac{x}{4}}$;   (5) $-2e^{-2x}$;
(6) $-20e^{-4x}$;   (7) $6e^{3x} + 8e^{-2x}$.

2. (1) $\frac{1}{2}e^{2x} + c$;   (2) $-\frac{1}{4}e^{-4x}$;   (3) $20e^{\frac{x}{4}}$;   (4) $\frac{2}{9}e^{-3x}$.

3. (1) $2xe^x + e^x x^2$;   (2) $e^{2x}(6x^3 + 9x^2)$;   (3) $-e^{-4x}(4x^{-2} + 2x^{-3})$;
(4) $e^x(\sin x + \cos x)$;   (5) $e^{3x}(3 \cos 4x - 4 \sin 4x)$;
(6) $ke^{ax}(a \sin bx + b \cos bx)$;   (7) $-e^{-2t}(2 \cos 3t + 3 \sin 3t)$;
(8) $e^{4x}(\frac{1}{4}x^{-3} - 3x^{-4})$;   (9) $ake^{-kt}(\cos kt - \sin kt)$.

4. (1) $3 \sinh 3x$;   (2) $4 \cosh 3x$;   (3) $\sinh \frac{x}{3}$.

5. (1) $\cos x e^{\sin x}$;   (2) $6 \cos 2x e^{3 \sin 2x}$;
(3) $e^{-x}[(2a - b)x + b - c - ax^2]$.

6. (1) $\log_e a \cdot a^x$;   (2) $\log_e 3 \cdot 3^x$;   (3) $\log 16 \cdot 4^{2x}$;
(4) $-3 \log 5 \cdot 5^{-3x}$.

7. (1) $3^5 e^{3x}$;   (2) $2^6 e^{-2x}$.   **9.** (0).

10. $c^2 \sinh \frac{a}{c}$.   **11.** (1) $2e + \frac{3}{e}$;   (2) $4\sqrt{e} + \frac{6}{\sqrt{e}} - 10$.

12. (1) $\frac{1}{2}(e^2 - 1)$;   (2) $\left(1 - \frac{1}{e^2}\right)$.

EXERCISE 47
p. 270.

1. (1) $\frac{1}{x}$;   (2) $\frac{1}{x - 5}$;   (3) $\frac{1}{x + 2} - \frac{1}{x + 5}$;   (4) $\frac{3}{3x - 4}$;
(5) $\frac{2x + 3}{x^2 + 3x} - \frac{1}{x + 1}$;   (6) $\frac{8x}{4x^2 - 5} - \frac{10x}{5x^2 + 3}$.

2. (1) $x(1 + 2 \log x)$;   (2) $\frac{3x - 6(x + 1) \log (x + 1)}{x^3(x + 1)}$;
(3) $\cos x \log x + \frac{\sin x}{x}$;   (4) $-\frac{3 \log x}{(x + 1)^2} + \frac{3}{x(x + 1)}$;
(5) $e^{3x}\left(\frac{1}{x} + 3 \log x\right)$;   (6) $3e^{-3x}\left(\frac{1}{1 - x} - 3 \log (1 + x)\right)$;
(7) $3 \cos 3x \log (x^2 + x + 1) + \frac{(2x + 1) \sin 3x}{x^2 + x + 1}$;
(8) $\sec^2 x \log x + \frac{\tan x}{x}$;   (9) $\frac{0 \cdot 4343}{x}$;   (10) $\frac{0 \cdot 4343(6x + 1)}{3x^2 + x + 1}$.
(11) $\frac{2x}{5(x^2 + 1)}$;   (12) $\cot x + \frac{\sin x}{1 + \cos x}$;   (13) $\frac{1}{1 - x^2}$.

3. (1) $\log (x + 2) + c$; (2) $- 3 \log (2 - x)$; (3) $\frac{1}{2} \log (x^2 + 1)$;

   (4) $\log (1 + \sin x)$;   (5) $\log \dfrac{1}{1 + \cos x}$;   (6) $\log (3 + e^x)$;

   (7) $\frac{1}{3} \log (3x + 2)$; (8) $- \frac{5}{3} \log (4 - 3x)$; (9) $\dfrac{a}{2c} \log (b + cx^2)$;

   (10) $\frac{1}{2} \log (x^2 + 6x + 4)$; (11) $\log \sqrt{x^2 - 2x + 4}$.

4. $3 \log \dfrac{b}{a} + \dfrac{14}{3}\left(b^{\frac{3}{2}} - a^{\frac{3}{2}}\right)$.

5. (1) $\log_e \frac{4}{3}$; (2) $\frac{3}{2} \log_e 5$; (3) $\log_e 2$; (4) $\log_e 2$; (5) $\frac{1}{2} \log_e \frac{11}{4}$.

EXERCISE 48

p. 283.

1. (1) $2 \sqrt{x + 3} + C$; (2) $- 2 \sqrt{5 - x}$; (3) $\dfrac{2a}{c} \sqrt{b + cx}$.

2. (1) $x - 4 \log (x + 4)$;   (2) $\dfrac{x^2}{2} + 4x + 16 \log (x - 4)$;

   (3) $2x - 6 \log (x + 3)$; (4) $\dfrac{x}{2} - \dfrac{3}{4} \log (2x + 3)$.

3. (1) $\sin^{-1} \dfrac{x}{2}$; (2) $\sin^{-1} \dfrac{x}{\sqrt{2}}$; (3) $\dfrac{1}{\sqrt{2}} \sin^{-1} \dfrac{x}{2}$; (4) $\sin^{-1} \dfrac{x + 1}{3}$;

   (5) $\sin^{-1} \dfrac{x + 2}{4}$; (6) $\dfrac{1}{\sqrt{2}} \sin^{-1} \dfrac{x + 1}{\sqrt{3}}$.

4 (1) $\tan^{-1} x$; (2) $\dfrac{3}{2} \tan^{-1} \dfrac{x}{2}$; (3) $\dfrac{1}{4} \tan^{-1} \dfrac{x}{2}$; (4) $\dfrac{1}{2} \tan^{-1} \dfrac{x + 1}{2}$.

   (5) $\dfrac{1}{2} \tan^{-1} \dfrac{x - 2}{2}$; (6) $\dfrac{1}{\sqrt{31}} \tan^{-1} \dfrac{2x + 3}{\sqrt{31}}$;

   (7) $\dfrac{2}{3\sqrt{3}} \tan^{-1} \dfrac{2x + 3}{\sqrt{3}}$.

5. (1) $\dfrac{1}{2}\left(\dfrac{\cos 20}{2} - \dfrac{\cos 60}{6}\right)$; (2) $\dfrac{1}{2}\left(\dfrac{\cos 2x}{2} - \dfrac{\cos 8x}{8}\right)$;

   (3) $-\left(\dfrac{\cos 6t}{6} + \dfrac{\cos 2t}{2}\right)$; (4) $\left(\dfrac{\sin 2t}{2} - \dfrac{\sin 8t}{8}\right)$;

   (5) $\dfrac{1}{2}\left(\dfrac{\sin 8x}{8} + \dfrac{\sin 4x}{4}\right)$; (6) $2 \cos \dfrac{t}{2} - \dfrac{2}{3} \cos \dfrac{3t}{2}$.

6. (1) $\dfrac{\sin^4 \theta}{4}$; (2) $- \dfrac{1}{2} \cdot \dfrac{1}{\cos^2 \theta}$; (3) $- \dfrac{\cos^5 x}{5}$; (4) $\dfrac{\tan^4 \theta}{4}$;

   (5) $- \dfrac{\cos^4 \theta}{4} - \cos 0$.

EXERCISE 49

p. 289.

1. (1) $\log (x^2 - 1)$; (2) $3 \log (x - 3) - \log (x - 2)$;
(3) $\frac{9}{11} \log (x + 6) + \frac{13}{11} \log (x - 5)$; (4) $\frac{1}{2} \log (x^2 - 9)$.
(5) $\frac{2}{5} \log (x - 1) - \frac{1}{5} \log (3x + 2)$;

(6) $3 \log (x - 4) - \log (x - 1)$; (7) $2 \log \dfrac{x}{x + 2}$;

(8) $\frac{1}{6} \log \dfrac{x}{x + 2}$; (9) $\frac{17}{6} \log (x + 6) - \frac{2}{6} \log (x + 1)$.

2. (1) $\dfrac{1}{\sqrt{3}} \log \dfrac{x + \frac{1}{2} - \frac{\sqrt{3}}{2}}{x + \frac{1}{2} + \frac{\sqrt{3}}{2}}$; (2) $\dfrac{1}{6} \log \dfrac{x - 2}{x + 4}$;

(3) $\dfrac{1}{\sqrt{5}} \log \dfrac{x + \frac{3}{2} - \frac{\sqrt{5}}{2}}{x + \frac{3}{2} + \frac{\sqrt{5}}{2}}$; (4) $\dfrac{1}{2\sqrt{3}} \log \dfrac{x + 2 - \sqrt{3}}{x + 2 + \sqrt{3}}$;

(5) $\dfrac{\sqrt{2}}{4} \log \dfrac{t + 1 - \frac{1}{\sqrt{2}}}{t + 1 + \frac{1}{\sqrt{2}}}$.

EXERCISE 50

p. 293.

1. $e^x(x - 1) + C$; (2) $e^x(x^2 - 2x + 2)$; (3) $\frac{1}{4}e^{2x}(2x^2 - 2x + 1)$;
(4) $-\dfrac{e^{-2x}}{4}(2x + 1)$; (5) $\dfrac{e^{-3x}}{-3}\left(x^2 + \dfrac{2x}{3} + \dfrac{2}{9}\right)$.

2. (1) $\sin x - x \cos x$; (2) $x \sin x + \cos x$;
(3) $- x^2 \cos x + 2x \sin x + 2 \cos x$;

(4) $\dfrac{x}{4}(3 - 2x^2) \cos 2x + \dfrac{\sin 2x}{4}(3x^2 - \frac{3}{2})$;

(5) $2x \sin \dfrac{x}{2} + 4 \cos \dfrac{x}{2}$; (6) $x^2 \sin x - 2 \sin x + 2x \cos x$.

3. (1) $\dfrac{x^3}{3} \log x - \dfrac{x^3}{9}$; (2) $- \dfrac{1}{4x^2}(1 + 2 \log x)$; (3) $\frac{1}{2}(\log x)^2$.

4. (1) $\dfrac{e^x}{2}(\sin x - \cos x)$;　　(2) $\dfrac{e^x}{2}(\sin x + \cos x)$;

(3) $\dfrac{e^{2x}}{5}(2\sin x - \cos x)$;　　(4) $-\dfrac{e^{-2x}}{5}(2\sin x + \cos x)$;

(5) $\dfrac{e^{3x}}{13}(3\sin 2x - 2\cos 2x)$;　(6) $\dfrac{e^{1x}}{20}(2\sin 2x + 4\cos 2x)$;

(7) $\dfrac{e^{-x}}{10}(3\sin 3x - \cos 3x)$;　(8) $-\dfrac{e^{-2x}}{13}(2\sin 3x + 3\cos 3x)$.

5. (1) $\dfrac{e^{ax}}{a^2+b^2}(b\sin bx + a\cos bx)$;

(2) $\dfrac{e^{ax}}{a^2+b^2}(a\sin bx - b\cos bx)$.

EXERCISE 51
p. 304.

1. 63° 30′ (nearly).
4. (1) R = 4·47, α = 63° 26′;　　(2) R = 3·61, α = 33° 41′;
(3) R = 1·8, α = 33° 41′.
6. 0·698.　　　　　　　　　　**7.** 0·48.
9. $y = 6\sin\left(\dfrac{2\pi}{3}t + \dfrac{\pi}{3}\right)$, ($t$ in secs.).

10. minimum at $\dfrac{\pi}{2}$; maximum at 0·7 radians (40° 8′). Max.

value 2·152. Min. value = 1.

EXERCISE 52
p. 309.

1. (a) (2, 3);　　(b) (− 2, 1);　　(c) (5, 0);　　(d) (0, − 2);
(e) (1, − 2); (f) (0, 3).
2. (a) $-\dfrac{1}{2} \pm \dfrac{\sqrt{7}}{2}j$;　(b) $\dfrac{3}{4} \pm \dfrac{\sqrt{23}}{4}j$;　(c) $0·35 \pm 1·4j$.

EXERCISE 53
p. 316.

1. $11 + 7j$.　　　　　**2.** $-\dfrac{23}{8} + \dfrac{7}{4}j$.　　　**3.** $11·2 - 0·6j$.
4. 25.　　　　　　　　**5.** 4·25.　　　　　　**6.** $5 - 12j$.
7. $-11 + 2j$.　　　　**8.** $-7 - 24j$.　　　　**9.** $-10 + 5j$.
10. $40 - 20j$.　　　**11.** $\cos 75° + j\sin 75°$.
12. $\cos 30° + j\sin 30°$.　**13.** $\dfrac{6}{13} + \dfrac{4}{13}j$.　**14.** $\dfrac{5}{17} + \dfrac{14}{17}j$.
15. $\dfrac{5}{13} - \dfrac{15}{26}j$.　　**16.** $-\dfrac{17}{26} + \dfrac{3}{13}j$.　**17.** $-\dfrac{16}{13} + \dfrac{37}{13}j$.
18. 1.

EXERCISE 54

p. 320.

1. $5 \angle 53° 8'$. **2.** $5 \angle -53° 8'$. **3.** $3 \cdot 7 \angle 71° 2'$.

4. $6 \cdot 33 \angle -161° 35'$. **5.** $0 \cdot 58 \angle -149° 2'$.

6. $32 \cdot 2 \angle 178° 13'$. **7.** $3 \cdot 14 \angle -9° 8'$. **8.** $\dfrac{3\sqrt{3}}{2} + \dfrac{3}{2}j$.

9. $1 \cdot 71 + 1 \cdot 54j$. **10.** $4 \cdot 21 - 3 \cdot 06j$. **11.** $4 \cdot 68 - 4 \cdot 22j$.

12. $6 \angle 45°$. **13.** $6 \cdot 72 \angle 36°$. **14.** $3 \cdot 64 \angle -42°$.

15. $1 \cdot 5 \angle 30°$. **16.** $0 \cdot 75 \angle 18°$. **17.** $1 \cdot 5 \angle 90°$.

18. $1 \cdot 44 \angle 45°$. **19.** $2 \cdot 32 \angle 34° 6'$. **20.** $2 \cdot 24 \angle -26° 34'$.

21. $1 \cdot 53 \angle 6° 8'$. **22.** $0 \cdot 52 \angle -16° 51'$. **23.** $1 \angle 45°$.

24. $3 \angle -45°$. **25.** $0 \cdot 67 \angle 84° 47'$.

26. $1 \cdot 3 - 2 \cdot 1j$; $\dfrac{5\sqrt{3}}{2} - \dfrac{5}{2}j$; $\sqrt{79} \angle 103°$.

27. $1 - j$; $\dfrac{5}{4} - \dfrac{5\sqrt{3}}{4}j$; $\dfrac{5\sqrt{2}}{2} \angle -105°$.

MISCELLANEOUS EXERCISES

p. 321.

1. (a) $2\frac{1}{7}$; (b) $11 \cdot 4$. **2.** 973. **3.** $0 \cdot 857$.

4. $0 \cdot 537$. **5.** $0 \cdot 4703$. **6.** (a) 18; (b) $0 \cdot 4669$.

7. $15 \cdot 2$. **8.** $0 \cdot 385$. **9.** 2654.

10. (a) $0 \cdot 062$; (b) $0 \cdot 2738$.

11. (a) $x = \pm 3 \cdot 02$; (b) $x = 0 \cdot 75$; (c) $x = \frac{9}{2}$.

12. (a) $x = \frac{3}{10}$ or $\frac{3}{4}$; (b) $a = \frac{5}{4}$, $b = \frac{24}{25}$.

13. $a = \dfrac{4}{10^4}$, $b = \dfrac{732}{10^2}$, $c = -160$; 1695.

14. (a) $x = \frac{7}{5}$ or 4; (b) $x = 2 \cdot 8$; (c) $x = \pm 1 \cdot 123$.

15. (a) $R = 4$; (b) $a = -4$, $b = 256$.

16. $r = 0 \cdot 575$.

17. (a) $x = 7 \cdot 49$, taking $\sqrt{x} = 2 \cdot 737$; (b) $x = 0 \cdot 38$.

18. (a) $x = 1 \cdot 142$; (b) $x = 7\frac{1}{2}$, $y = -\frac{13}{3}$.

19. $C = 9 \cdot 712 \times 10^{-7}$.

20. (a) $n = 1 \cdot 5$, $k = 0 \cdot 4585$; (b) $x = 1 \cdot 3$. **21.** $42° 5'$.

22. (a) $A = \sqrt{a^2 + b^2}$. $\alpha = \tan^{-1} \dfrac{b}{a}$; (b) $0 \cdot 0561$.

23. $4 \cdot 95$; $30°$ with $\overline{AB}$. **24.** $21° 29'$.

25. $\frac{3}{2} + \frac{7}{2} \cos 2\theta$, $57° 42'$ or $122° 18'$.

26. $1 \cdot 4$ m.p.h., E. $25° 16'$ S. **27.** $7 \cdot 68$ sq. in.

28. $30°$ or $330°$. **29.** $5 \cdot 93$ in.

31. 905 yds. **32.** $4 \cdot 53$ in.; $6 \cdot 88$ in.

33. $\theta = 270°$; $61° 56'$ or $241° 56'$.

34. $30° 58'$ or $210° 58'$.   **35.** $116° 45'$.   **36.** 83 ft.

37. $r = 0.17$, $\alpha = 139° 46'$.   **38.** (ii) $0°$, $45°$, $135°$, $180°$.

39. 25·3 in., $12° 50'$.   **40.** 4903 ft.   N. $78° 29'$ W.

41. $A = 25$, $\alpha = 16° 15'$.   (a) When $\theta = 73° 45'$; (b) $20° 37'$ or $126° 53'$.   **42.** (a) 1340 yds.; (b) 1214 yds.

43. 2054 ft.   **45.** $Z = 10.18$, $\cos \phi = 0.9829$.

46. (i) $6x^2 + \dfrac{3}{x^4}$; (ii) $e^x(1-x)$; (iii) $\dfrac{2}{(3x+2)^2}$; -20.

47. (a) $4.51 \cos x - 2.5 \sin x$; (b) $61°$; (c) 7.01.

48. (a) $12\frac{1}{2}$; (b) $\cos \theta - \theta \sin \theta$.   **49.** $x = 6$, $H = 180$.

50. (a) $36x^2 + 18x - 4$; (b) $\dfrac{e^x \cdot (2-x)}{(1-x)^2}$; (c) $-(5\sqrt{3} + \frac{3}{2})$.

51. $\dfrac{3}{2}$, $-\sqrt{3}$, $-\dfrac{2\sqrt{3}}{3}$.   **52.** (a) 4; (b) 1.

53. (a) $1 + \log_e x$; (b) $\dfrac{-2a}{(a+x)^2}$, $13°$, $23°$, $144°$.

56. Side = base = 12 in.   **57.** 6·43 in.

58. (a) 5; (b) $-\dfrac{2}{3}$; (c) $\dfrac{3}{5\pi}$.   **59.** (a) 17·21; (b) $\dfrac{5}{6}$; (c) $\dfrac{10}{\pi}$.

60. $y = x^3 - x^2 - 5x - 3$; $x = \dfrac{5}{3}$.   **61.** $0.48 \log_e \dfrac{10}{Q}$.

62. $\dfrac{8}{3}$.   **63.** $\dfrac{128\pi}{3}$.   **65.** $y = \dfrac{(10-x)^4}{144 \times 100} + \dfrac{10x}{36} - \dfrac{25}{36}$.

66. (a) $\dfrac{10\sqrt{2}}{3}$, $\dfrac{5}{2}$; $\dfrac{10}{\pi}$; (b) $8.1 \cdot \pi$.

68. (a) $\frac{7}{6}$; (b) 9.34; (c) 1; (d) $11\frac{7}{8}$ lb.

69. $x^3 - x^5 + C$, 18, $\frac{1}{3}$.   **70.** (a) $\dfrac{13}{3}$; (b) $\dfrac{x^5}{5} - \dfrac{1}{3x^3} + C$; (c) 2.

71. 0·997.   **72.** ± 0.02.   **73.** 6 in.   1088 in.⁴.

74. $130a + 66$. $l = 3.0385$.   **75.** 288 in.⁴.   922 in.⁴.

76. 2·03.   **77.** (a) $\dfrac{bd^3}{3}$ in.⁴; (b) $\dfrac{\pi d^4}{32}$.

78. $\dfrac{ml^3}{3}$. lb. in.². $\dfrac{ml^3}{12}$. lb. in.².   **79.** $3\sqrt{2}$, $45°$.

80. 36 in. 182π.   **81.** 2·5, 1.

82. rad. = 4 in.   BC = $4\sqrt{3}$, CD = $2\sqrt{3}$; (c) $8\sqrt{3}$.

83. 520 cu. in.   **84.** $3\frac{1}{3}$, $\frac{24}{25}$.   **85.** -1, 2·5, 0.

86. $109° 28'$.   Max. = $\sqrt{2}$.   Hyp. = $\dfrac{10}{1 + \sin \theta + \cos \theta}$.   Min. = 4·14.

87. $1 + \dfrac{x}{2} + \dfrac{x^2}{2} + \dfrac{7x^3}{12}$, $x = 0.04$, value = 1·0208.

88. $\dfrac{4r}{3\pi}$, $\dfrac{\pi^2}{4}\left(3 - \dfrac{2}{3\pi}\right)$.   **89.** $13°$.

NATIONAL CERTIFICATE MATHEMATICS

The complementary volumes in this series are:—

Volume I

FIRST YEAR COURSE

BY

P. ABBOTT, B.A.

Formerly Head of the Mathematics Department.
the Polytechnic, Regent St., W.1; and

C. E. KERRIDGE, B.Sc.

Formerly Lecturer in Mathematics at the Polytechnic, Regent St., W.1

336 pages with 119 diagrams

Price 7s. 6d. net

Synopsis of Contents

NATIONAL CERTIFICATE MATHEMATICS

The complementary volumes in this series are:—

Volume II

SECOND YEAR COURSE

BY

P. ABBOTT, B.A.

Formerly Head of the Mathematics Department, the Polytechnic,
Regent Street, W. 1

AND

H. MARSHALL, B.Sc.

Late Lecturer in Mathematics at the Polytechnic, Regent St., W.1

316 pages with 98 diagrams   **Price 8s. 6d. net**

SYNOPSIS OF CONTENTS